Technology and Society
A Spectrum of Issues
for the 21st Century

Linda S. Hjorth, *Coordinator*
Barbara A. Eichler
Ahmed S. Khan
John Morello
DeVry Institute of Technology

McGraw-Hill, Inc.
College Custom Series

New York St. Louis San Francisco Auckland Bogotá
Caracas Lisbon London Madrid Mexico Milan Montreal
New Delhi Paris San Juan Singapore Sydney Tokyo Toronto

Technology and Society
A Spectrum of Issues for the 21st Century

1 2 3 4 5 6 7 8 9 0 PCP PCP 9 0 9 8 7 6 5

ISBN 0-07-029144-6

Editor: Reaney Dorsey

Text Preparation: Architext

Cover Design: Ahmed S. Khan

Printer/Binder: Port City Press

Table of Contents

Preface

Technology. Hard to define, hard to avoid, and today even harder to live without. The technological advances come with dizzying speed; we barely get used to one only to have it replaced by another. Even more difficult is our ability to understand technology's hold on our lives and its rightful **place** in our lives. And, what about its rightful **use?** If technology isn't fully understood, can we be sure it's being used properly? Safely? Appropriately?

The 1990's and the following decades will usher in a most urgent challenge to humankind's intellect; the resolution of our technological, environmental and social worlds. The issues of industrial societies' use of energy resources, and its impact on the remaining three-fourths of the world and their economic and social development have become unavoidable in world growing more interdependent each day. Therefore, our ability to understand the impact of technology on our lives, the lives of our neighbors and succeeding generations are essential to reaching the goals of survival, peaceful coexistence, prosperity and safety.

This reader attempts to address all these issues, but in no particular order. The collaborative nature of its assembly, involving an engineer, a psychologist, an environmentalist and an historian testifies to the proposition that technology touches all spectrums of life and study, and that no one interest group has a monopoly on truth or wisdom. The articles we have selected are designed to stimulate, inspire and even provoke.

Chapter one will feature basic definitions and a general history of technology. Many references to technology imply a type of skill, tool, general capability or 'state of the art'. This ambiguity is evident when we can speak of a bicycle's technology on one end of the spectrum and state of the art technology such as fiber optics on the other. Technology involves not only knowledge and capability, but also its development, support and maintenance in society. It refers to all the political, economic, and industrial activity that support that activity. Chapter one, as you have no doubt guessed will be important in trying to clarify and sort out the many ways we look at and define technology.

Chapter two will investigate the impact of technology on energy development and conservation. Given the unknown condition of the world's traditional energy sources, and the unstable political environment of the areas where those resources are found, it will be important to consider the costs of going on the way we have, or using technology to try something new. Appropriately, environmental concerns will be the focus of attention of the articles included in Chapter three. Articles addressing the relationship of population and technology comprise Chapter four. The impact of technology on war and politics will be covered in Chapter five, followed in Chapter six by articles confronting the issues of technological use and social responsibility. This chapter will feature a discussion of ethics, whistleblowing and an examination of several technological disasters and how they were resolved. One article will include a discussion by Roger Boisjoly, an engineer on the ill-fated Challenger Shuttle mission of 1986. It was Boisjoly who 'blew the whistle' about faulty seals on the Shuttle. His story is a reminder that ethics has a heavy price tag. No reader on technology would be complete without some mention of the challenges and opportunities it presents to science and medicine; our contribution appears in Chapter seven. Chapter eight features articles dealing with the state and impact of technology on the less developed or so called Third World societies, and finally Chapter nine focuses on the future of technology and society in the coming years. The sources of our articles are as eclectic as the team the helped pull them together; some are scholarly efforts; some are of popular origin. But all of them were looked at by each member of our committee and vigorously discussed before finding their way between these covers. Each chapter concludes with questions drawn from the readings. We hope that this effort will stimulate the reader the same way it has stimulated those of us who were fortunate enough to be involved in its assembly.

No book is possible without the support and collaboration of others. We would like to thank Bryan Minogue for his help in creating the textbook cover design. We would also like to thank the editor Reaney Dorsey and assistant Jane Williams for the hours they dedicated to this project, and the patience that they shared as we sorted through reams of Social Issues in Technology readings.

Linda Hjorth
Barb Eichler
Ahmed S. Khan
John Morello

January, 1995

ACKNOWLEDGMENTS

Brown Jr., George E., "Technology's Dark Side," The Chronicle of Higher Education, American Association for the Advancement of Science, June 1993, Section B2. Reprinted with permission from The Chronicle of Higher Education and the author.

Diamond, Jared, "The Great Leap Forward," Discover Magazine, Walt Disney Magazine Publishing Inc., May 1989, pp. 50-60. Reprinted with permission from Walt Disney Magazine Publishing Inc.

Brinton, Crane, Etal., "A History of Civilization Volume II," 1648 to the Present, Prentice-Hall, New York: 1995, pp. 59-71. This material reproduced with permission from Prentice-Hall.

Barbour, Ian "Chapter Five: Energy," Ethics in an Age of Technology, HarperCollins Publishers, Inc., 1992, pp. 116-145. ©Copyright 1992 by Ian Barbour. Reprinted with permission from HarperCollins Publishers, Inc.

Melville, Keith, Managing Editor, "Energy Options: Finding a Solution to the Power Predicament," National Issues Forums, 1992. ©Copyright 1992 National Issues Forums. Reprinted with permission from McGraw-Hill, Inc.

Feiveson, Harold, "Dismantling the Doomsday Machine," Technology Review, MIT Press, May-June 1992, pp. 61-69. ©Copyright 1992. Reprinted with permission from Technology Review.

Flavin, Christopher, "Beyond the Gulf Crisis: An Energy Strategy for the '90s," Challenge the Magazine of Economic Affairs, M. E. Sharpe, Inc., Nov.-Dec. 1990, pp. 4-10. ©Copyright 1990. Reprinted with permission from M. E. Sharpe, Inc.

Durning, Alan, "The Grim Payback of Greed," International Wildlife Magazine, National Wildlife Federation, May-June 1991, pp. 36-39. ©Copyright 1991. Reprinted with permission from Copyright Clearance Center, Inc.

Schmidt, Karen, "Can Superfund Get On Track," National Wildlife Magazine, May-April 1994, pp. 10-17. Reprinted with permission from the National Wildlife Federation.

Pratt, Gil Andrews, "EV's On the Road Again," Technology Review, MIT Press, 1992, pp. 50-59. ©Copyright 1992. Reprinted with permission from Technology Review.

Glasgow, Dale, Data from Population Reference Bureau graph as it appears in Paul R. Enrilch, "Earth 88," National Geographic, Dec. 1988. Reprinted with permission from The Population Reference Bureau.

Hinrichsen, Don, "Putting the Bite on Planet Earth," International Wildlife Magazine, National Wildlife Federation, Sept.-Oct. 1994, pp. 36-35. Reprinted with permission from National Wildlife Federation.

Bongaarts, John, "Can the Growing Population Feed Itself?" Scientific American, March 1994, 36-42. ©Copyright 1995. Reprinted with permission from Scientific American, Inc. All rights reserved.

Callahan, David, "Air Power Comes of Age: War, Politics, and Technology," Technology Review, MIT Press, Aug.-Sept. 1994, pp. 62-70. ©Copyright 1994. Reprinted with permission from Technology Review.

Budiansky, Stephen, Etal., "The Cold War Experiments," U.S. News & World Report, Jan. 1994, pp. 32-38. Reprinted with permission from U.S. News & World Report.

INTRODUCTION

Technology's Dark Side

George E. Brown, Jr.

When I was a boy, it didn't perturb me that the radio took five minutes to warm up. Nor was I particularly bothered that I had to talk to an operator to place a telephone call. As a young man, I don't recall feeling irritated that a flight from New York to Europe took 22 hours and stopped in Gander and Shannon on the way to Paris. When I was in my 40's, I believe that I was perfectly satisfied with my black-and-white TV, my dial telephone, my electric typewriter, and even my slide rule.

Today, though, I'm less tolerant. I can't stand it when the remote gets buried under a pile of papers on my desk, and I have to get out of my chair to turn on the television. I can't stand it when my flight to Los Angeles is delayed by half an hour or when the fax machine in my district office is busy or—God forbid—when I lose the audio on a video-teleconference with Moscow. What I never dreamed of yesterday, I can't do without today. Invention often seems to be the mother of necessity, not vice versa.

We need to think more clearly about the role that technology is playing in modern society. The role of technological and economic development is often explained in a straight-forward manner. A recent report by the Bush Administration's Council on Competitiveness stated: "Throughout America's history, technology has been a major driver of economic growth.... Because of our great technological strength, U.S. manufacturing has stood head and shoulders above other nations in world markets." The 1993 Economic Report of the President—one of the last documents issued by the Bush Administration—completed the argument: "Strong and sustained economic growth is the key to providing

Americans with rising real incomes and the resources to meet their needs, desires, and aspirations."

I think there is considerable reason to reexamine this conventional, straightforward view of the relations between technology, economic growth, and quality of life. One concrete example is the recently documented decline in infant mortality in the United States. Although we still rank near the bottom of the list of industrialized nations in infant mortality, we have recently risen from number 22 to number 20. The improvement results primarily from technological innovations that allow for more effective treatment of under-developed lungs—a major source of death for premature and underweight infants.

But there is a dark side to our progress. As our overall infant mortality rate declined, the disparity between white and black infant mortality continued to increase. The benefit of the technologies that treat underdeveloped lungs is limited to those who can afford fine medical care.

No doubt technological development is an efficient, market-driven approach to this medical problem. But it can also displace more equitable—and cheaper—nontechnological solutions. Many premature and underweight births could be prevented by wider access to adequate prenatal care. We know how to provide this care; we just don't manage to deliver it to poor people.

Why does the market-driven approach follow the technological route, instead of the preventative route? Because there are more profits to be made in treating the premature infants of mothers who can afford medical care than in preventing the premature infants of mothers who cannot. Thus, the market-driven technological approach provides a solution to the medical problem that actually exacerbates societal inequity. Such cases are not rare.

Another example of how technology-led economic growth can contribute to social inequity is found in the increased use of computers in elementary and secondary science education. Wealthier school districts tend to benefit from this trend more than poor districts, since wealthier parents have computers at home that their children can use. The government plans to link the nation's grade schools to a national computer network over the next several years; meanwhile urban libraries can't afford to stay open or buy new books. Disparity of opportunity is magnified by technology-driven forces. If you can't read, it won't do you much good to log on.

The current U.S. economic recovery offers a more general example. As we know, the current recovery is not generating many new jobs. It appears that increased profitability is being fueled in part by technological innovation, with no need for additional workers. In fact, companies are improving their profitability by *firing* workers. The economy is growing, the recession is ending, and corporations are behaving in an economically rational manner: adopting new technologies, increasing efficiency, decreasing payrolls, boosting profits.

Looking more broadly, we find that the global distribution of wealth has become increasingly concentrated in the past 30 years, in spite of significant worldwide economic growth. In 1960, those nations with the wealthiest 20 per cent of the world's population accounted for 70 per cent of the world's annual gross profit. In 1989, the concentration of profit in the wealthiest nations had growth to 83 percent. Trade, commercial lending, domestic investment and savings, and foreign private investment show similar trends.

I realize that global patterns of income, wealth, and economic growth reflect the extraordinarily complex political economy of international relations. Yet the role of technology in these relations is always viewed as a plus. Technology-driven economic growth in the industrialized world is supposed to promote investment in less-developed countries.

This investment then allows those nations to purchase technologies and take advantage of their cheap and abundant labor, in turn fueling their own economic development. Eventually, the conventional theory holds, the less-developed countries become sort of like us.

But how do we know that these simple relationships will hold up in a high-technology world, where human physical labor becomes increasingly irrelevant to the production of wealth? In a high-technology world, how do we know whether market incentives will serve to mitigate or magnify economic disparity?

Further, the ability of human beings to achieve a basic measure of human dignity does not depend on advanced technologies. A nation's capacity to provide food and nutrition, education and literacy, clean water, decent housing, and basic health care does not correlate with technological sophistication, great wealth, or operation of market economies. Nations such as Costa Rica, North Korea, China, Sri Lanka, Jamaica, Cuba, and the former Soviet Union all managed to relieve most of their population from the elemental struggle for survival. Other nations, especially in the oil-producing Middle East, have accumulated great wealth, but have been less successful in meeting basic human needs.

Once basic needs are met, satisfaction with our lives cannot be said to depend on the amount of things we acquire, use, and consume. If that were the case, modern U. S. society would be the happiest in history, an assertion that would be difficult to support.

In terms of the social contract, we justify more growth because it is supposedly the most efficient way to spread economic opportunity and social well-being. But I believe that this reasoning is simplistic and often specious. When economic growth does not lead to greater public good, we do not blame dumb objects—technologies. Rather, we blame imperfections in the market system. The sources of such market imperfections go by names such as collusion, monopoly, pollution, nationalism, protectionism, authoritarianism, injustice, and war. These imperfections may all be grouped under a category commonly known as "reality."

Suppose that we viewed economic markets as an imperfect artifact of human culture, instead of vice versa. In this context, we might first ask: What type of technology policy would best serve the goals of human culture, such as reduction of injustice and inequity? The role of markets in promoting an optimal distribution of technologies would then become subservient to more fundamental objectives.

What would a socially oriented technology policy look like? We know that good health and quality education for the vast majority of human beings can be provided with little technological assistance. This point is so basic that it sounds almost asinine: Clean water, a good diet, and exercise would provide most Americans with a long and healthy life. Well-trained and dedicated teachers are the key to good education. Yet the average life expectancy of a black male in our inner cities is less than in many of the poorest developing nations, and we continue to graduate students from high school who can barely read or do math. Technology-driven economic growth didn't cause these problems, but it may be making it more difficult to solve them.

A social-technology policy might actually proscribe some types of technological solutions to social problems. This is not as insane as it sounds. The Japanese do it in a limited way. By limiting automation in agriculture, for example, Japanese agribusiness companies accept the cost of reduced productivity in order to insure fuller employment for their work forces.

Other aspects of a social-technology policy might encourage the development of technologies that decentralize political power and economic resources, to minimize the control that large institutions have over the lives of individuals. The federal government has spent 50 years subsidizing research and development on nuclear fission and nuclear fusion, while largely neglecting research into a wide range of renewable and generally decentralized energy sources that could help the world meet its energy needs in a more flexible and equitable way. These include solar and hydrothermal energy and hydrogen-derived power. The reason we took the nuclear path is obvious: Those who had a stake in nuclear energy—be it economic, political, or intellectual—were those already in power. Perhaps we can learn from this mistake, which has implications for an almost incredible range of social and economic phenomena, from dependence on imported oil to deterioration of the environment.

If we are to reduce technology-driven concentration of power—that is, if we are to achieve a world at once more equitable and more just—we must recognize that technology is a means, not an end. There is no invisible hand that ministers to the wise and equitable application of technology. We must provide that guiding hand through a conscious process of democratic action. Science and technology can and must be advanced in concert with the search for more justice in our society

In his book *Steady-State Economics*, first published more than 15 years ago, Herman Daly, an economist at the World Bank, wrote: "The usual objection to limiting growth, made ostensibly in the name of the poor, only illustrates the extent of [our spiritual] void because it views growth as an alternative to sharing, which is considered unrealistic. For the traditional religious attitude, there is such a thing as material sufficiency, and beyond that admittedly vague and historically changing amount, the goal of life becomes wisdom, enjoyment, cultivation of the mind and soul, and community. It may even be that community requires a certain degree of scarcity, without which cooperation, sharing, and friendship would have no organic reason to be, and hence community would atrophy.... The answer to a failure of brotherhood is not simply more growth but is to be found mainly in more sharing."

How can someone like me, who has spent the last 30 years of his life enmeshed in the hard-headed world of Washington politics, take such utopian notions seriously? For the past 50 years this nation has focused its resources on building weapons of inconceivable destructive power, and we have viewed the rest of the world as a chess board designed to play out our own ideological struggle. We propped up governments that murdered nuns, priests, nurses, and children, and we provided high-technology weaponry to dictatorships. We undercut democratically elected governments, in some instances to protect the profits of U.S. companies.

We turned a blind eye while our tactical allies acquired the components necessary to build nuclear weapons, and we condoned authoritarian government in the name of the free flow of oil. Our vision during the cold war was cynical in the extreme. "Mutual assured destruction" was a U.S. philosophy of international relations; the "Peacekeeper" was a ballistic missile armed with nuclear warheads.

Now the cold war is over, and our excuse for this behavior is gone. We need a new and better vision. Neither technology nor economics can answer questions of values. Is our path into the future to be defined by the literally mindless process of technological evolution and economic expansion, or by a conscious adoption of guiding moral precepts? Progress is meaningless if we don't know where we're going. Unless we try to visualize what is beyond the horizon, we will always occupy the same shore.

CHAPTER ONE
HISTORY OF TECHNOLOGY

The Great Leap Forward

Jared Diamond

One can hardly blame nineteenth-century creationists for insisting that humans were separately created by God. After all, between us and other animal species lies the seemingly unbridgeable gulf of language, art, religion, writing, and complex machines. Small wonder, then, that to many people Darwin's theory of our evolution from apes appeared absurd.

Since Darwin's time, of course, fossilized bones of hundreds of creatures intermediate between apes and modern humans have been discovered. It is no longer possible for a reasonable person to deny that what once seemed absurd actually happened—somehow. Yet the discoveries of many missing links have only made the problem more fascinating, without fully solving it. When and how did we acquire our uniquely human characteristics?

We know that our lineage arose in Africa, diverging from that of chimpanzees and gorillas sometime between 6 million and 10 million years ago. For most of the time since then we have been little more than glorified baboons. As recently as 35,000 years ago western Europe was still occupied by Neanderthals, primitive beings for whom art and progress scarcely existed. Then there was an abrupt change. Anatomically modern people appeared in Europe, and suddenly so did sculpture, musical instruments, lamps, trade, and innovation. Within a few thousand years the Neanderthals were gone.

Insofar as there was any single moment when we could be said to have become human, it was at the time of this Great Leap Forward 35,000 years ago. Only a few more dozen millennia—a trivial fraction of our 6-to-10 million-year history—were needed for us to domesticate animals, develop agriculture and metallurgy, and invent writing. It was then but a short further step to those monuments of civilization that distinguish us from all other animals—monuments such as the *Mona Lisa* and the Ninth Symphony, the Eiffel Tower and Sputnik, Dachau's ovens and the bombing of Dresden.

What happened at that magic moment in evolution? What made it possible, and why was it so sudden? What held back the Neanderthals, and what was their fate? Did Neanderthals and modern peoples ever meet, and if so, how did they behave toward each other? We still share 98 percent of our genes with chimps; which genes among the other 2 percent had such enormous consequences?

Understanding the Great Leap Forward isn't easy; neither is writing about it. The immediate evidence comes from technical details of preserved bones and stone tools. Archeologists' reports are full of such terms as "transverse occipital torus," "receding zygomatic arches," and "Chatelperronian backed knives." What we really want to understand—the way of life and the humanity of our various ancestors—isn't directly preserved but only inferred from those technical details. Much of the evidence is missing, and archeologists often disagree over the meaning of the evidence that has survived.

I'll emphasize those inferences rather than the technical details, and I'll speculate about the answers to those questions I just listed above. But you can form your own opinions, and they may differ from mine. This is a puzzle whose solution is still unknown.

To set the stage quickly, recall that life originated on Earth several billion years ago, the dinosaurs became extinct around 65 million years ago, and, as I mentioned, our ancestors diverged from the ancestors of chimps and gorillas between 6 and 10 million years ago. They then remained confined to Africa for millions of years.

Initially, our ancestors would have been classified as merely another species of ape, but a sequence of three changes launched them in the direction of modern humans. The first of these changes occurred by around 4 million years ago: the structure of fossilized limb bones shows that by men our ancestors, in contrast to gorillas and chimps, were habitually walking upright. The upright posture freed our forelimbs to do other things, among which toolmaking would eventually prove to be the most important.

The second change occurred around 3 million years ago, when our lineage split in two. As background, remember that members of two animal species living in the same area must fill different ecological roles and do not normally interbreed. For example, coyotes and wolves are obviously closely related and, until wolves were exterminated in most of the United States, lived in many of the same areas. However, wolves are larger, they usually hunt big mammals like deer and moose, and they often live in sizable packs, whereas coyotes are smaller, mainly hunt small mammals like rabbits and mice, and normally live in pairs or small groups.

Now, all modern humans unquestionably belong to the same species. Ecological differences among us are entirely a product of childhood education: it is not the case that some of us are born big and habitually hunt deer while others are born small, gather berries, and don't marry the deer hunters. And every human population living today has interbred with every other human population with which it has had extensive contact.

Three million years ago, however, there were hominid species as distinct as wolves and coyotes. On one branch of the family tree was a man-ape with a heavily built skull and very big cheek teeth, who probably ate coarse plant food; he has come to be known as *Australopithecus robustus* (the "robust southern ape"). On the other branch was a man-ape with a more lightly built skull and smaller teeth, who most likely had an omnivorous diet; he is known as *Australopithecus africanus* (the "southern ape of Africa"). Our lineage may have experienced such a radical division at least once more, at the time of the Great Leap Forward. But the description of that event will have to wait.

There is considerable disagreement over just what occurred in the next million years, but the argument I find most persuasive is that *A. africanus* evolved into the larger-brained form we call *Homo habilis* ("man the handyman").

Complicating the issue is that fossil bones often attributed to *H. habilis* differ so much in skull size and tooth size that they may actually imply another fork in our lineage yielding two distinct *habilis*-like species: *H. habilis* himself and a mysterious "Third Man." Thus, by 2 million years ago there were at least two and possibly three protohuman species.

The third and last of the big changes that began to make our ancestors more human and less apelike was the regular use of stone tools. By around 2.5 million years ago very crude stone tools appear in large numbers in areas of East Africa occupied by the protohumans. Since there were two or three protohuman species, who made the tools? Probably the light-skulled species, since both it and the tools persisted and evolved. (There is, however, the intriguing possibility that at least some of our robust relatives also made tools, as recent anatomical analyses of hand bones from the Swartkrans cave in South Africa suggest. See "The Gripping Story of Paranthropus," by Pat Shipman, in last month's issue.

With only one human species surviving today but two or three a few million years ago, it's clear that one I or two species must have become extinct. Who was our ancestor, which species ended up instead as a discard in the trash heap of evolution, and when did this shakedown occur?

The winner was the light-skulled *H. habilis,* who went on to increase in brain size and body size. By around 1.7 million years ago the differences were sufficient that anthropologists give our lineage the new name *Homo erectus* ("the man who walks upright"—*H. erectus* fossils were discovered before all the earlier ones, so anthropologists didn't realize that *H. erectus* wasn't the first protohuman to walk upright). The robust man-ape disappeared somewhat after 1.2 million years ago, and the Third Man (if he ever existed) must have disappeared by then also.

As for why *H. erectus* survived and *A. robustus* didn't, we can only speculate. A plausible guess is that the robust man-ape could no longer compete: *H. erectus* ate both meat and plant food, and his larger brain may have made him more efficient at getting the food on which *A. robustus* depended. It's also possible that *H. erectus* gave his robust brother a direct push into oblivion by killing him for meat.

The shakedown left *H. erectus* as the sole protohuman player on the African stage, a stage to which our closest living relatives (the chimp and gorilla) are still confined. But around one million years ago *H. erectus* began to expand his horizons. His stone tools and bones show that he reached Near East, then the Far East (where he is represented by the famous fossils known as Peking man and Java man) and Europe. He continued to evolve in our direction by an increase in brain size and in skull roundness. By around 500,000 years ago some of our ancestors looked sufficiently like us, and sufficiently different from earlier *H. erectus*, to be classified as our own species, *Homo sapiens* (the "wise man"), although they still had thicker skulls and brow ridges than we do today.

Was our meteoric ascent to *sapiens* status half a million years ago the brilliant climax of Earth history, when art and sophisticated technology finally burst upon our previously dull planet? Not at all: the appearance of *H. sapiens* was a non-event. The Great Leap

Forward, as proclaimed by cave paintings, houses, and bows and arrows, still lay hundreds of thousands of years in the future. Stone tools continued to be the crude ones that *H. erectus* had been making for nearly a million years. The extra brain size of those early *H. sapiens* had no dramatic effect on their way of life. That whole long tenure of *H. erectus* and early *H. sapiens* outside Africa was a period of infinitesimally slow cultural change.

So what was life like during the 1.5 million years that spanned the emergence of *H. erectus* and *H. sapiens*? The only surviving tools from this period are stone implements that can, charitably, be described as very crude. Early stone tools do vary in size and shape, and archeologists have used those differences to give the tools different names, such as hand-ax, chopper, and cleaver. But these names conceal the fact that none of these early tools had a sufficiently consistent or distinctive shape to suggest any specific function. Wear marks on the tools show that they were variously used to cut meat, bone, hides, wood, and nonwoody parts of plants. But any size or shape tool seems to have been used to cut any of these things, and the categories imposed by archeologists may be little more than arbitrary divisions of a continuum of stone forms.

Negative evidence is also significant. All the early stone tools may have been held directly in the hand; they show no signs of being mounted on other materials for increased leverage, as we mount steel ax blades on wooden handles. There were no bone tools, no ropes to make nets, and no fishhooks.

What food did our early ancestors get with those crude tools, and how did they get it? To address this question, anthropology textbooks usually insert a long chapter entitled something like "Man the Hunter." The point they make is that baboons, chimps, and some other primates prey on small vertebrates only occasionally, but recently surviving Stone Age people (like Bushmen) did a lot of big-game hunting. There's no doubt that our early ancestors also ate some meat. The question is, how much meat? Did big-game hunting skills improve gradually over the past 1.5 million years, or was it only since the Great Leap Forward—a mere 35,000 years ago—that they made a large contribution to our diet?

Anthropologists routinely reply that we've long been successful big-game hunters, but in fact there is no good evidence of hunting skills until around 100,000 years ago, and it's clear that even then humans were still very ineffective hunters. So it's reasonable to assume that earlier hunters were even more ineffective.

Yet the mystique of Man the Hunter is now so rooted in us that it's hard to abandon our belief in its long-standing importance. Supposedly, big-game hunting was what induced protohuman males to cooperate with one another, develop language and big brains, join into bands, and share food. Even women were supposedly molded by big-game hunting: they suppressed the external signs of monthly ovulation that are so conspicuous in chimps, so as not to drive men into a frenzy of sexual competition and thereby spoil men's cooperation at hunting.

But studies of modern hunter gatherers, with far more effective weapons than those of early *H. sapiens*, show that most of a family's calories come from plant food gathered by women. Men catch rats and other small game never mentioned in their heroic campfire stories. Occasionally they get a large animal, which does indeed contribute significantly to protein intake. But it's only in the Arctic, where little plant food is available, that big-game hunting becomes the dominant food source. And humans didn't reach the Arctic until around 30,000 years ago.

So I would guess that big-game hunting contributed little to our food intake until after we had evolved fully modern anatomy and behavior. I doubt the usual view that hunting was the driving force behind our uniquely human brain and societies. For most of our history we were not mighty hunters but rather sophisticated baboons.

To return to our history: *H. sapiens*, you'll recall, took center stage around half a million years ago in Africa, the Near East, the Far East, and Europe. By 100,000 years ago humans had settled into at least three distinct populations occupying different parts of the Old World. These were the last truly primitive people. Let's consider among them those whose anatomy is best known, those who have become a metaphor for brutishness: the Neanderthals.

Where and when did they live? Their name comes from Germany's Neander Valley, where one of the first skeletons was discovered (in German, *thal*— nowadays spelled *tal*—means "valley"). Their geographic range extended from western Europe, through southern European Russia and the Near East, to Uzbekistan in Central Asia, near the border of Afghanistan. As to the time of their origin, that's a matter of definition, since some old skulls have characteristics anticipating later "full-blown" Neanderthals. The earliest full-blown examples date from around 130,000 years ago, and most specimens postdate 74,000 years ago. While their start is thus arbitrary, their end is abrupt: the last Neanderthals died around 32,000 years ago.

During the time that Neanderthals flourished, Europe and Asia were in the grip of the last ice age. Hence Neanderthals must have been a cold-adapted people—but only within limits. They got no farther north than southern Britain, northern Germany, Kiev, and the Caspian Sea.

Neanderthals' head anatomy was so distinctive that, even if a Neanderthal dressed in a business suit or a designer dress were to walk down the street today, all you *H. sapiens* would be staring in shock. Imagine converting a modern face to soft clay, gripping the middle of the face from the bridge of the nose to the jaws, pulling the whole mid-face forward, and letting it harden again. You'll then have some idea of a Neanderthal's appearance. Their eyebrows rested on prominently bulging bony ridges, and their nose and jaws and teeth protruded far forward. Their eyes lay in deep sockets, sunk behind the protruding nose and brow ridges. Their foreheads were low and sloping, unlike our high vertical modern foreheads, and their lower jaws sloped back without a chin. Yet despite these startlingly primitive features, Neanderthals' brain size was nearly 10 percent greater than ours! (This does not mean they were smarter than us; they obviously weren't. Perhaps their larger brains simply weren't "wired" as well.) A dentist who examined a Neanderthal's teeth would have been in for a further shock. In adult Neanderthals front teeth were worn down on the outer surface, in a way found in no modern people. Evidently this peculiar wear pattern resulted from their using their teeth as tools, but what exactly did they do? As one possibility, they may have routinely used their teeth like a vise, as my baby sons do when they grip a milk bottle in their teeth and run around with their hands free. Alternatively, Neanderthals may have bitten hides to make leather or wood to make tools.

While a Neanderthal in a business suit or a dress would attract your attention, one in shorts or a bikini would be even more startling. Neanderthals were more heavily muscled, especially in their shoulders and neck, than all but the most avid bodybuilders. Their limb bones, which took the force of those big muscles contracting, had to be considerably thicker than ours to withstand the stress. Their arms and legs would have looked stubby to us, because the lower leg and forearm were relatively shorter than ours. Even their hands were much more powerful than ours; a Neanderthal's handshake would have been bone-crushing. While their average height was only around 5 feet 4 inches, their weight was at least 20 pounds more than that of a modern person of that height, and this excess was mostly in the form of lean muscle.

One other possible anatomical difference is intriguing, although its reality as well as its interpretation are quite uncertain—the fossil evidence so far simply doesn't allow a definitive answer. But a Neanderthal woman's birth canal may have been wider than a modern woman's, permitting her baby to grow inside her to a bigger size before birth. If so, a Neanderthal pregnancy might have lasted one year, instead of nine months.

Besides their bones, our other main source of information about Neanderthals is their stone tools. Like earlier human, tools, Neanderthal tools may have been simple hand-held stones not mounted on separate parts such as handles. The tools don't fall into distinct types with unique functions. There were no standardized bone tools, no bows and arrows. Some of the stone tools were undoubtedly used to make wooden tools, which rarely survive. One notable exception is a wooden thrusting spear eight feet long, found in the ribs of a long-extinct species of elephant at an archeological site in Germany. Despite that (lucky?) success, Neanderthals were probably not very good at big-game hunting; even anatomically more modern people living in Africa at the same time as the Neanderthals were undistinguished as hunters.

If you say "Neanderthal" to friends and ask for their first association, you'll probably get back the answer "caveman." While most excavated Neanderthal remains do come from caves, that's surely an artifact of preservation, since open-air sites would be eroded much more quickly. Neanderthals must have constructed some type of shelter against the cold climate in which they lived, but those shelters must have been crude. All that remain are postholes and a few piles of stones.

The list of quintessentially modern human things that Neanderthals lacked is a long one. They left no unequivocal art objects. They must have worn some clothing in their cold environment, but that clothing had to be crude, since they lacked needles and other evidence of sewing. They evidently had no boats, as no Neanderthal remains are known from Mediterranean islands nor even from North Africa, just eight miles across the Strait of Gibraltar from Neanderthal-populated Spain. There was no long-distance overland trade: Neanderthal tools are made of stones available within a few miles of the site.

Today we take cultural differences among people inhabiting different areas for granted. Every modern human population has its characteristic house style, implements, and art. If you were shown chopsticks, a Schlitz beer bottle, and a blowgun and asked to associate one object each with China, Milwaukee, and Borneo, you'd have no trouble giving the right answers. No such cultural variation is apparent for Neanderthals, whose tools look much the same no matter where they come from.

We also take cultural progress with time for granted. It is obvious to us that the wares from a Roman villa, a medieval castle, and a Manhattan apartment circa 1988 should differ. In the 1990s my sons will look with astonishment at the slide rule I used throughout the 1950s. But Neanderthal tools from 100,000 and 40,000 years ago look essentially the same. In short, Neanderthal tools had no variation in time or space to suggest that most human of characteristics, *innovation*.

What we consider old age must also have been rare among Neanderthals. Their skeletons make clear that adults might live to their thirties or early forties but not beyond 45. If we lacked writing and if none of us lived past 45, just think how the ability of our society to accumulate and transmit information would suffer.

But despite all these subhuman qualities, there are three respects in which we can relate to Neanderthals' humanity. They were the first people to leave conclusive evidence of fire's regular, everyday use: nearly all well-preserved Neanderthal caves have small areas of ash and charcoal indicating a simple fireplace. Neanderthals were also the first people who regularly buried their dead, though whether this implies religion is a matter of pure speculation. Finally, they regularly took care of their sick and aged. Most skeletons of older Neanderthals show signs of severe impairment, such as withered arms, healed but incapacitating broken bones, tooth loss, and severe osteoarthritis. Only care by young Neanderthals could have enabled such older folks to stay alive to the point of such incapacitation. After my litany of what Neanderthals lacked, we've finally found something that lets us feel a spark of kindred spirit in these strange creatures of the Ice Age— human, and yet not really human.

Did Neanderthals belong to the same species as we do? That depends on whether we would have mated and reared a child with a Neanderthal man or woman, given the opportunity. Science fiction novels love to imagine the scenario. You remember the blurb on a pulpy back cover: "A team of explorers stumbles on a steep-walled valley in the center of deepest Africa, a valley that time forgot. In this valley they find a tribe of incredibly primitive people, living in ways that our Stone Age ancestors discarded thousands of years ago. Are they the same species as us?" Naturally, there's only one way to find out, but who among the intrepid explorers—male explorers, of course—can bring himself to make the test? At this point one of the bone-chewing cavewomen is described as beautiful and sexy in a primitively erotic way, so that readers will find the brave explorer's dilemma believable: Does he or doesn't he have sex with her?

Believe it or not, something like that experiment actually took place. It happened repeatedly around 35,000 years ago, around the time of the Great Leap Forward. But you'll have to be patient just a little while longer.

Remember, the Neanderthals of Europe and western Asia were just one of at least three human populations occupying different parts of the Old World around 100,000 years ago. A few fossils from eastern Asia suffice to show that people there differed from Neanderthals as well as from us moderns, but too few have been found to describe these Asians in more detail. The best characterized contemporaries of the Neanderthals are those from Africa, some of whom were almost modern in their skull anatomy. Does this mean that, 100,000 years ago in Africa, we have at last arrived at the Great Leap Forward?

Surprisingly, the answer is still no. The stone tools of these modern-looking Africans were very similar to those of the non-modern-looking Neanderthals, so we refer to them as Middle Stone Age Africans. They still lacked standardized bone tools, bows and arrows, art, and cultural variation. Despite their mostly modern bodies, these Africans were still missing something needed to endow them with modern behavior.

Some South African caves occupied around 100,000 years ago provide us with the first point in human evolution for which we have detailed information about what people were eating. Among the bones found in the caves are many of seals and penguins, as well as shellfish such as limpets; Middle Stone Age Africans are the first people for whom there is even a hint that they exploited the seashore. However, the caves contain very few remains of fish or flying birds, undoubtedly because people still lacked fishhooks and nets.

The mammal bones from the caves include those of quite a few medium-size species, predominant among which are those of the eland, an antelope species. Eland bones in the caves represent animals of all ages, as if people had somehow managed to capture a whole herd and kill every individual. The secret to the hunters' success is most likely that eland are rather tame and easy to drive in herds. Probably the hunters occasionally managed to drive a whole herd over a cliff: that would explain why the distribution of eland ages among the cave kills is like that in a living herd. In contrast, more dangerous prey such as Cape buffalo, pigs, elephants, and rhinos yield a very different picture. Buffalo bones in the caves are mostly of very young or very old individuals, while pigs, elephants, and rhinos are virtually unrepresented.

So Middle Stone Age Africans can be considered big-game hunters, but just barely. They either avoided dangerous species entirely or confined themselves to weak old animals or babies. Those choices reflect prudence: their weapons were still spears for thrusting rather than bows and arrows, and—along with drinking a strychnine cocktail—poking an adult rhino or Cape buffalo with a spear ranks as one of the most effective means of suicide that I know. As with earlier peoples and modern Stone Age hunters, I suspect that plants and small game made up most of the diet of these not-so-great hunters. They were definitely more effective than baboons, but not up to the skill of modern Bushmen and Pygmies.

Thus, the scene that the human world presented from around 130,000 years ago to somewhat before 50,000 years ago was this: Northern Europe, Siberia, Australia, and the whole New World were still empty of people. In the rest of Europe and western Asia lived the Neanderthals; in Africa, people increasingly like us in anatomy; and in eastern Asia, people unlike either the Neanderthals or Africans but known from only a few bones. All three populations were still primitive in their tools, behavior, and limited innovativeness. The stage was set for the Great Leap Forward. Which among these three contemporary populations would take that leap?

The evidence for an abrupt change—at last!—is clearest in France and Spain, in the late Ice Age around 35,000 years ago. Where there had previously been Neanderthals, anatomically fully modern people (often known as Cro-Magnons, from the French site where their bones were first identified) now appear. Were one of those gentlemen or ladies to stroll down the Champs Elysées in modern attire, he or she would not stand out from the Parisian crowds in any way. Cro-Magnons' tools are as dramatic as their skeletons; they are far more diverse in form and obvious in function than any in the earlier archeological record. They suggest that modern anatomy had at last been joined by modern innovative behavior.

Many of the tools continue to be of stone, but they are now made from thin blades struck off a larger stone, thereby yielding roughly ten times more cutting edge from a given quantity of raw stone. Standardized bone and antler tools appear for the first time. So do unequivocal compound tools of several parts tied or glued together, such as spear points set in shafts or ax heads hafted to handles. Tools fall into many distinct categories whose function is often obvious, such as needles, awls, and mortars and pestles. Rope, used in nets or snares, accounts for the frequent bones of foxes, weasels, and rabbits at Cro-Magnon sites. Rope, fishhooks, and net sinkers explain the bones of fish and flying birds at contemporary South African sites.

Sophisticated weapons for killing dangerous animals at a distance now appear also—weapons such as barbed harpoons, darts, spear-throwers, and bows and arrows. South African caves now yield bones of such vicious prey as adult Cape buffalo and pigs, while European caves are full of bones of bison, elk, reindeer, horse, and ibex.

Several types of evidence testify to the effectiveness of late Ice Age people as big-game hunters. Bagging some of these animals must have required communal hunting methods based on detailed knowledge of each species' behavior. And Cro-Magnon sites are much more numerous than those of earlier Neanderthals or Middle Stone Age Africans, implying more success at obtaining food. Moreover, numerous species of big animals that had survived many previous ice ages became extinct toward the end of the last ice age, suggesting that they were exterminated by human hunters' new skills. Likely victims include Europe's woolly rhino and giant deer, southern Africa's giant buffalo and giant Cape horse, and—once improved technology allowed humans to occupy new environments—the mammoths of North America and Australia's giant kangaroos.

Australia was first reached by humans around 50,000 years ago, which implies the existence of watercraft capable of crossing the 60 miles from eastern Indonesia. The occupation of northern Russia and Siberia by at least 20,000 years ago depended on many advances: tailored clothing, as evidenced by eyed needles, cave paintings of parkas, and grave ornaments marking outlines of shirts and trousers; warm furs, indicated by fox and wolf skeletons minus the paws (removed in skinning and found in a separate pile); elaborate houses (marked by postholes, pavements, and walls of mammoth bones) with elaborate fireplaces; and stone lamps to hold animal fat and light the long Arctic nights. The occupation of Siberia in turn led to the occupation of North America and South America around 11,000 years ago.

Whereas Neanderthals obtained their raw materials within a few miles of home, Cro-Magnons and their contemporaries thought Europe practiced long-distance trade, not only for raw materials for tools but also for "useless" ornaments. Tools of obsidian, jasper, and flint are found hundreds of miles from where those stones were quarried. Baltic amber reached southeast Europe, while Mediterranean shells were carried to inland parts of France, Spain, and the Ukraine.

The evident aesthetic sense reflected in late Ice Age trade relates to the achievements for which we most admire the Cro-Magnons: their art. Best known are the rock paintings from caves like Lascaux, with stunning polychrome depictions of now-extinct animals. But equally impressive are the bas-reliefs, necklaces and pendants, fired-clay sculptures, Venus figurines of women with enormous breasts and buttocks, and musical instruments ranging from flutes to rattles.

Unlike Neanderthals, few of whom lived past the age of 40, some Cro-Magnons survived to 60. Those additional 20 years probably played a big role in Cro-Magnon success. Accustomed as we are to getting our information from the printed page or television, we find it hard to appreciate how important even just one or two old people are in preliterate society. When I visited Rennell Island in the Solomons in 1976, for example, many islanders told me what wild fruits were good to eat, but only one old man could tell me what other wild fruits could be eaten in an emergency to avoid starvation. He remembered that information from a cyclone that had hit Rennell around 1905, destroying gardens and reducing his people to a state of desperation. One such person can spell the difference between death and survival for the whole society.

I've described the Great Leap Forward as if all those advances in tools and art appeared simultaneously 35,000 years ago. In fact, different innovations appeared at different times: spear-throwers appeared before harpoons, beads and pendants appeared before cave paintings. I've also described the Great Leap Forward as if it were the same everywhere, but it wasn't. Among late Ice Age Africans, Ukrainians, and French, only the Africans made beads out of ostrich eggs, only the Ukrainians built houses out of mammoth bones, and only the French painted woolly rhinos on cave walls.

These variations of culture in time and space are totally unlike the unchanging monolithic Neanderthal culture. They constitute the most important innovation that came with the Great Leap Forward: namely, the capacity for innovation itself. To us innovation is utterly natural. To Neanderthals it was evidently unthinkable.

Despite our instant sympathy with Cro-Magnon art, their tools and hunter-gatherer life make it hard for us to view them as other than primitive. Stone tools evoke cartoons of club-waving cavemen uttering grunts as they drag women off to their cave. But we can form d more accurate impression of Cro-Magnons if we imagine what future archeologists will conclude after excavating a New Guinea village site from as recently as the 1950s. The archeologists will find a few simple types of stone axes. Nearly all other material possessions were made of wood and will have perished. Nothing will remain of the multistory houses, drums and flutes, outrigger canoes, and world-quality painted sculpture. There will be no trace of the village's complex language, songs, social relationships, and knowledge of the natural world.

New Guinea material culture was until recently "primitive" (Stone Age) for historical reasons, but New Guineans are fully modern humans. New Guineans whose fathers lived in the Stone Age now pilot airplanes, operate computers, and govern a modern state. If we could carry ourselves back 35,000 years in a time machine, I expect that we would find Cro-Magnons to be equally modern people, capable of learning to fly a plane. They made stone and bone tools only because that's all they had the opportunity to learn how to make.

It used to be argued that Neanderthals evolved into Cro-Magnons within Europe. That possibility now seems increasingly unlikely. The last Neanderthal skeletons from 35,000 to 32,000 years ago were still full-blown Neanderthals, while the first Cro-Magnons appearing in Europe at the same time were already anatomically fully modern. Since anatomically modern people were already present in Africa and the Near East tens of thousands of years earlier, it seems much more likely that such people invaded Europe rather than evolved there.

What happened when invading Cro-Magnons met the resident Neanderthals? We can be certain only of the result: within a few thousand years no more Neanderthals. The conclusion seems to me inescapable that Cro-Magnon arrival somehow caused Neanderthal extinction. Yet many anthropologists recoil at this suggestion of genocide and invoke environmental changes instead—most notably, the severe Ice Age climate. In fact, Neanderthals thrived during the Ice Age and suddenly disappeared 42,000 years after its start and 20,000 years before its end.

My guess is that events in Europe at the time of the Great Leap Forward were similar to events that have occurred repeatedly in the modern world, whenever a numerous people with more advanced technology invades the lands of a much less numerous people with less advanced technology. For instance, when European colonists invaded North America, most North American Indians proceeded to die of introduced epidemics; most of the survivors were killed outright or driven off their land; some adopted European technology (horses and guns) and resisted for some time; and many of those remaining were pushed onto lands the invaders did not want, or else intermarried with them. The displacement of aboriginal Australians by European colonists, and of southern African San populations (Bushmen) by invading Iron Age Bantu-speakers, followed a similar course.

By analogy, I suspect that Cro-Magnon diseases, murders, and displacements did in the Neanderthals. It may at first seem paradoxical that Cro-Magnons prevailed over the far more muscular Neanderthals, but weaponry rather than strength would have been decisive. Similarly, humans are now threatening to exterminate gorillas in central Africa, rather than vice versa. People with huge muscles require lots of food, and they thereby gain no advantage if less-muscular people can use tools to do the same work.

Some Neanderthals may have learned Cro-Magnon ways and resisted for a while. This is the only sense I can make of a puzzling culture called the Chatelperronian, which coexisted in western Europe along with a typical Cro-Magnon culture (the so-called Aurignacian culture) for a short time after Cro-Magnons arrived. Chatelperronian stone tools are a mixture of typical Neanderthal and Cro-Magnon tools, but the bone tools and art typical of Cro-Magnons are usually lacking. The identity of the people who produced Chatelperronian culture was debated by archeologists until a skeleton unearthed with Chatelperronian artifacts at Saint-Césaire in France proved to be Neanderthal. Perhaps, then, some Neanderthals managed to master some Cro-Magnon tools and hold out longer than their fellows.

What remains unclear is the outcome of the interbreeding experiment posed in science fiction novels. Did some invading Cro-Magnon men mate with some Neanderthal women? No skeletons that could reasonably be considered Neanderthal-Cro-Magnon hybrids are known. If Neanderthal behavior was as relatively rudimentary and Neanderthal anatomy as distinctive as I suspect, few Cro-Magnons may have wanted to mate with Neanderthals. And if Neanderthal women were geared for a 12-month pregnancy, a hybrid fetus might not have survived. My inclination is to take the negative evidence at face value, to accept that hybridization occurred rarely if ever, and to doubt that any living people carry any Neanderthal genes.

So much for the Great Leap Forward in western Europe. The replacement of Neanderthals by modern people occurred somewhat earlier in eastern Europe, and still earlier in the Near East, where possession of the same area apparently shifted back and forth between Neanderthals and modern people from 90,000 to 60,000 years ago. The slowness of the transition in the Near East, compared with its speed in western Europe, suggests that the anatomically modern people living around the Near East before 60,000 years ago had not yet developed the modern behavior that ultimately let them drive out the Neanderthals.

Thus, we have a tentative picture of anatomically modern people arising in Africa over 100,000 years ago, but initially making the same tools as Neanderthals and having no advantage over them. By perhaps 60,000 years ago, some magic twist of behavior had been added to the modern anatomy. That twist (of which more in a moment) produced innovative, fully modern people who proceeded to spread westward into Europe, quickly supplanting the Neanderthals. Presumably, they also spread east into Asia and Indonesia, supplanting the earlier people there of whom we know little. Some anthropologists think that skull remains of those earlier Asians and Indonesians show traits recognizable in modern Asians and aboriginal Australians. If so, the invading moderns may not have exterminated the original Asians without issue, as they did the Neanderthals, but instead interbred with them.

Two million years ago, several protohuman lineages existed side-by-side until a shakedown left only one. It now appears that a similar shakedown occurred within the last 60,000 years and that all of us today are descended from the winner of that shakedown. What was the Magic Twist that helped our ancestor to win?

The question poses an archeological puzzle without an accepted answer. You can speculate about the answer as well as I can. To help you, let me review the pieces of the puzzle: Some groups of humans who lived in Africa and the Near East over 60,000 years ago were quite modern in their anatomy, as far as can be judged from their skeletons. But they were not modern in their behavior. They continued to make Neanderthal-like tools and to lack innovation. The Magic Twist that produced the Great Leap Forward doesn't show up in fossil skeletons.

There's another way to restate that puzzle. Remember that we share 98 percent of our genes with chimpanzees. The Africans making Neanderthal-like tools just before the Great Leap Forward had covered almost all of the remaining genetic distance from chimps to us, to judge from their skeletons. Perhaps they shared 99.9 percent of their genes with us. Their brains were as large as ours, and Neanderthals' brains were even slightly larger. The Magic Twist may have been a change in only 0.1 percent of our genes. What tiny change in genes could have had such enormous consequences?

Like some others who have pondered this question, I can think of only one plausible answer: the anatomical basis for spoken complex language. Chimpanzees, gorillas, and even monkeys are capable of symbolic communication not dependent on spoken words. Both chimpanzees and gorillas have been taught to communicate by means of sign language, and chimpanzees have learned to communicate via the keys of a large computer-controlled console. Individual apes have thus mastered "vocabularies" of hundreds of symbols. While scientists argue over the extent to which such communication resembles human language, there is little doubt that it constitutes a form of symbolic communication. That is, a particular sign or computer key symbolizes a particular something else.

Primates can use as symbols not just signs and computer keys but also sounds. Wild vervet monkeys, for example, have a natural form of symbolic communication based on grunts, with slightly different grunts to mean *leopard*, *eagle*, and *snake*. A month-old chimpanzee named Viki, adopted by a psychologist and his wife and reared virtually as their daughter, learned to "say" approximations of four words: *papa*, *mama*, *cup*, and *up*. (The chimp breathed rather than spoke the words.) Given this capability, why have apes not gone on to develop more complex natural languages of their own?

The answer seems to involve the structure of the larynx, tongue, and associated muscles that give us fine control over spoken sounds. Like a Swiss watch, our vocal tract depends on the precise functioning of many parts. Chimps are thought to be physically incapable of producing several of the commonest vowels. If we too were limited to just a few vowels and consonants, our own vocabulary would be greatly reduced. Thus, the Magic Twist may have been some modifications of the protohuman vocal tract to give us finer control and permit formation of a much greater variety of sounds. Such fine modifications of muscles need not be detectable in fossil skulls.

It's easy to appreciate how a tiny change in anatomy resulting in capacity for speech would produce a huge change in behavior. With language, it takes only a few seconds to communicate the message, "Turn sharp right at the fourth tree and drive the male antelope toward the reddish boulder, where I'll hide to spear it." Without language, that message could not be communicated at all. Without language, two protohumans could not brainstorm together about how to devise a better tool. or about what a cave painting might mean. Without language, even one protohuman would have had difficulty thinking out for himself or herself how to devise a better tool.

I don't suggest that the Great Leap Forward began as soon as the mutations for altered tongue and larynx anatomy arose. Given the right anatomy, it must have taken humans thousands of years to perfect the structure of language as we know it—to hit on the concepts of word order and case endings and tenses, and to develop vocabulary. But if the Magic Twist did consist of changes in our vocal tract that permitted fine control of sounds, then the capacity for innovation that constitutes the Great Leap Forward would follow eventually. It was the spoken word that made us free.

This interpretation seems to me to account for the lack of evidence for Neanderthal-Cro-Magnon hybrids. Speech is of overwhelming importance in the relations between men and women and their children. That's not to deny that mute or deaf people learn to function well in our culture, but they do so by learning to find alternatives for an existing spoken language. If Neanderthal language was much simpler than ours or nonexistent, it's not surprising that Cro-Magnons didn't choose to associate with Neanderthals.

I've argued that we were fully modern in anatomy and behavior and language by 35,000 years ago and that a Cro-Magnon could have been taught to fly an airplane. If so, why did it take so long after the Great Leap Forward for us to invent writing and build the Parthenon? The answer may be similar to the explanation why the Romans, great engineers that they were, didn't build atomic bombs. To reach the point of building an A-bomb required 2,000 years of technological advances beyond Roman levels, such as the invention of gunpowder and calculus, the development of atomic theory, and the isolation of uranium. Similarly, writing and the Parthenon depended on tens of thousands of years of cumulative developments after the Great Leap Forward—developments that included, among many others, the domestication of plants and animals.

Until the Great Leap Forward, human culture developed at a snail's pace for millions of years. That pace was dictated by the slowness of genetic change. After the Great Leap Forward, cultural development no longer depended on genetic change. Despite negligible changes in our anatomy, there has been far more cultural evolution in the past 35,000 years than in the millions of years before. Had a visitor from outer space come to Earth before the Great Leap Forward, humans would not have stood out as unique among the world's species. At most, we might have been mentioned along with beavers, bowerbirds, and army ants as examples of species with curious behavior. Who could have foreseen the Magic Twist that would soon make us the first species, in the history of life on Earth, capable of destroying all life?

Article Questions

1. What three changes took place in human development to distinguish them from apes?

2. What physical characteristics are evident in the development of *homo erectus*?

3. Approximately when did the Great Leap Forward occur?

4. What misconceptions does the author mention regarding popular beliefs about Neanderthals?

5. What conclusions might be drawn from the fact that tools used 40,000 years ago by Neanderthals differed little from those used by him 100,000 years ago?

6. What human behaviors have been found in the investigation of Neanderthal societies?

7. What are some basic differences between the Neanderthal and the Cro-Magnon of the Great Leap Forward?

8. Speculate why today's society would find a more comfortable link with Cro-Magnon society.

9. Discuss why a possible encounter between Cro-Magnon and Neanderthal societies might have meant an end to Neanderthal life.

from A History of Civilization

Crane Brinton, John Christopher, Robert Lee Wolff, and Robin Winks

When the Liverpool and Manchester Railway line opened in September of 1830, the railway train—drawn by the *Rocket*, then the fastest and strongest of the locomotives— ran down and killed William Huskisson, a leading British politician and an ardent advocate of improving transport and communication, who had underestimated its speed. This, the first railway accident in history, was symbolic of the new age to come, which benefited many, brought destruction to some, and transformed society far more rapidly than anyone had predicted. In due course the railroad would tie continents together with ribbons of steel, virtually changing how people calculated distance. After the railway age, travelers in England would speak of distances in terms of the time it took to travel them, rather than in terms of miles.* More than any other new instrument of technology, the railroad was indicative of the changes wrought in human lives by the Industrial Revolution.

The Industrial Revolution would, in time, produce a global economy in which developments in a remote corner of a colonial empire would influence price, population, and social customs in European metropolitan centers. The Industrial Revolution proceeded in stages—none so clearly marked as economic historians once assumed, though with relatively clear links of cause and effect between one industrial, financial, or technological development and another—the speed and sometimes sequence of which differed in different nations. Along with an economic revolution in Britain, a political revolution continued in France, which deeply influenced industrial development. This dual revolution led to patterns of cause and effect that are so complex that philosophers, economists, and political scientists continue to argue about their meanings today. These arguments—in defense of capitalism, in support of socialism, in advocacy of communism—produced ideologies so powerful that their exponents often dominated the intellectual history of their time: Marxism, Leninism, and the array of attacks upon the capitalist mode of production grew out of debates in the Industrial Revolution.

Frequently necessity did prove to be the mother of invention. As each new machine, each new adjustment in manufacturing technique produced the need for yet another new machine or another adjustment in the laboring force, inventors, entrepreneurs, and managers showed remarkable innovative capacity. Urbanization accelerated because industry worked best on the basis of concentrated centers of production. Concentrated in these specific centers of production and often working at the same job, laborers developed a sense of class consciousness. Periodic dislocations in the market, overproduction, or perhaps the failure to procure a needed supply of raw materials sometimes led to unemployment and the insecurity of not knowing whether one would, though employed today, be employed tomorrow. The cities thus became centers for both the laboring classes and "the dangerous classes"—those who through discontent, anger, despair, or the inability to find a role to play in an increasingly complex, specialized working class, turned to lives of crime. Simultaneously, a transportation revolution—the railroad on land and the steamship by sea—brought the problems and the successes of one area ever more quickly to another.

The Industrial Revolution was truly a revolution in both senses of the word. It transformed the lives of millions of people, first in western Europe and the United States but eventually in central and eastern Europe and in the overseas empires of the European powers. And it proceeded to "revolve," to unfold at greater speed, to influence those who thought of themselves as distant from the centers of production or unconcerned with the changes brought to society. Just as mechanization of one stage of textile manufacturing virtually demanded mechanization of the next stage, so did changes in the relationships between stages of production lead to changes in the nature of labor, of the family, of nutrition, and of disease. Even though most nineteenth-century Europeans continued to be agricultural laborers despite industrialization, the great economic crises of the century— in the 184()s, in 1857, and most dramatically in 1873—affected all. By the end of the century the tensions between nations, between classes, and between the various reform-minded and conservative groups became acute. By the 1890s the Industrial Revolution had produced an industrial society.

The industrial society developed different tastes in art, literature, and music. Interest in science became increasingly utilitarian: science that could be applied to industry was valued above science that was purely speculative. In the middle of the nineteenth century the revolutionary theory of evolution—applied originally to biology but quickly adapted to economics, society, and even politics—reinforced an emphasis on competition, on survival by contest. The search for knowledge became less intuitive, less romantic, and more capable of being quantified, more open to statistics, research, and the "objective" gathering of data. Competition between nations, between businesses, even between individuals and teams through organized athletics, would mark the industrial society. Realistic and naturalistic fiction would reflect a growing sense of historical determinism. Yet there would also be a continuity of optimism, from the "springtime of the peoples" in 1848 to "the century of hope"—a widely felt sense that the future held virtually unlimited progress for all humanity.

I. Stages of Industrial Growth

Economic change generally takes place gradually, and therefore some historians feel it is misleading to speak of an industrial *revolution*, since the process was clearly evolutionary, rather than revolutionary. However, growth did not proceed at an even pace, and developments in one country or one sector of industry often altered circumstances so rapidly as virtually to transform styles of life and modes of work within a generation or less. Generally, the growth of industry was identified with the introduction of machine production, making mass markets possible and the factory system essential.

A History of Civilization

Historians once believed that production expanded most rapidly at moments of economic "take-off," when various factors that had blocked sustained growth were removed by the forces of capitalism. Among the factors often credited with the economic take-off that ushered in the nineteenth century were the rise of a merchant class during the Renaissance, colonialism and mercantilism, the American and French revolutions, the rise of the competitive state system, the Protestant emphasis on hard work and material progress as signs of salvation, the rise of modern science, and the social theories of the philosophers. Obviously these all played a role, though historians no longer generally agree that a sharp line separated the Industrial Revolution from the years that preceded it. They do, however, generally agree that between the 1820s and the 1890s industrialization spread from England across Europe and eventually to Russia in four stages; the textile industry was generally the first to be mechanized, followed by metals, chemicals, and ultimately electricity. The first stage was a transition from agricultural to industrial priorities for society. Industrial expansion accelerated as capital was mobilized, raw materials were secured through treaty or annexation, managerial skills were developed, and unified national states turned to the business of competition for markets, influence, and prestige.

The first developments were in textiles, in which Britain led. The second stage was in metallurgy, in which Belgium joined Britain in leadership until Germany overtook both around 1900 (and the United States, in turn, overtook them). In the third stage the chemical industry developed from improvements in mining techniques. By the 1850s new methods for recovering minerals from the earth meant that potassium, phosphate, sulfur, and rock salt were the center of attention; these, in turn, made the development of new fertilizers possible, vastly increasing the productivity of the soil. The fourth stage came after the 1890s, first in Britain and Germany, when electronics marked the move to a new form of industry based on more specialized skills. By 1914 Germany led the world in the production of lights, cables, generators, transformers, ultimately transforming both public and private life by bringing appliances within reach of thousands of purchasers. The age of the consumer had begun.

As each stage led to another, profits built up, so that capital tended to move from the west, where capital was first amassed, to the east. Investment in industry soon led to significant growth in all forms of transportation and in mining. Thus a factory working class was created throughout Europe, drawn largely from rural areas to cities near the resources most needed: Birmingham in England, Mulhouse in France, Kiev in Russia. Industrial growth occurred in the traditional commercial centers as well.

British Leadership, 1760-1850

The process of industrialization began in Britain. After the 1760s England enjoyed a long period of relative economic prosperity. England's growth rate was little more than one percent a year in the volume of goods and services produced, but this modest growth was constant, and its cumulative effect was substantial. Starting in the sixteenth century, a new group of landed proprietors— squires and townspeople—saw land as an investment; thus they were concerned with improved production and profit. The enclosure movement had, in effect, transformed estates into compact farms, set off from others by fences or hedgerows. Their relatively small, private owners were less interested in family inheritance than in sustained growth. Marginal cottagers and garden farmers were eliminated, landowners were freed from manorial restrictions on farming practices, and the division of markets and of labor stimulated individual and geographically localized productivity.

A sharp rise in the price of grain, caused by wars and by industrialization in local centers such as Manchester, meant that more land was put into crops, leading to a greater demand for labor. Waste lands were put into production for vegetable crops to feed to animals, and eastern England in particular became a center of experimentation with new fertilizers, crops, and methods of crop rotation. Wealthy, aristocratic proprietors adopted the new methods and also financed canals, roads, mines, and eventually railroads to carry their produce to market. By 1800 English agriculture was probably the most efficient in Europe.

This increased productivity led to a rapid growth in population in England and Wales—from seven and a half million in 1751 to twenty-one million in 1851—creating a large pool of workers for the new industries. A long, sustained series of victories over foreign enemies—the Church of Rome and the Spain of Philip II in the sixteenth century, the Dutch in the seventeenth, and the French in the eighteenth—had given England the self-confidence, unity, and pride to take advantage of economic good fortune.

This good fortune was enhanced not only by ample supplies of capital from foreign and colonial trade but also by the possession of large deposits of coal and iron. The geographical compactness of the British Isles made shipments from mine to smelter and from mill to seaport short, fast, and cheap. The marginal farmers, and also the Irish, driven from their overpopulated and famine-ridden island, formed a large reservoir of eager labor, so that managers could accurately predict levels of productivity and meet orders faithfully, earning Britain an early reputation for dependability in trade. The Napoleonic wars further stimulated the demand for metal goods and the invention of new machines. The construction of great new docks along the lower Thames between 1802 and 1807 further assured London of its position as the economic center of Europe.

Thus the twin needs of economic activity were met: labor and capital. The rising population became a market for simple manufactured goods while also supplying labor. Women and children were employed, especially in the textile industries, because thy could be paid less and were best suited to jobs requiring dexterity of hand and eye rather than a strong back. The large landowners had capital to spare, and from their ranks, and even more from the ranks of the middle class, came the entrepreneurs who, though not inventors, knew how to adapt the inventions of others to new problems for a profit. The middle class enjoyed a secure social status, as they did not on the Continent, for the law of primogeniture (by which land passed undivided to the eldest son) prevented the division of estates into uneconomic small parcels. Since second sons could not inherit the estate though they were gentlemen in birth and education, they could enter trade, the military, the church, and the colonial service without serious social stigma. To be a "counter-jumper" (a merchant) while not aristocratic, was no disgrace in England, as it continued to be in parts of the Continent. Economically, socially, and politically, Britain was in an excellent position for the first phase of its Industrial Revolution, from the 1760s to the 1850s.

Textiles, Coal and Iron

The textile industry, based in Lancashire and especially in Manchester, was the first to exploit the potentialities of power-driven machinery. Beginning with the spinning jenny in the 1760s, the use of machinery gradually spread to other processes. In 1793 an American, Eli Whitney (1765-1825), devised the cotton gin, an engine that separated the fibers of raw cotton from the seeds and enabled a single slave to do what had previously required the hand labor of fifty slaves. Meanwhile, British inventors perfected a power-driven loom for weaving cotton thread into cloth. By 1830 Britain operated more than fifty thousand power looms, and cotton goods accounted for half of its exports. By 1851 the British census listed more than half a million workers employed in cotton manufacturing alone.

Advances in mechanical engineering made this rapid expansion possible. Earlier, for instance, the difficulty of procuring exactly fitting parts had restricted the output of Watt's steam engine. Then British engineers, by studying the precision techniques of watchmakers, devised a lathe that turned screws of almost perfect regularity. They also developed machines for sawing,, boring, and turning the pulley blocks used by British ships in the Napoleonic wars. Meantime, Eli Whitney undertook important experiments at his arms factory in Connecticut, using the concept of standardized and interchangeable parts, one of the basic principles of mass production.

New processes in industry were not uniformly adopted, of course. The revolutionary implications of Whitney's experiments with standardization, for example, were long ignored by manufacturers. The survival of handicraft techniques and the workers' fear that they would be displaced by machines also slowed down the process of mechanization. Even in the cotton industry, weaving on the hand loom continued in areas with an especially large reservoir of cheap labor, like Ireland and central Europe, where peasants could produce cloth in the privacy of their cottages and be paid by the piece. In the woolen and clothing industries, mechanization did not come until the 1850s, when Britain produced a machine for combing, wool, and an American, Isaac Singer (1811-1875), popularized the sewing machine.

Coal ranked with cotton as an industry that pioneered in the solution of technical problems. Steam engines were used to pump water from the mines; ventilating shafts and power fans supplied them with fresh air; and safety lamps gave miners some protection against dangerous underground gases. The coal output of Britain, the world's leading producer, rose steadily from about sixteen million tons in 1816 to sixty-five million in 1856. The consumption of coal mounted because of its increased use as a household fuel in wood-short Britain, its importance in producing steam power, and its vital contribution to the expanding iron industry, which required large quantities of coal to make the coke used in smelting.

The efficiency of smelting advanced rapidly after the development of the blast furnace (1828), in which fans provided a blast of hot air to intensify the action of the hot coke on the iron. Thanks to the blast furnace, Britain produced iron strong enough for use in bridges and in factory buildings. Yet the best grade of iron lacked the tremendous strength of steel, which is iron purified of all but a minute fraction of carbon by a process of prolonged, intense heating. Steel for industrial purposes could be made in the early 1800s, but only by ruinously expensive methods. Then in 1856 the Englishman Henry Bessemer (1813-1898) invented the converter, which accelerated the removal of impurities by shooting jets of compressed air into the molten metal. A decade later William Siemens (1823-1883), a German living in England, devised the open-hearth process, which utilized scrap as well as new iron, and which handled larger amounts of metal than the converter could. The inventions of Bessemer and Siemens lowered the cost of making steel so substantially that the world output increased tenfold between 1865 and 1880. The nineteenth century ushered in a new iron age.

Transport and Communication

Steam, coal, and iron brought the railway age. Coal powered the railways and the railways carried coal. Though railways based on wooden rails were known from the sixteenth century, iron and steel rails made it possible to carry huge weights and mount giant locomotives to pull long trains; and three hundred tons of iron were required to lay a single mile of railroad track. Canals and hard-surfaced roads had preceded railroads in Europe and North America. A Scot, John McAdam (1756-1836), had devised a means of surfacing ("macadamizing") roads so that they could be traveled in all weather, but extra heavy shipments nonetheless broke the road's surface. The railway was the answer, once cast iron rails were developed by Abraham Darby's foundry in 1767. By the 1820s only mechanization remained to be accomplished. George Stephenson (1781-1848) and others put the steam engine on wheels and created the modern locomotive. Thus it was that Stephenson's *Rocket* traversed twelve miles in fifty-three minutes on the new Liverpool and Manchester Railway in 1830! The railroad-building boom was soon in full swing: Britain had 500 miles of track in 1838, 6,600 miles in 1850, and 15,500 in 1870.

Steam also affected water transport, though at a less revolutionary pace. Robert Fulton's (1765-1815) steamboat, the *Clermont*, made a successful trip on the Hudson River in 1807, and soon paddle-wheel steamers plied the inland waterways of the United States and Europe. Ocean-going steamships, however, were uneconomical to operate because of the inefficiency of their engines. When the Scot Samuel Cunard inaugurated the first regular transatlantic steamer service (between Liverpool and Boston in 1840), the coal required for the voyage took up almost half the space on his vessels. Consequently, only passengers and mail went by steamship, most freight being handled by sailing ships. Finally, in the 1860s, the development of improved marine engines and the substitution of the screw propeller for the paddle wheel forecast the doom of the commercial sailing vessel.

These many improvements in transport by sea and land promoted industrial expansion by creating the need for machines to make the new equipment, by facilitating shipments of raw materials and finished products, and by opening up almost the whole world as a potential market.

Communications also experienced radical improvement. In 1840 Great Britain inaugurated the penny post, which enabled a letter to go from London to Edinburgh, for instance, at the cost of one penny, less than a tenth of the old rate. This provided an inexpensive means by which a family, perhaps separated by the need to look for work, could stay in touch. More dramatic was the utilization of electricity for instantaneous communication, beginning with the first telegraph message, from Baltimore to Washington in 1844. Then came the first submarine cable (under the English Channel) in 1851, the first transatlantic cable in 1866, and the first telephone in 1876.

This communications revolution was not limited to Britain. Belgium also used the turnpike principle, establishing all-weather roads financed by tolls, so that by 1850 most major centers were reachable even in the worst weather. The industrializing Rhineland provinces of Prussia improved their roads, as did France, which also built an ambitious system of canals. The Ruhr River valley, made navigable by 1780, was tied in by roads and canals to the rest of Germany, France, and the Low Countries. But canals were frequently built too soon, before there was enough traffic to pay for them. It was the railways, which could satisfy many objectives, such as transporting goods, passengers, and armies, and eventually providing access to seaside resorts as a taste for leisure developed, that truly transformed the Continent as they had Britain.

Though the first British railroad opened in 1830, the rest of Europe was not far behind: France in 1832, Germany and Belgium in 1835, Russia in 1837, Austria in 1838, Italy and Holland in 1839, Denmark and Switzerland in 1847, Spain in 1848. By 1870, 897,000 miles of rails had been laid in western Europe, the United States had its own transcontinental line, and railroads were flourishing in Canada and in faraway Australia. The lines differed in one important respect, however. In Britain traffic for the lines existed before they were built, and railway companies could easily find private capital for finances. In western Europe and in much of the United States, however, lines were built as traffic grew to require them, and private capital needed a government guarantee or subsidy, since the profit margin was precarious. In eastern Europe lines were built well before there was enough traffic to make them profitable, and state financing was necessary. Thus a varying pattern of private capital, state-aided capital, foreign capital, and state-controlled capital developed. In Britain the railways boosted an industrial revolution already in progress; in western Europe the railways often created the revolution; in eastern Europe, to which the iron, rails, locomotives, engineers, and capital all had to be imported, the railway boom led countries into debt and threatened ruin. Thus the railroad was a true symbol of the diversity of responses to industrialization and modern capitalism.

Money, Banking, and Limited Liability

The exploitation of these new developments required a constant flow of fresh capital. From the first, the older commercial community supported the young industrial community. The slave traders of Liverpool financed the cotton mills of Lancashire, thereby increasing the demand for American cotton fiber and for slaves to work the plantations. Tobacco merchants of Glasgow provided the funds that made their city the foremost industrial center of Scotland, and tea merchants in London and Bristol aided the ironmasters of South Wales. Bankers played such an important role that the Barings of London and the international house of Rothschild were among the great powers of Europe. In the early nineteenth century each of five Rothschild brothers, sons of a German Jewish banker, established himself in an important economic center—London, Paris, Frankfurt, Naples, and Vienna. The Rothschilds prospered because, in an age of frequent speculation, they avoided unduly risky undertakings, and because they facilitated investment by residents of one state in the projects of other states. The Paris Rothschild, for instance, negotiated the investment of British capital in the construction of French railroads during the 1840s.

Banks further assisted economic expansion by promoting the use of checks and banknotes in place of coins. During the Napoleonic wars, when the shortage of coins forced some British mill owners to pay their workers in goods, the British government empowered local banks to issue paper notes supplementing the meager supply of coins. But whenever financial crises occurred—and they came frequently before 1850—dozens of local banks failed, and their notes became valueless. Parliament therefore encouraged the absorption of shaky banks by the more solid institutions, and in 1844 it gave the Bank of England a virtual monopoly on issuing banknotes, thus providing a reliable paper currency. It also applied, first to railroads and then to other companies, the principle of limited liability (indicated by "Ltd." after the name of British firms). Earlier, the shareholders in most British companies were subject to unlimited liability, and they might find their personal fortunes seized to satisfy the creditors of an unsuccessful company. The practice of limiting each shareholder's liability to the face value of that person's shares encouraged investment by diminishing its risks.

By the midnineteenth century, the tangible signs of Britain's economic predominance were evident on every hand—in the teeming docks and thriving financial houses of London, in the mushrooming factory and mining towns of the Midlands, the north of England, and Scotland, and in other quarters of the globe as well. British capital and thousands of skilled British workers participated in the construction of French railroads. American trains ran on rails rolled in British mills and on the capital from British investors. Cotton goods made in Lancashire clothed a sizable part of the world's population, and British entrepreneurs and investors would finance the opening of great cattle ranches in the American West in the next decades

Yet Britain, even in the heyday of its leadership, did not monopolize inventive skill. The French, for example, devised the chlorine process of bleaching cloth and the Jacquard loom for weaving intricate patterns. German technicians led the world in agricultural chemistry and in the utilization of the valuable byproducts of coal. And from the United States came Eli Whitney and the cotton gin, Samuel F.B. Morse (1791-1872) and the telegraph, Singer and the sewing machine, and the young Cyrus McCormick (1809-1884), whose reaper (1831) was the first of many agricultural machines developed for the vast agricultural expanse of America. In a sense, the whole North Atlantic world, European and North American, constituted an economic, commercial, and financial community.

British Decline

After 1850 Britain began to lose its advantage in this economic community. Politically its leaders had positioned it well to the forefront. The Reform Act of 1832 had put Parliament into the hands of the propertied classes, so that they might pass legislation favorable to industry. In 1846 Parliament had repealed the Corn Laws (in Britain "corn" meant all forms of grain), which had limited the import of grain, and the nation began eighty-five years of nearly tariff-free trade. But the food supply was no longer keeping up, and while the growing empire—the sheep stations of Australia and New Zealand, the vast stretches of prairie in Canada—might meet the need, nearby supplies from Denmark or Holland were obviously cheaper, especially as dietary needs moved from grain and beef to fruit, poultry, and vegetables. With the abolition of the Corn Laws, Britain accepted the principle of heavy specialization, of full commitment to private initiative, private property, and the mechanism of the market place. But this also made Britain increasingly dependent on others for certain necessities, so that it had to be able to assure itself of a supply of those necessities by colonial or foreign policy.

As the middle class became more comfortable and the working class more demanding, the possibilities for peaceful innovation decreased. A period of prolonged inflation, from 1848 to 1873, and another of depression, from 1873 to 1896, intensified the perception of inequalities of wealth. After 1873 British agriculture could no longer compete with the Continent or the United States; agriculture began to stagnate, and the overall rate of British growth decreased.

In the new phase of the Industrial Revolution in Britain, the initial advantage was slowly lost—to Germany, to Belgium, and to the United States. Britain had become a nation of shopkeepers, teacher to the world, but the world had learned to well and had come to the industrial scene later, with newer and better equipment, while Britain continued to work with methods that, while once innovative, were now outmoded. The lead in developing new techniques passed in agricultural machinery to the Americans, in chemical and steel production to the Germans, in electricity to both. England, and particularly London, remained the undoubted financial center of the world, but by 1890 industrial leadership had passed elsewhere, including to Czarist Russia and to Japan.

Industrial and agricultural changes are often mutually dependent. For sustained growth, industry relies on an efficient agriculture for its raw materials and for additions to its labor force, recruited from surplus workers no longer needed on mechanized farms. Agriculture depends on industry for the tools and fertilizers that enable fewer workers to produce more, and to transform farms into agrarian factories. In the nineteenth century factory-made implements like the steel plow and the reaper improved the cultivation of old farmlands and permitted the opening of vast new areas, like the North American prairies, that could scarcely have been touched if the pioneers had had to rely on hand labor alone. The mechanical cream separator raised the dairy industry to a big business, and railroads and steamers sped the transport of produce from farm to market. The processes of canning, refrigeration, and freezing—all industrial in origin and all first applied on a wide scale during the last third of the century—permitted the preservation of many perishable commodities and their shipment halfway around the world.

Farmers found steadily expanding markets both in the industrial demand for raw materials and in the food required by mining and factory towns. International trade in farm products increased rapidly during the second half of the nineteenth century. The annual export of wheat from the United States and Canada rose from 22,000,000 bushels in the 1850s to 150,000,000 in 1880. Imported flour accounted for a quarter of the bread consumed in Britain during the 1850s and for half by the 1870s. Denmark and the Netherlands increasingly furnished the British table with bacon, butter, eggs, and cheese; Australia supplied its mutton, and Argentina its beef.

Germany now partly assumed Britain's old role as the pioneer of scientific agriculture. Shortly after 1800 German experimenters had extracted sugar from beets in commercially important quantities, thus ending Europe's dependence on the cane sugar of the West Indies. In the 1840s the German chemist Justus Liebig (1803-1873) published a series of influential works on the agricultural applications of organic chemistry. Plant growth, Liebig argued, depended on three basic elements: nitrogen, potassium, and phosphorus. But the production of crops and fodder leached these elements from the soil; they had to be returned to it. Liebig's warnings promoted even wider use of fertilizers: guano from the nesting islands of sea birds off the west coast of South America, nitrate from Chile, and potash from European mines.

Generally, farming progressed and prospered in the nineteenth century as never before. Yet the agricultural revolution exacted a price. Faced with the competition of beet sugar, the sugar-cane islands of the west Indies went into a depression from which they did not recover. In the highly industrialized countries the social and political importance of agriculture began to decline. Farming was no longer the principal occupation of the English in the nineteenth century, and land was no longer the yardstick of wealth and power. The urban merchants and manufacturers demonstrated their dominance in British politics when they won, through the Anti-Corn Law League, their campaign to abolish the tariffs on grain, which, they said, kept the price of food high. Decisive in the abolition of the Corn Laws in 1846 was an attack of black rot that devastated the Irish potato crop for two years and made it essential to bring in cheap substitute foods. Even so, the great potato famine in Ireland continued to have disastrous results there, leading to massive abandonment of the land.

Meanwhile, across the Channel, France was industrializing far more slowly. Public finance continued to be unstable, capital formation was far more difficult, and France remained wed to tariff protection, which retarded change. Railways were built far more slowly, and the revolution of 1848, caused by an economic crisis, made French financiers even more hesitant. The French economy remained especially sensitize to movements in world prices, creating more dramatic alterations in growth rates than in Britain. Agriculture remained especially important, and both farm and city workers in France were reluctant to innovate. An "aristocracy of labor" set crafts workers apart from manual laborers, and some of the working class—such as the glassworkers of Carmaux, who occupied an elite position though they lived virtually side by side with lower-class miners—successfully resisted mechanization into the 1890s. To the inhibitions of small farms and inadequate capital was added the effect of equal inheritance laws, which led to the division of land into tiny parcels so that the peasant could not accumulate capital to take risks on new crops. Businesses were owned by single families, who could not be protected by limited liability laws or easily recruit new managers. Since bankruptcy had to be avoided above all else, owners could not afford to take risks with new products or new methods. Economic and social conservatism thus limited efforts to create large-scale production or a high degree of specialization. The social attitudes of the Old Regime persisted down to 1914, the economic attitudes even into the 1930s.

II. Economic and Social Change

The Population Explosion and the Standard of Living

When Britain abandoned any pretense of raising all the basic foods its people needed, its population was growing so rapidly that self-sufficiency was no longer possible. Despite substantial emigration, especially to the colonies, the number of inhabitants in England and Wales more than tripled during the nineteenth century, from about 9,000,000 in 1800 to 32,500,000 in 1900. There is no clear agreement why. Some demographers have attributed this population explosion not to a higher birth rate but to the lowered death rate resulting from the improved food and sanitation—especially cheap, washable cotton materials—brought by industrialism. Others claim that neither diet nor sanitation improved until the second half of the century, and that the population increase in the first half may be attributed to the rural areas and not to the cities, which had a much higher death rate. It is also pointed out that in Russia, still an agrarian country in a preindustrial stage, the population increased proportionately (36,000,000 in 1800, about 100,000,000 in 1900) almost as fast as it did in Britain.

A similar controversy is focused on the extent to which the Industrial Revolution improved the standard of living not just of the new capitalist and managerial classes but of the workers themselves. The overall standard of living in Britain did not begin to improve steadily until after the Napoleonic wars and the immediate postwar slump. After about 1820 the purchasing power of the workers seems to have grown very gradually, as more and cheaper goods became available. Opportunities for steady, regular employment also grew, as did chances for laborers to climb up the economic ladder a rung or two by mastering a skill and getting a better-paying job. But all these factors varied in their effect from industry to industry and from one locality to another; they also fluctuated with the ups and downs of the economic cycle. Many people, consequently, appear to have found that their standard of living was declining.

There is little debate about one most important social result of industrialism—the truly revolutionary changes it caused in the structure and distribution of the population.

Wherever mines and factories were opened, towns and cities appeared. Large areas of once rural England became urban England and a similar transformation was beginning in the lowlands of Scotland around Glasgow, in the northern French plain around Lille, in the Rhineland, and along the rivers of the northeastern United States. The growth of an urban population increased the numbers and influence of the two social classes that form the backbone of an industrial society: business people and workers. Industrialists, bankers, investors, managers, and promoters of every sort joined the already established capitalists to form the modern middle class, or bourgeoisie. Millhands, railway workers, miners, some artisans, clerks, and a host of other recruits swelled the ranks of wage-earning workers.

The impact of capital and labor upon the life of industrial nations was becoming increasingly evident by the middle of the nineteenth century. Some of the signs pointed to steady material progress—better food and the conquest of space by the railroad, the steamship, and the telegraph. Other signs, however, foretold serious dislocation and violent change. The repeal of the Corn Laws buried an old agrarian way of life in Britain, and the collapse of the French railroad boom in the late 1840s suggested that economic slumps in an industrial society might have alarming consequences, for the hundreds of thousands thrown out of work aggravated the political unrest that culminated in the June Days of 1848 in Paris.

The remarkable rise of population tested the earth's resources and environment even before people thought in these terms. Perhaps ten thousand years ago the total population of the globes was under ten million. By 1750, when the modern rise was beginning, the figure was seven hundred and fifty million. By 1930 it was two billion, and only forty-five years later, in 1975, it was double that. Thus, human population expanded to reach its first thousand million over hundreds of thousands of years; the second thousand million was added in a single century; the third in only thirty years, and the fourth in only fifteen. This uncontrollable explosion in population, with its untold impact on the planet's resources, was made evident in the nineteenth century as people flocked to the cities, which grew far more rapidly than sanitation, police or education could provide for, creating teeming slums that bred disease, crime, and discontent. Population growth in England and Wales was even more striking than these figures indicate, as England, and later Belgium, became the most crowded nations in the West; indeed, England had already reached a population density as early as 1600 that the United States would not reach until 1961.

In the midst of the Industrial Revolution, fewer people worried about overpopulation than rejoiced in the growth of the labor force and the increase in potential consumers. Changing moral concerns influenced traditional methods of limiting fertility and births. While population increased in many societies, the growing acceptance of contraceptive methods in post-Revolutionary France and a rise in abortions, despite church opposition to both practices, contributed to a decline in the French birth rate. The death rate had declined in France from about 1800: after 1870 both the death and birth rates declined in England and Wales. Birth rates were related in part to marriage rates, which were related to economic circumstances: as real wages increased, so did marriage rates. In Ireland postponement of marriage was increasingly common, reducing the total number of children a woman might bear in her lifetime. Yet by modern standards the mortality rate remained very high in the first half of the century, largely owing to infectious disease, and while families grew larger in Victorian times because the comfortable middle class could afford to clothe, house, and educate larger families, mortality also increased with increasing family size. Many wives died in childbirth, and men frequently had a succession of children by two or three wives. Cholera, in particular, had a devastating impact on urban populations at midcentury.

However, despite crowded living conditions in cities, overall mortality rates declined throughout Europe, especially after 1850. This was due in good measure to a decline in certain communicable diseases, as scientific research found both causes and cures, often as a by-product of research conducted for military or commercial purposes. Murder, infanticide, and death in war remained commonplace, but starvation and infectious disease were slowly reduced as causes of death, as greater agricultural productivity, better nutrition, and more rapid movement of foodstuffs from area of production to area of need reduced starvation to a local phenomenon in the West. Certain airborne diseases increased—bronchitis, pneumonia, influenza—as people lived and worked closer together, and by 1901 the death rate was higher than in 1854. Some diseases were reduced marginally, despite crowded conditions, as medicine developed means of combating them; measles, whooping cough, and scarlet fever were reduced to common occurrences in childhood but did not normally lead to death, as they once had done. The death rate from tuberculosis, diphtheria, and smallpox was cut drastically. Thus a death rate in 1700 of thirty persons per thousand was reduced most dramatically by bringing infectious diseases under control. Deaths from industrial accidents, war, localized famine, and physical attack remained relatively high, however. Since these forms of death could be attributed to a seen, known cause, much of the element of mystery once attached to death through the intervention of an "unseen hand"—unidentified infections air- or water-born diseases—was removed. Though death remained a frequent occurrence in any family, and though the consolations of religion remained important at the moment of death, men and women of the industrial society nonetheless had reason to think optimistically of the future.

The expectation of the enjoyment of good health, as distinct from the fear of an early death, also increased in the industrial society. Purification of water, efficient disposal of sewage (both requiring public measures, usually by municipalities), and better hygiene—for example, in the introduction of the water closet, or flush toilet; more frequent bathing as water became more readily available; and cleaner bedding—all helped reduce the incidence of typhus. The condition of food improved, though milk—important to childhood diets—remained unpasteurized until after 1900. Because surgery was increasingly performed in well-equipped hospitals with effective anesthesia and antiseptics, especially after the introduction of ether in 1846, certain medical problems no longer led to death—except on the battlefield, where far more soldiers died of disease and infection during surgery than from their wounds. Epilepsy responded to treatment, and new medicines were introduced for many chronic problems.

From the time of Hippocrates to the nineteenth century, few significant new drugs had been developed, and often treatment was totally wrong, according to present-day medical knowledge for a specific disease; for example, sufferers from malaria were subjected to leeching (the drawing of blood from the body, often by blood-sucking insects), which caused dehydration at a time when their bodies needed all their strength and an increase in liquids. But the kind of research on a mass basis that is possible to conduct only on the battlefield or in a hospital led first to the isolation of infectious patients in separate hospital wards after 1875, and then to specific studies of specific diseases, so that a modern pharmacopeia began to emerge from research hospitals by 1900. While some diseases increased, notably cancer, the chances of surviving to die of old age were materially greater at the end of the century than at the beginning. For this decline in mortality, most historians credit contraception, medical care, better nutrition, and new drugs; after amputation, for example, in which over 50 percent of patients had customarily died from shock and loss of blood, blood coagulants and anesthetics reduced the death rate to 35 percent. However, since access to such improvements in health often depended upon the ability to pay, death rates varied substantially according to class.

Class Grievances and Aspirations

Both business people and workers nourished grievances—and aspirations. In the Britain of the 1820s, the new industrialists had small opportunity to mold national policy. Booming industrial cities like Manchester and Birmingham sent not a single representative to the House of Commons. A high proportion of business leaders belonged not to the Church of England but to non-Anglican Protestant "chapels"; nonconformists, as these dissenters were termed, still suffered discrimination when it came to holding public office or sending their sons (not to speak of their daughters) to Oxford or Cambridge. Even in France, despite the gains made since 1789, the bourgeoisie often enjoyed only second-class status.

In Western Europe the middle classes very soon won the place they felt they deserved; in Britain a gradual process of' reform gave them substantially all they wanted. The high spot was the Reform Bill of 1832, which extended the suffrage to the middle class. In 1830 the French bourgeoisie got their citizen-king, and their Belgian counterparts scored a very great advance in political power. In Piedmont the middle class found a sympathetic leader in the aristocratic Cavour and secured at least a narrowly liberal constitution in 1848. In southern and central Europe, by contrast, the waves of revolution that crested in 1848 left the bourgeoisie frustrated and angry.

The grievances of workers were more numerous than those of their masters, and they seemed harder to satisfy. The difficulties may be illustrated by the protracted struggle of laborers to secure the vote and to obtain the right to organize and to carry on union activities. In Britain substantial numbers of workers first won the vote in 1867, a generation after the middle class did. In France universal male suffrage began in 1848. The unified German Empire had a democratic suffrage from its inception in 1871, but without some other institutions of democracy. Elsewhere, universal manhood suffrage came slowly—not until 1893 in Belgium, and not until the twentieth century, in Italy, Austria, Russia, Sweden, Denmark, the Netherlands, and the United States.

During most of the nineteenth century, labor unions and strikes were regarded by employers as improper restraints on the free operation of natural economic laws; accordingly, a specific ban on such a "combinations," as they were termed, was imposed by the British Combination Acts at the close of the eighteenth century.

Parliament moderated the effect of these acts in the 1820s but did not repeal them until 1876. Continental governments imposed similar restrictions, and the July Monarchy in particular repressed strikes with great brutality. France's Le Chapelier Law of 1791 was only relaxed in the 1860s and repealed in 1884. Everywhere labor slowly achieved full legal recognition of the legitimacy of union activities: in 1867 Austria, in 1872 in the Netherlands, and in 1890 in Germany.

Labor's drive for political and legal rights, however, was only a side issue during the early Industrial Revolution. Many workers faced the more pressing problems of finding jobs and making ends meet on wages that ran behind prices. The modern Western world had long experienced the business cycle, with its alternation of full employment and drastic layoffs; the Industrial Revolution intensified the cycle, making boom periods more hectic and widespread depressions, such as the one in the late 1840s, more severe. At first factories made little attempt to provide a fairly steady level of employment. When a batch of orders came in, machines and workers were pushed to capacity until the orders were filled: this was the "brisk time." Then the factory simply shut down to await the next orders.

Excessively long hours, low pay, rigorous discipline, and dehumanizing working conditions were the most common grievances of early industrial workers. Many plants neglected hazardous conditions, and few had safety devices to guard dangerous machinery. Cotton mills maintained the heat and the humidity at an uncomfortable level because threads broke less often in a hot, damp atmosphere. Many workers could not afford decent housing, and if they could afford it, they could not find it. Some few of the new factory towns were well planned, with wide streets and space for yards and parks. Some had an adequate supply of good water and arrangements for disposing of sewage. But many had none of these necessities, and in rapidly growing London the Thames became an open sewer so foul that riverside dwellers were reluctant to open their windows. The life expectancy of a boy born to a working-class family in Manchester was only half that of one born to rural laborers.

The industrial nations also threatened to remain nations of semiliterate; until they made provision for free public schools during the last third of the nineteenth century, education facilities were grossly inadequate. In England, as often as not, only the Sunday school gave the millhand's child a chance to learn the ABCs. A worker with great ambition and fortitude might attend an adult school known as a "mechanics' institute." In the 1840s a third of the men and half of the women married in England could not sign their names on the marriage register and simply made their mark. And no wonder that Benjamin Disraeli, the Tory reformer, in his novel *Sybil* (1845), called Britain "two nations"—the rich and the poor.

Laborers did attempt to join the ranks of the middle class by adhering to the precepts of thrift, hard work, and self-help. Samuel Smiles (1812-1904) pointed the way in a number of books with didactic titles such as *Character, Thrift,* and *Duty,* which preached a doctrine of self-salvation. Through joining a temperance society and by regular attendance at a worker's institute, a laborer might rise to become a master cotton spinner, a head mechanic, even a clergyman, shopkeeper, or schoolmaster. For some, the demands of hard work, self-reliance, and adherence to duty paid off in upward social mobility; for others, whether ill, lazy, unintelligent, rebellious, or simply confused, life was a round of exploitation, poverty, and demoralization. For many, the use of alcohol was a way of forgetting the demands of the day, prostitution a means of income, rigid religious observance a path to peace of mind. Flight into anonymity in another city and perhaps descent into a life of casual crime were equally commonplace. For each success story there was a horror story; for each "improving landlord" there was a district of hovels and tenements where rats spread disease; for each great lady who provided alms for the poor there was a lunatic committed to an asylum for failing to adjust to the industrial society.

Preceding the revolutions of 1848, Europeans discussed at length the "social question," or, as it was as called in Britain, "the condition-of-England question"; these terms were code language for pauperism and the evident decline of the lower classes. Pauperism was most visible in the cities, though conditions of poverty may in fact have been harsher in the countryside. Many social observers, while welcoming the clear benefits arising from industrialization, predicted that social calamity lay ahead. Some thought overpopulation was the main problem and suggested that "redundant populations" be sent overseas to colonies; others thought the problem lay in the decline of agriculture, forcing mechanically unskilled workers to migrate to the cities; yet others thought the oppressive conditions were limited to specific trades and locations. None could agree whether the overall standard of living was increasing for the majority, if at the cost of the minority—nor can historians agree today.

Historians generally do agree on some conclusions, however. There was an aggregate rise in real wages, which went largely, however, to the skilled worker, so that the working class was really two or more classes. Prices for the most basic foodstuffs declined, so that starvation was less likely. Conditions of housing worsened, however, and the urgency of work increased. Workers in traditional handicrafts requiring specialized skills might now have meal on their table three times a week, but workers displaced by a new machine might not have meat at all. Fear of unemployment was commonplace. A millhand could barely earn enough to feed a family of three children if fully employed; economic necessity compelled him to limit the size of his family, even by means morally repugnant to him, and he had to remain docile at work to assure that he would remain employed. Dependence on public charity, with its eroding effects on self-confidence, was necessary during periods of layoffs in the factory. Women and children were drawn increasingly into the labor force, since they would work at half a man's wage or less, and this led to tension between the sexes, since men saw their jobs being taken by women. In Britain, France, Belgium, and Germany half the mill employees were boys and girls under eighteen.

Work began at dawn and ended at dusk; there was no time for leisure, and often the only solace was in sex, increasing the size of the family and adding to the economic burdens of the parents. Food consumption was dreary and often unhealthy: bread, potatoes, some dubious milk, turnips, cabbage, on occasion bacon. Meat was a luxury; in the sixteenth century the average German was estimated to consume two hundred pounds of meat in a year: in the nineteenth century, forty pounds. The workingman and workingwoman, as well as the workingchild, lived at the margin of existence. Yet they did live, as their predecessors might not have done. The statistics support both those who are pessimistic—poverty was widespread—and those who are optimistic—life at a minimal level was now more likely for all. The very concept of the cycle of life had changed; there was a "hierarchy of wretchedness" that was relative rather than absolute, but now was felt all the more acutely.

*While today the clocks of the Trans-Siberian express that makes its way across the Soviet Union are always set on Moscow time, however far from the capital city the train may be, in the United States the railroads have promoted the idea of time *zones*, reflecting more closely the realities of the position of the sun in relation to the speed of travel, so that California is reckoned to be three hours "earlier" than New York.

Article Questions

1. Describe how technological development affected 19th century urbanization.

2. What four areas experienced the greatest rate of technological advancement in the 19th century?

3. What impact did Eli Whitney's invention have on cotton production and, indirectly, slavery?

4. Describe the Bessemer process.

5. Analyze the following statement: "Steam, coal and iron helped produce the railroad age."

6. Generally speaking, what role did industrial technologies play in the improvement of 19th century living standards?

7. What problems, especially for working classes, emerged as a result of the industrial revolution?

8. All things considered, did industrialization produce positive or negative results for society in the 19th century?

Discussion Questions

1. Define Technology. How does Technology differ from science ?

2. Compare the following countries in terms of technological achievement using the criteria listed in the table below.

Countries:
- USA
- Burma
- Amazon Indians

- England
- Pakistan
- Aborigine

- Japan
- Brazil
- The Hottentot

- Singapore
- Vietnam
- Amish

Criterion	Highly Developed Country	Emerging Society	Tribal Society
Population			
Education			
Politics			
Economics			
Communication			
Technology			
Environment			
Language			
Energy			
Religion			

4. Discuss the aspect of technology from cultural views, technical views, and organizational "infra-structure." Do these aspects all have to be included in understanding the focus of technology?

5. How old is the world according to archaelogists? How old is the species of modern man according to anthropologists? What would you consider modern technology? When did modern technology begin?

6. When did man begin to use and make tools? What were some significant characteristics that caused man to progress to to modern man in the way he used his tools and knowledge?

7. What is culture? How does culture interface with technology?

8. Tool development progressed from naturally made tools to industrialized tools to today's highly conceptual informational tools. How has the change of tools changed man, his needs, values, views, and dependencies?

9. For a nation to grow economically, what type of technology do they need? How can this technology be tailored for their needs?

10. There are an estimated 15,000 different cultures on earth, but they are becoming rapidly extinct and many of these cultures will be lost within the next generation. MIT linguist Ken Hale estimates that 3000 of the world's 6000 languages will disappear and that only 300 languages have a secure future. (Reference: *Time*, Sept. 23 '91 - pp. 46-48.) What is lost with this loss of culture and language? How does this tie into technology?

CHAPTER TWO
ENERGY

Energy

Ian Barbour

Until 1800, all world civilizations were based on wood, wind, water, and animal power. The Industrial Revolution in the nineteenth century was the product of technologies powered by coal. The growth of twentieth-century industrial nations was fueled by coal and cheap oil. In the 1960s it was hoped that nuclear reactors would supply much of the world's future energy needs. But by the 1980s it was clear that each of these sources entails high environmental and social costs. Yet we have done little to develop the renewable sources that might replace them or the conservation and efficiency measures that could reduce energy demand.

One-fifth of the world's population now accounts for 70 percent of the world's energy use, which is more than nine times as much per person as in the remaining four-fifths of the world. One person in Western Europe uses as much energy as eighty people in sub-Saharan Africa.[1] A U.S. citizen uses as much as 330 citizens of Bangladesh.[2] The world as a whole could not sustain the rate of energy consumption now enjoyed by industrial nations, which industrialized when coal and oil were relatively cheap. The Third World is trying to industrialize at a time when high energy prices are hindering development plans and adding to already staggering debt loads.

Values are present in energy decisions, whether recognized or not. There are inescapable trade-offs among diverse values: health, justice, participation, economic development, environmental protection, and sustainability. We will look mainly at the social and ethical issues in energy choices, but we cannot ignore technical and economic questions. We must ask both what is technically feasible and what is ethically desirable. Who benefits and who bears the costs and risks of various energy systems? Which technologies accelerate the concentration of economic and political power? Which sources are most promising for developing countries? Which policies take into account the needs of future generations? We will look successively at fossil fuels, nuclear power, renewable sources, and the possibilities for conservation.

I. Fossil Fuels

Oil, natural gas, and coal contain energy that arrived from the sun for millions of years, captured in prehistoric plant life and preserved in the geological strata of a few regions of the earth. Fossil fuels supply 88 percent of the world's purchased energy (excluding nonmarket fuels such as firewood). It is estimated that identified global reserves of oil would last for 44 years, natural gas for 60 years, and coal for three centuries at current depletion rates.[3] However, their geographical distributions are very uneven and their political and environmental costs are very high.

1. Oil and Global Justice

Since 1900, oil has been central in the *military and political involvement* of Britain, France, Germany, Turkey, and then the United States in the Middle East. Japan attacked Pearl Harbor in 1941 because its oil supplies had been cut off and its stores of oil were running low.[4] More recently, three oil price shocks—caused by the OPEC oil embargo in 1973, the Iranian crisis in 1979, and Iraq's invasion of Kuwait in 1990—have brought home the world's dependence on Middle Eastern oil. World oil reserves were 50 percent higher in 1990 than in 1973, but most of the new discoveries were in the Middle East which now holds two-thirds of the world's reserves.[5]

Oil production has been declining in the U.S. since 1970, and it is now falling in the former Soviet Union, Britain, and several other non-OPEC nations. The cost of drilling for deeper deposits and in inaccessible locations (such as Alaska and the North Sea) has been growing. Higher prices encouraged some conservation measures, and world oil consumption fell during the early 1980s. But following the price drop in 1986 it rose again and by 1990 was back to the levels of the late seventies. In 1990, the United States imported almost half its oil, and its current policies will lead to increased dependence on imports in the future.[6]

The prospect that Saddam Hussein might control or influence a large part of *Middle Eastern oil production* was clearly a major factor in the 1991 military intervention by the United States (with some support from other allies). Iraq's invasion of Kuwait and efforts to acquire nuclear weapons posed a threat of further aggressive actions. In the future, nations dependent on Middle Eastern oil will continue to be vulnerable to political changes in a region of long-standing conflicts and great inequalities. Saudi Arabia's autocratic royal family will be under great pressure from Islamic fundamentalists and from impoverished Arab countries that lack oil resources. Imported oil is the largest and fastest-growing component of the U.S. trade deficit. In addition, the military costs of oil imports should really be included in their true costs. For example, keeping shipping lanes open in the Gulf in 1985 cost $200 per barrel of oil shipped, eight times its world price.[7]

Dependence on imported oil has had a devastating impact on the *Third World*. We have seen that oil is crucial for agriculture because it is the main feedstock for fertilizer and petrochemicals as well as the fuel for tractors and irrigation pumps. The profligate use of oil in industrial nations together with OPEC policies in the seventies drove up world prices, and by 1981 developing nations were spending an average 61 percent of their export earnings on oil imports.[8] The high price of kerosene, an oil derivative, accelerated the depletion of firewood and other traditional sources used for heating and cooking.

Within industrial countries, *the politics of oil* are extremely complicated because oil plays such a large part in national life. In the past, oil use has been heavily subsidized through depletion allowances, import quotas, and highway construction funds. A powerful lobby was formed by a coalition of diverse interests: oil companies and oil-producing states; auto, insurance, and highway construction companies; and labor unions. The oil lobby has made large contributions to the campaign funds of the members of Congress who are on committees dealing with energy, and it has actively opposed all attempts to raise auto fuel economy standards. Of the 20 largest U.S. companies 7 are oil companies, and many other industries, such as autos, plastics, and petrochemicals, are dependent on oil.[9] Oil companies have also reduced competition by "vertical integration" (control of oil imports, domestic production, refining, pipelines, and service stations). They have used extensive television and magazine advertising to present their interpretation of the energy situation and the policies they favor.

The use of oil also has serious *environmental consequences*. The Exxon Valdez accident off the Alaska coast in 1989 dramatized the damage to wildlife and coastal beauty that a single human error can perpetrate. Other oil spills have been caused by severe storms, and we can expect such spills to continue, though we could reduce some of the consequences by requiring double-hulled tankers and better standby equipment for more rapid containment. The fuel burned in cars and trucks is a major contributor to urban air pollution, which constitutes a serious hazard to human health. According to the American Lung Association, auto air pollution adds $40 billion to annual American medical bills.[10] The nitrogen oxides and ozone-forming hydrocarbons can be controlled by catalytic converters. But the combustion of any oil product adds carbon dioxide to the air, accelerating global warming from the greenhouse effect discussed below.

The *reduction of oil use* by industrial nations is thus essential for world peace and global justice and also for environmental protection and long-term sustainability. Since transportation accounts for two-thirds of U.S. oil use, and more than half the oil used in many other countries, auto fuel economy standards, alternative fuels, and public transportation are promising starting points, as we will see in section IV. Most conservation measures and renewable energy sources have low environmental impacts, and they rely on local or regional materials, diminishing the international competition for fossil fuels that are so unevenly distributed geographically.

2. Coal and the Environment

The known reserves of coal are larger than those of oil, but the human and environmental costs are greater.

1. Human and Environmental Costs of Mining

The long history of *mine accidents and black lung disease* is a classic instance of high risks falling on one group while benefits accrue to other people. The appalling conditions faced by generations of miners have gradually improved in response to labor union demands and legislated safety standards. Following the U.S. mine safety law passed in 1969, fatalities per million working hours fell from 1.2 in 1970 to 0.3 in 1977, and the incidence of lung disease also dropped sharply. Since then enforcement of safety and ventilation standards has improved somewhat, but even stricter standards and better enforcement would not impose an unreasonable economic cost.[11]

It is sometimes claimed that it is justifiable for *workers to be exposed to higher risks* than the public because the risks are voluntarily accepted. However, a coal miner usually has little geographical mobility or job mobility and may have no alternative to working in a mine. Another defense of occupational hazards is that high-risk jobs, such as the construction of tall buildings, often offer a wage premium. But rates of compensation for comparable risks vary widely, and mine workers have usually been poorly paid compared to industrial workers. Some compensation for injury has been provided under workman's compensation laws and under specific legislation providing payments to miners with black lung disease. It would serve the interests of justice and offer greater incentives to safety if the cost of these payments were paid by those who benefit, such as the consumers of coal-fired electricity.

There are also considerable *environmental impacts* from the mining of coal. Deep-mining wastes have depressed land values, polluted streams, and marred areas of great natural beauty around the world. The strip mining of surface coal has left large areas denuded and subject to rapid erosion. In the United States, a 1977 law required replanting and reclamation measures to be sustained for five years (or ten years in arid areas) with costs passed on to coal users. But reclaimed land often can only be used for pasture, and in semiarid regions, with fragile ecosystems and scarce water, it will take decades for healthy plant life to be restored and some areas will probably remain wastelands.[12]

2. Air Pollution and Acid Rain

Burning coal has even greater human and environmental costs than mining it. Coal contains sulfur compounds which form sulfur dioxide in stack emissions, and these in turn combine with moisture to produce sulfates. These sulfates in *urban air* are a major source of respiratory illness and fatality. Tall smokestacks reduce local sulfate levels but at the expense of increased acid rain at distant points.

Since the late sixties the effects of *acid rain* on the forests and lakes of Europe and North America have been increasing. By 1988, 52 percent of the forests in West Germany had been affected. The U.N. Environmental Program estimates that more than a third of Europe's total forest area has been damaged. In some parts of Eastern Europe, only bare trunks and eroded hillsides mark what were once great forests. Crop losses from sulfates and ozone are difficult to determine, but one recent study puts losses at 5 to 10 percent of production in the United States. In half of the lakes in eastern North America, many species of fish and plants have been wiped out by acidification. In Greece, public monuments and statues have deteriorated more in the last 25 years than in the previous 2400 years.[13]

Effective *pollution control technologies* for acid emissions can be installed. Passing the combustion gases through limestone scrubbers removes 85 percent of the sulfur dioxide. Scrubbers and use of low-sulfur coal account for most of the 28 percent drop in sulfur dioxide emissions in the United States between 1970 and 1987. In 1977, Congress required scrubbers on all new plants, but during the eighties the utilities and eastern coal-producing states lobbied effectively against legislation to require the installation of scrubbers on older plants. By 1990, only 30 percent of U.S. coal-fired capacity had scrubbers, compared to 85 percent in West Germany and over 90 percent in Japan. Japan and Germany are also adding catalytic reducers to remove the nitrogen oxides that produce smaller amounts of acid rain. In Japan, pollution control adds 25 percent to the cost of coal-generated power, but an air pollution disaster has been averted. Newer "clean coal technologies," such as fluidized bed combustion and multistage combustion, offer the prospect of cheaper control of both these air pollutants.[14]

The technology to control sulfur and nitrogen emissions is available, and its installation is primarily a matter of *political will*. The cost of the damage from the emissions clearly exceeds the costs of the control technology, but indirect costs do not appear on industrial balance sheets. During the eighties the U.S. administration gave economic growth priority over environmental preservation, and the conflict of regional interests undermined repeated congressional attempts to strengthen clean air laws. However, greater public interest in clean air and a more pragmatic administration finally produced tighter air emission laws, though still below the standards sought by environmentalists; the 1990 Clean Air Amendments required cutting sulfur dioxide emissions in half by the year 2000. A 1988 directive of the European Economic Community seeks to lower sulfur dioxide levels to 57 percent of the 1980 levels by 2003, and a group of nine countries has pledged a 50 percent reduction.[15]

3. Global Warming: The Greenhouse Effect

The burning of all fossil fuels entails the formation of *carbon dioxide* (CO_2). The enormous quantities released into the air by fossil fuels have increased the CO_2 content of the air by 25 percent in the past hundred years. At the present emission rate it will have doubled by 2030. Coal is the worst offender, releasing 24 kilograms of CO_2 per billion joules of heat produced; oil is next (20 kg.), and natural gas produces least (14 kg.). In the United States, coal-burning utilities account for a third of the CO_2 emitted, oil-burning vehicles another third, and fuels burned in homes and industry the final third.[16]

The average annual temperature fluctuates erratically from year to year. Nevertheless, there is a very high correlation between past CO_2 levels and the general *trend of temperature changes*. Core samples from glaciers substantiate this correlation over a period of 160,000 years (including a large temperature change during the last ice age), and it holds for the past 130 years for which there are historical records. In the latter period the change in average temperature has been small, amounting to only 1°F. But the five warmest years in the last century were all in the 1980s. It is known on theoretical grounds that CO_2 increases the reflectivity of the upper atmosphere, trapping more heat in the lower atmosphere.

The prediction of *future global warming* is uncertain because climate effects are very complex and only partially understood. Computer models for atmospheric conditions involve simplifying assumptions about winds, humidity, clouds, oceans, and so forth. One widely quoted study concludes that at present emission rates the CO_2 concentration would double by 2030, and the average surface temperature would rise between 3 and 5.5° C (5 to 10° F), with larger changes in the earth's temperate zones.[17] The melting of polar ice would raise sea levels by somewhere between 8 inches and 5 feet, flooding some coastal areas and contaminating groundwater with salt. Wind and rainfall patterns would be drastically changed, affecting agriculture in many parts of the world. (These effects would of course be worse if emission rates increased or if they continued for a longer time interval.) Climatologists recognize the uncertainties in these calculations, but they are virtually unanimous that the magnitude of the potential consequences are so great that we must not only intensify research on the problem but initiate preventive policies.[18] Such polices would be a form of insurance. The greenhouse effect may turn out to be smaller than current estimates, but it could be greater, and it would be much more difficult to reverse later.

The main way to reduce global warming is to *reduce the use of fossil fuels*. If this is accomplished by conservation measures and greater efficiency, the reduction will at the same time cut down on other environmental impacts from fossil fuels. A report by the National Academy of Sciences says that the United States could cut its carbon emissions by 40 percent with no impact on life-styles.[19] Forests absorb CO_2 from the atmosphere as well as providing wildlife habitats and protection against soil erosion. Slowing the destruction of forests would slow global warming, and in the tropics it would help to preserve endangered species and highly erodible soil. Planting trees would have many environmental benefits, but it will have to be done very extensively to make a dent on the CO_2 accumulation.

Apart from conservation, switching from coal and oil to *natural gas* is the most effective way of reducing carbon dioxide emissions during the next decade. Natural gas is more abundant globally than oil and more widely dispersed, including extensive known deposits in the Third World (and many areas have not yet been explored). Gas fueled combined-cycle plants are highly efficient in generating electricity because the burning gases are used to drive one turbine directly and then the heat is used to generate steam to drive a second turbine. The greater efficiency, together with the smaller amount of CO_2 released per unit of heat, means that only two-fifths as much CO_2 is emitted as a coal-burning plant of equivalent capacity, and the sulfur dioxide emissions are negligible. Several nations are experimenting with vehicles driven by cylinders of compressed natural gas. Mexico City is planning to use them on its city buses to reduce air pollution. Natural gas development is also much less environmentally destructive than coal mining. Natural gas is the most promising fuel during the transition to sustainable sources.[20]

A *carbon tax* would be an effective way for industrial nations to reduce carbon dioxide emissions, but it would have to be introduced gradually to avoid severe economic dislocations. Such a tax would favor natural gas over coal and oil, and it would strongly favor nuclear, solar, and conservation technologies that release no CO_2 once they are installed. If part of the tax receipts was invested in efficiency improvements, and part was offset by reductions in other taxes, the economy as a whole would be strengthened rather than weakened. By 1991, Finland, Sweden, and the Netherlands had introduced small carbon taxes, and the European Community was making plans for a carbon tax to be instituted in all European nations.[21] Some Third World countries, especially China, have extensive coal deposits and will find it very difficult to avoid expanding their use of coal as they seek more rapid economic growth. But the efforts of industrial nations to develop alternatives to fossil fuels would help all developing nations in making the transition to sustainable sources.

II. Nuclear Power

In 1990, 421 nuclear plants were operating in twenty-six countries (with 96 more under construction), generating 17 percent of the world's electricity. In many industrial nations the percentage of electricity coming from nuclear plants was even higher: 19 in the U.S., 22 in Britain, 28 in Japan, 34 in the former West Germany, 45 in Sweden, and 75 in France.[22] But in virtually every Western nation, plans to start construction of new plants have been halted by public opposition and by escalating costs (now estimated as twice those for coal-fired plants per kilowatt-hour). All orders for new nuclear plants in the United States since 1973 were subsequently canceled. The industry blames additional safety requirements, regulatory delays, and high interest payments during long construction times (up to eighteen years) for costs of up to $5 billion per plant, ten times the original estimates. A few of the critics of nuclear power are reconsidering it in the light of the greenhouse dangers of coal and the possibility of new "inherently safe" reactor designs. Let us look successively at reactor safety, radioactive waste disposal, and prospects for the future.

1. Reactor Safety and Risk Acceptability

The history of nuclear reactors in the United States supports the *contextualist thesis*, presented in chapter 1, that the design of a technology is not inevitable but is the product of choices made in particular social contexts. In the early 1950s, reactor designers had a choice of fuels (natural uranium, enriched uranium, or plutonium), moderators (light water, heavy water, or graphite), coolants (water, liquid metal, or gas), temperature (boiling water, pressurized water, or high temperatures), and reactor size and configuration. The U.S. Navy urgently wanted a nuclear submarine, which required a high energy density and a readily available design—most easily fulfilled by a pressurized light water reactor (LWR) using enriched uranium. The first commercial LWR at Shippingport was designed to serve also as the prototype for an aircraft carrier reactor.

These choices strongly influenced subsequent decisions. By the time the Atomic Energy Commission (AEC) and the private utilities and reactor contractors chose designs for commercialization in the late fifties, LWRs had a substantial head start from the navy program. Their decisions were based more on cost and current availability than on safety considerations (though liquid sodium coolants were ruled out partly for safety reasons). In Congress, the Joint Committee on Atomic Energy concurred that these decisions were in the national interest.[23]

The next crucial stage was *the very rapid upscaling* in size and numbers that occurred between 1965 and 1970. A hundred reactors were ordered, many of them seven times as large as the largest with which there had been any operating experience. At such sizes, containment structures could not be counted on to withstand a major accident, and plants were being built near population centers. As successive problems emerged, new safety equipment was added on (such as emergency cooling systems and redundant pumps and instruments), but the basic design was not changed. Until 1965, nuclear technology still had considerable flexibility, but by 1970 large-scale light water reactors had developed a momentum of their own, sustained by heavy financial investment and institutional commitments. The industry was locked in before it could learn from experience.[24] In Britain nuclear reactors were owned by the government and alternative designs were tried, but similar problems were present. Long lead times and huge capital investment in large plants with which there had been no previous experience produced an inflexible system, and mistakes were difficult and costly to correct.[25]

The U.S. Atomic Energy Commission's mandate to *regulate* nuclear power was compromised by its conflicting mandate to *promote* nuclear power. The AEC was secretive, suppressed information and internal dissent, and virtually excluded participation by citizens or independent experts. As often happens, a "cozy triangle" of a government agency, a legislative committee, and a private industry shared a common interest in promoting a particular technology.[26]

During the seventies the nuclear industry faced a variety of *unexpected problems*. Demand for electricity grew much more slowly than had been anticipated, As new safety measures were added, regulations became more complex and delays in construction and licensing extended the construction time to 10, 12, or in one case 18 years. High interest rates further escalated construction costs. Vocal opposition to nuclear plants was often associated with the growing plans and antiwar movements. Communities woke up to plans for nearby plants, formulated without their involvement, and they protested vehemently and started court challenges. Some of the objections were wildly overblown, but others pointed to problems that turned out to be valid. Public confidence in both government bureaucracies and large corporations was eroding. One could no longer simply "trust the experts," for knowledgeable experts now spoke out on both sides. The Nuclear Regulatory Commission was established in 1974 with authority only for regulation, but much of its staff and many of its attitudes and procedures were taken over with little change from the AEC.

Then came two major *reactor accidents*. At Three Mile Island in 1979, a partial meltdown occurred and 90 percent of the fuel rods burst, but very little radiation escaped from the containment vessel. At Chernobyl in 1986 an explosion and fire in a graphite-moderated reactor spread large quantities of radiation across Europe. Thirty-one workers at the plant died within a few weeks. It has been estimated that the radiation will result in the death of 28,000 from delayed cancer over the next fifty years.[27] Both accidents were the result of human errors, which in the Three Mile Island case were compounded by a stuck valve and misread instruments. Previous calculations of reactor risks had failed to allow adequately for unlikely combinations of mechanical failures, system interactions, and operator misjudgments. With complex, tightly coupled systems it is impossible to anticipate all possible linkages among human errors and component failures, and events can occur too rapidly for analysis and corrective action.[28] The credibility of reassurances from the industry and the government was undermined, and public support of nuclear power dwindled in both the United States and Europe.

How should we deal with the risk of reactor accidents? Risk analysis defines risk as the *probability* of an event multiplied by the *magnitude* of its harmful consequences. Current estimates of the probability of a nuclear accident are higher than those in the midseventies, but the calculated risk remains less than many other risks that we accept, such as those in driving an auto. Nuclear proponents say that public anxiety about nuclear accidents is therefore irrational. In reply, social scientists point out that the *acceptability of a risk* involves many factors in addition to probability and consequences. In general, we are more willing to accept risks that are familiar, voluntarily accepted, personally controlled, reversible, and equitably distributed—and necessary to obtain a desired benefit. Nuclear power scores poorly on all these characteristics.[29] Nuclear power is thus less acceptable than conventional risk analysis suggests.

In addition, there may be valid reasons for giving *low-probability catastrophes* more weight than risk-benefit analysis assigns. One accident with 50,000 victims is more socially disruptive and receives more media coverage than 50,000 one-victim accidents. A study by a national laboratory in 1982 calculated that a major nuclear accident near an urban area with unfavorable winds could cause losses as high as $150 billion and 140,000 deaths.[30] The probability of rare events and human errors can seldom be estimated with the same accuracy as high-probability events, and underestimation of the probability of a disaster would have enormous consequences. Again, complex large-scale systems are more vulnerable to disruption than smaller and simpler systems, and they can create human overloads. Finally, risk analysis of nuclear plants assumes stable social conditions and leaves out the possibility of wars, civil conflicts, or deliberate acts of sabotage, terrorism, or threat.

Any evaluation of technological risks will be influenced by assumptions about *human nature* and *social institutions*. The biblical understanding of human fallibility would lead one to be cautious about situations in which errors can have disastrous consequences. I suggested earlier that the social dimension of sin is expressed in institutional self-interest. It should be no surprise that organizations put their own goals ahead of the public interest or underestimate risks that could be reduced by expenditures on safety. If we live in a world of stark injustice and growing gaps between rich and poor nations, it seems unrealistic to leave out the effects of social unrest and political instability. Nuclear reactors would be vulnerable in situations of conflict, and they would be tempting targets for blackmail by terrorists. Moreover, their large scale and cost represent a concentration of economic and hence political power that makes if difficult for citizens to participate in decisions about them. In short, catastrophe avoidance should be given heavier weight than traditional risk analysis assigns, but it cannot be the only criterion for choosing technologies, since benefits and alternatives must be considered along with risks.

2. Radioactive Wastes and Future Generations

The risks from high-level radioactive wastes extend over very long periods of time. Many of the waste products must be isolated for a thousand years, and plutonium itself is still dangerous after 100,000 years. A huge backlog of military and commercial wastes has already accumulated around the world. Several nations are hoping to create *permanent repositories* in which solidified wastes would be stored in concrete casks in tunnels excavated deep in salt beds or solid rock. The repositories must be isolated from groundwater, since even very slow leaching would contaminate underground aquifers. Most scientists believe that suitable geological formations can be found, but at each of the sites proposed so far, geologists have been concerned about possible changes in groundwater flow induced by fractures, earthquakes, or climate changes.

Both *scientific uncertainties* and *public opposition* have plagued all attempts to establish such repositories. In Germany, the Gorleben salt dome was selected as the first site, but it was discovered that groundwater is eroding the salt and the geological structures are not stable. Gorleben has been the scene of large public protests, and the repository opening has been put off from 1998 to 2008 at the earliest. In France, the opening of a repository has been postponed to 2010, and no site has yet been named. Japan hoped to locate a burial site in a remote and poor prefecture, but despite the offer of a large subsidy, opposition from the governor and the diet was strong. Japan has signed an agreement with China to conduct research on an underground facility in Shanxi province, in return for assistance with the Chinese nuclear program.[31]

Three ethical issues can be identified in planning for nuclear waste disposal.

1. Regional Justice

Radioactive waste disposal is an extreme case of local risks for national benefits. Utilitarians may assert that the total benefits outweigh the total risks, but justice is violated if some people benefit and others sustain the risks. People recognize that the wastes must go somewhere, but they assert, "Not in my backyard." The U.S. National Waste Policy Act of 1982 permitted an individual state to veto a site within its borders, but the veto could be overridden by a majority of both houses of Congress. In 1987 Congress instructed the Department of Energy (DOE) to proceed with detailed underground studies at Yucca Mountain, Nevada, and to abandon plans to study two other western sites concurrently. Both DOE and Congress also capitulated to political pressures to abandon plans to investigate possible sites for a second repository in several eastern states. Nevada has responded by a series of court challenges. The date for opening the first repository has been postponed from 1998 to 2010, to allow for further negotiation and scientific studies.

Fairness in *selection procedures* can help to mitigate the injustice in sacrificing local interests for the national good. But DOE did such a poor job of scientific research that it was criticized by several other government agencies. And Nevadans felt that they had been betrayed politically when the original agreement to build one western and one eastern site was violated. Another way of mitigating injustices is to require the beneficiaries to compensate those who bear the risks. The 1982 act authorizes DOE to provide *compensation to host states*, paid for by a users' fee on the electricity generated from nuclear fuel. In 1987 amendments to the act, the state hosting the first site would receive $10 million per year until the site opens and $20 million per year thereafter. This seems inadequate compensation when there are uncertain health risks, social impacts, and public fears that might stigmatize local communities. Another form of compensation would be the funding of hospitals and health care centers in the area to monitor radiation risks and to provide greater local participation in health decisions.[32] But we must resist the temptation to buy off depressed communities or Native American reservations and to deprive them of an ongoing voice in their own health and safety.

2. Intergenerational Justice

Justice is violated when the current generation benefits from electricity and passes on to future generations some of the resulting risks. According to Rawls, an intergenerational decision is fair if you would accept it when you did not know in which generation you would live. I also mentioned in chapter 3 the biblical view of a covenant between generations and the idea that God's purposes span the generations. Here is a case where the longevity of the risks forces us to think beyond the short time frame of political processes and economic calculations. The present generation has a responsibility to pay for the costs of reducing the risks to posterity. The standards of the Environmental Protection Agency (EPA) specify that radiation released from a nuclear waste depository should not cause more than 1,000 deaths in 10,000 years (which is the time it will take for the level of radiation in typical reactor wastes to fall to that of the uranium ore from which the fuel was extracted).

If we considered the welfare of future generations, would we favor storing radioactive wastes permanently or retrievably? While a *permanent* site costs more initially, it entails no future maintenance costs, and sabotage and terrorism could not occur because the wastes are buried in solid rock. But a *retrievable* site offers two advantages: it would be far easier and cheaper to get at the wastes if problems did show up; and the wastes would be accessible if future generations wanted to reprocess them (to reclaim some of the potential nuclear energy still present) or to use them in a future technology not now imagined.

Alvin Weinberg advocates *retrievable storage* with tight security measures to guard against flooding, drilling, or sabotage. He describes it as a "Faustian bargain" of energy growth at the expense of long-term vigilance. He says it would require a "nuclear priesthood" of highly disciplined technicians to maintain surveillance and guard the buried wastes.[33] But is it realistic to count on the stability of social institutions on a time scale of 10,000 years? No social order in history has lasted more than a few centuries. The occurrence of two world wars and many smaller wars and revolutionary upheavals in this century suggests that in a fast changing world we should use methods that do not depend on human institutions over periods of many generations.

On balance it seems to me that our obligations to future generations would best be fulfilled by *permanent sealed repositories*, but that the first couple of sites should be left open and carefully monitored for leakage or other problems for several decades so that any modifications could be made before they are sealed. From current fees a substantial endowment fund should be set aside, and interest from it would cover future monitoring and modification costs and underwrite insurance against accidents. It is conceivable that a new technology might allow long-lived isotopes in plant wastes to be transmuted into isotopes with shorter half-lives, in order to keep more of the risks within our own generation. But with current technologies this would be extremely expensive, and permanent sealed repositories seem a more promising way of avoiding significant risks to future generations.

3. Public Confidence

In many nations, including France, Britain, the United States, and the Soviet Union, the *credibility of government agencies* planning nuclear wasted disposal was undermined by their secrecy and their historic failure to protect the public and the environment. In many cases the same agency was responsible for nuclear weapons production, nuclear power generation, and nuclear waste disposal—and for public health and safety regulations. A 1982 report by the Office of Technology Assessment (OTA) of the U.S. Congress noted the erosion of public confidence in the Department of Energy and proposed an independent Waste Management Agency to sponsor scientific research and to encourage greater participation by citizens, state agencies, and independent experts.[34] But DOE has continued to manage the disposal of wastes, and public confidence has not been restored. While some public hearings have been held, DOE has provided only limited opportunities for access to information and for independent scientific review, and it has not been sensitive to the diversity of interests involved or the intensity of public opposition.[35] The controversies over waste disposal, like those over reactor safety, point to the importance of public involvement and the full inclusion of social and environmental costs in the planning of large scale technological projects.

3. The Future of Nuclear Power

If waste disposal problems can be solved, should nuclear power be reconsidered now that coal seems to pose such a threat to the environment? A 1984 OTA study concluded that a revival of the nuclear industry could occur only under two conditions. First, public trust in the government agencies and in the utilities would have to be restored. Second, only simpler, smaller reactors with inherent safety features and standardized designs might achieve acceptable safety and reduce construction and licensing times.[36] By 1990 DOE and the reactor vendors were considering smaller, standardized modular reactors that could be built in factories rather than on site and that would incorporate passively stable features.[37]

Passively stable ("inherently safe") reactors rely on the laws of nature, rather than on human intervention or mechanical systems, to limit the effects of any malfunctions. In smaller reactors, emergency cooling can be obtained by gravity flow from water in elevated tanks or by the natural circulation of water, helium, or air—without the use of complex systems of controls, pumps, and valves. Reactor cores can be designed so that the reaction itself slows down as the temperature rises. The uranium fuel can be formed into pellets, each surrounded by layers of graphite and ceramic that withstand temperatures far higher than do the metal-clad fuel rods currently used. A 135-megawatt graphite-moderated helium-cooled reactor (one-seventh the size of many current reactors) and a 155 megawatt reactor cooled by liquid sodium are among the designs under consideration in the United States. Canada's 300-megawatt heavy water reactor has an excellent operating record, and Sweden is working on a light water reactor in which naturally circulating borated water is used to slow down the reaction and to cool the core.[38]

Morone and Woodhouse hold that if we learn from the mistakes of the past we would develop a second generation of nuclear reactors only *slowly and cautiously*. We would incorporate safety in the initial design rather than by complex add-on systems. We would do research for a decade on diverse types of passive design, and then for a second decade we would develop prototypes of several alternatives for testing at a remote site so that we could learn from experience and make modifications. The whole process would be open to scrutiny by the OTA, independent experts, and environmentalists. After two decades, when both the greenhouse effect and the prospects for solar energy are clearer, a decision about commercialization could be made.[39]

Such a cautious research program on smaller passively stable reactors would *keep options open*. Along with a satisfactory resolution of waste disposal, it might lead to a restoration of public confidence in the nuclear industry. But I could support such a program only if it were funded at a level considerably lower than that for research on conservation and renewable sources. Moreover, given current attitudes in the industry and DOE, the program is not likely to be cautious and open or to restore public confidence. It would probably divert funds from alternatives and encourage the belief that we do not have to take conservation seriously. For at least the next decade, measures to *conserve* electricity will almost certainly cost less than the *production* of an equivalent amount of electricity from a new generating plant of any kind. During that interval we can expect the cost of solar sources to continue to fall if we allocate more funds to research on them. Even if smaller standardized reactors do achieve an acceptable level of safety, they are not likely to be competitive with solar sources if the true costs of the whole nuclear fuel cycle are included.

In the past, nuclear power has been *heavily subsidized* by public funds. The initial research was publicly funded, and free enriched uranium was supplied to private reactors. The Price-Anderson Act of 1957 limits a utility's liability from a reactor accident to $60 million, even though recent government studies put the damage from the maximum credible accident at $150 billion. Federal subsidies to the nuclear industry were still $12 to $15 billion a year in the mideighties. Waste disposal research and management will undoubtedly cost many times the disposal fees collected to date, and the safe dismantling of reactors at the end of their useful life (thirty or forty years) could cost up to $30 billion each.[40] The British government, as part of its privatization program, tried to sell off its nuclear plants in 1989, but private investors were not interested when they discovered the estimated costs of decommissioning and waste disposal.[41] Even with simpler modular reactors, the high cost of all these processes would have to be included in any realistic appraisal.

Breeder reactors and the *reprocessing* of spent fuel would reduce the cost of nuclear fuel. Breeder reactors are highly efficient, deriving sixty times as much energy from a ton of uranium as light water reactors do and extending reserves by making low-grade ores economical. Reprocessing plants are operating in Britain, France, and India; they take spent fuel and separate out the plutonium so that it can be recycled as reactor fuel. Japan is planning to ship its used fuel to Europe and bring the reprocessed plutonium back again in convoys, which would be a tempting target for terrorists. The United States rejected both breeders and reprocessing because they involve the transportation of plutonium, of which a small quantity could easily be diverted to make nuclear weapons. A nation that wants to make nuclear weapons now has to set up breeders or reprocessing or uranium enrichment plants—all of which are complex, expensive, large-scale operations. But if plutonium were circulating in nations around the world, it would be easy for terrorist groups to steal a small quantity. It takes only 20 pounds of plutonium to make a bomb, and 100,000 pounds would be available each year if spent fuel at current levels were being reprocessed and recycled. Plutonium can be handled with relative ease, and theft during storage or shipment would be tempting to small nations or evolutionary groups.[42]

It is of course difficult to prevent *the proliferation of nuclear weapons*. There are several routes for acquiring them. Several nations have not signed the Nonproliferation Treaty of 1968, and they do not allow the inspection of their facilities by the International Atomic Energy Agency. Even with stricter and universal international inspection, some diversion of weapons-grade material could occur. But the widespread circulation of plutonium would make acquisition of a bomb much easier. Even if it were intended only for purposes of extortion, events could get out of hand, especially in the midst of tensions between major powers or Middle Eastern rivalries. If nuclear war is the largest catastrophe that threatens both humanity and the planet, anything that even slightly increases the risk of its occurrence must weigh heavily in policy choices. Effective and verifiable arms control would be easier if plutonium were not readily available. I would thus be opposed to breeders and reprocessing even if they posed no safety problems. I also support proposals for international jurisdiction over the crucial portions of the current fuel cycle (uranium enrichment and waste disposal), preferably at regional international centers.[43]

I have not discussed *fusion* because the temperatures necessary for a self-sustaining reaction have proved so difficult to achieve even in the laboratory. In 1991 a European team produced a fusion reaction of 1.7 million watts for two seconds, releasing much less energy than was used to initiate the reaction but more than had been released in any previous experiments. The experimenters cautioned that commercial fusion remains at least fifty years away.[44] Fusion has the advantage that its main fuel, heavy hydrogen, is present in small quantities in ordinary water; if tritium is also needed, it could be produced in the fusion installation. Fusion technology would escape the problems of highly radioactive fuels and wastes that occur with fission, but the temperatures of millions of degrees and the local radioactivity produced would entail their own risks. Moreover, if commercial fusion can be achieved it will probably be only with very large-scale equipment that could not be scaled down.[45]

In short, I would favor a modest program of research on small passively stable reactors and on fusion, in order to keep future options open. But I believe that most of our efforts should be directed toward renewable sources and conservation because they are more promising alternatives for the next few decades.

III. Renewable Sources

Renewable energy sources contribute to sustainability and justice, and in most cases the environmental impacts are lower than those of fossil fuels. Many forms of renewable energy involve decentralized systems amenable to local ownership and participation by individuals and communities. Their direct economic costs are only just beginning to be competitive with coal and oil, but these costs could be reduced by appropriate policy initiatives, and the indirect costs are far lower.

1. Solar Energy And Sustainability

An inherent feature of all renewable sources is their sustainability. Their energy will keep on arriving from the sun without depletion for millions of years. Using solar energy is living off income, whereas using fossil fuels is living off capital. One nation's use of solar energy does not affect the amount available to other nations or to future generations. While solar technologies often require considerable initial investment, the fuel itself is free; using it does not drive up the price for other people. Moreover, sunlight is available in all parts of the earth. There are regional variations in the duration and intensity of sunshine, but these are smaller than the huge geographical disparities in the distribution of fossil fuel and uranium reserves. Solar sources are thus compatible with both international and intergenerational Justice. They fulfill Rawls's criterion of justice: they are the sort of technology you would try to develop if you did not know in which nation or in which generation you would live.

The main obstacle to renewable energy has been the costs, though in most cases costs have fallen dramatically and would undoubtedly fall faster with more research and with mass production. There are also some environmental problems, though these are seldom as serious as those from fossil fuels. In particular, none of these technologies produces the main greenhouse gas, carbon dioxide, and none of them except biomass produces air pollutants or soil erosion. Renewable systems cannot be turned into military weapons, and they cannot produce sudden catastrophes (except for the failure of large dams). The very diversity of solar technologies and their geographical dispersal would diversify the risks. By reducing dependence on foreign oil, they would contribute to world stability and peace and reduce balance-of-payment deficits. In terms of environmental impacts, renewable sources appear in general to be worse than nuclear plants operating normally, but better than coal or oil, for equivalent energy production. But the materials and the fabrication of the equipment for renewable technologies require energy that in many cases would come initially from fossil fuels.

1. Hydroelectricity. Electricity generated from water power has for decades been cheaper than that from any other source. Nearly a fifth of the world's electricity is now water generated. North America has developed 59 percent of its potential hydropower, Europe 36 percent, Asia 9 percent, Latin America 8 percent, and Africa only 5 percent. But large dams entail great environmental costs: inundation of forests, farmland, and homes; accumulation of sediments; and harm to fish migration and aquatic life. In some parts of the world, small dams produce electricity with only modest environmental impacts. China, for example, has 90,000 small water turbines providing electricity in rural areas.[46]

2. Water and Space Heating. In Israel, 65 percent of domestic water heating comes from rooftop solar collectors, which since 1980 have been required on all new residences up to nine stories high. In most countries, space heating with passive solar design and good insulation pays for itself in fuel savings in a decade or two, but most consumers want a more rapid payback on their investment. Building contractors are more interested in keeping the initial home price down than in reducing long-term costs. Retrofitting old houses is expensive, so solar heating does little to help low-income families. But if the cost of oil and gas rises, solar heating will become more attractive when combined with conservation measures.[47]

3. *Biomass.* Twelve percent of the world's primary energy today comes from organic matter, mainly wood, but a serious fuelwood crisis has occurred in the Third World from the cutting of trees with little replanting. Brazil obtains 62 percent of its automotive fuel from sugar cane converted to ethanol, which was competitive with oil in 1981; but with oil prices lower in the late eighties, government subsidies were continued largely because the program creates 450,000 jobs and helps rural development instead of sending billions of dollars overseas for oil. But ethanol from crops uses scarce agricultural land. If 40 percent of the entire U.S. corn crop were converted to ethanol it would meet only 10 percent of the nation's auto fuel demand.[48]

A more promising alternative is the planting of fast-growing trees, shrubs, or grasses on marginal land or rangeland, or the integrated cultivation of trees and crops (agroforestry). The burning or fermenting of forest and municipal wastes is another energy source. Crop and animal wastes can be fermented in tanks to create a biogas fuel, with the residue returned to the land as fertilizer. The growth of such biomass absorbs as much carbon dioxide as is released when it is burned, so it produces no net greenhouse effect, and sulfur emissions are low, but careful design and management is needed to limit soil erosion.[49]

4. *Wind Power.* Electricity generated by turbines at windy sites now costs 6 to 8 cents per kilowatt-hour (kwh), which is competitive with current U.S. utility purchases during peak demand periods (when utilities pay a premium in order to avoid having to build new plants) and is approaching the cost of electricity from new coal plants (5 cents per kwh). After some failures in the 1970s, the wind industry expanded in the early 1980s, especially in California, but it has slowed since 1985 when oil prices fell, federal tax credits were eliminated, and federal funds for research on renewable sources were cut by 85 percent. Turbines at windy sites could supply 20 percent of current U.S. electricity demand, and costs would fall with improved designs and mass production. They could be located in mountains or deserts or on farming and ranching lands, with little interference to other activities. India is planning for 10,000 turbines producing 1000 megawatts by 1995, and the Netherlands hopes to reach the same goal by 2000.[50]

5. *Solar Thermal Electricity.* Sunlight can be concentrated by parabolic reflectors to produce steam to drive generators. In California, 350 megawatts of solar thermal electricity are being produced at costs competitive with peak rates, and the costs are expected to fall in the nineties as larger and more efficient units are installed. Already their costs (8 cents per kilowatt-hour) are lower than that of electricity from recent nuclear plants (10 to 12 cents per kwh). Solar steam can also be used for process heat in nearby industries.[51]

6. *Photovoltaic Cells.* Electricity from PVs has the greatest potential for the future. The costs of both crystalline silicon and thin films of amorphous silicon fell dramatically in the eighties but are still prohibitive except for remote locations (communications, navigation aids, or isolated villages). In 1991 Texas Instruments announced plans to market flexible solar roof panels that look like metallic sandpaper; because they are made from metallurgical grade silicon, they are expected to cost a fifth of current PVs and would be competitive with coal-generated electricity. PVs create no carbon dioxide or air pollution

(except in the fabrication of the equipment). The materials used—iron and silicon—are abundant. The land area needed for solar cells is comparable to that for coal plants of equivalent capacity if land strip-mined during thirty years is included. Panels in deserts, rocky areas, roadside rights-of-way, or on factory or home rooftops would avoid competing with other land uses. Their modular character is adaptable to small or large arrays. PVs to supply all current U.S. electricity would require a square of land 100 miles on a side—a ninth the area of Arizona, or a fifth of the national area used by the U.S. military.[52]

Wind, solar thermal, and PVs share one limitation: they all provide energy *intermittently*, varying with time of day and weather. They are useful for feeding electricity into a grid, thereby reducing the consumption of fossil fuels and avoiding the construction of new plants for daytime peak loads. Solar thermal can be combined with gas turbines in hybrid systems; gas takes over when there is no sunlight. But before wind or PVs could be used as the main source for baseloads, less expensive ways of *storing electricity* must be found. A dozen auto manufacturers, including Ford, GM, and Toyota, are planning to produce electric cars by 1995. Sodium-sulfur or nickel-cadmium batteries are an improvement on lead-acid batteries, but they are bulky and expensive.[53]

Photovoltaic-generated electricity passing through water releases *hydrogen* that can be stored and used for transportation or residential heating. Hydrogen produced from PVs in sunny desert areas could be compressed and distributed inexpensively in a pipeline system like that now used for natural gas. Autos would have to carry the hydrogen in high-compression tanks or in the form of metal hydrides. Hydrogen could also be burned in fuel cells on electric-powered cars, with twice the efficiency of internal combustion motors. If 150,000 square miles (2 percent of the world's desert areas) were used for PVs producing hydrogen, they could supply as much energy as all fossil fuels today. Hydrogen appears very promising in the long run, since it burns so cleanly; it emits no carbon dioxide, sulfur dioxide, or particulates. But extensive research is still needed on its production, storage, and combustion.[54]

Only *a combination of these renewable sources* could reduce the consumption of fossil fuels significantly. By one recent estimate, if total energy consumption remains constant, the U.S. supply in 2020 could be 7 percent nuclear, 4 percent hydro, 6 percent wind, 18 percent biomass, 24 percent solar, and 42 percent fossil fuels (as compared to 86 percent today).[55] But such a shift will take a concerted effort.

Under the influence of market forces alone the transition will be slow because market prices neglect many *environmental and human costs*, even when some of the externalities have been internalized through emission standards and environmental and safety regulations. As I have said, the market takes a short-term view and discounts costs and risks to future generations. When irreplaceable resources such as oil are used up, potential benefits are transferred from the future to the present. Neither the environment nor our grandchildren enter current economic calculations. A study in the former West Germany estimates the external costs of coal (not including global warming) at 2.4 to 5.5 cents per kilowatt-hour, and those of nuclear power at 6 to 13 cents.[56] In the United States, the state regulatory agencies often compare alternatives (including conservation) before they approve the plans of utilities for constructing new plants. The Wisconsin agency adds 15 percent to coal plant figures to reflect external costs, and in New York 25 percent is added.[57]

Moreover, fossil and nuclear fuels have been *heavily subsidized* in the past. For decades, oil was subsidized by depletion allowances, tax credits, highway construction funds, and regulated prices. Some of the subsidies to the nuclear industry were mentioned earlier. By one estimate the total annual U.S. energy subsidy in 1984 was $44 billion, mostly for coal, oil, and nuclear fuels.[58] Because the energy industry has invested heavily in these technologies, most of its research and its political influence supports continued use of these fuels. The cumulative expenditures on solar research since World War II are a minute fraction of that spent on other sources, so it is not surprising that it lags behind. Of the $7 billion that twenty-one industrial nations spent on energy research in 1989, 47 percent went to nuclear fission, 15 percent to fossil fuels, 12 percent to fusion, and only 7 percent to renewables and 5 percent to conservation.[59]

In the late 1970s under Carter, *national policies* to simulate renewable energy technologies were adopted in the United States, but these were mostly revoked during the 1980s under Reagan. Federal funding for renewable research and development fell from $718 million in 1980 to $115 million in 1989. With the new concern for global warming and the dangers of dependence on imported oil, the time has come to reinstate tax credits for renewables and restore research and development funds at least to their former level. These could be financed by a tax on imported oil, higher taxes at the pump, or the proposed carbon tax. Or they could be paid for by a small fraction of the funds released if the space station and Star Wars research were canceled. Purchases of solar equipment and fuels for government facilities, offices, and vehicles would also help to create economies of scale. The diverse long-term benefits of renewable energy would justify such policies.

2. Decentralization and Participation

In chapter 2, I defined freedom *as participation in the decisions that affect one's life*. I distinguished three forms of freedom: (1) participation in policy decisions through political processes, (2) participation in economic decisions through the marketplace, and (3) participation in work-related decisions through activities in the workplace. All three forms of participation are very limited when the individual faces a large centralized organization, such as those that produce fossil or nuclear energy. Oil companies are among the world's largest financial institutions, wielding immense economic and political power. Nuclear plants require huge capital investments, so they can be built only by large private utilities or government agencies.

By contrast, some forms of solar technology can be owned and controlled by *individuals and communities*, which would encourage local self-reliance and a plurality of centers of decision—counteracting the trend toward the concentration of economic and political power. Biomass involves many actors: growers, harvesters, processors, and distributors. A biomass system would be coordinated by the market and by government policy, but it would have room for many local initiatives. Economies of scale may rule out very small operations, but intermediate-scale activities can be efficient. Solar heating and insulation and rooftop photovoltaics offer scope for small businesses in the installation and repair of equipment, drawing on local skills and shops that would integrate well with existing building trades. Solar technology is more labor-intensive than coal-fired plants and oil refineries, which produce fewer jobs per dollar than any other major industry. The manufacturing and installation of solar components would be well dispersed geographically.[60]

Community-level systems can be run as cooperatives, small companies, or municipal utilities. The burning of municipal wastes to produce electricity helps to solve the waste disposal and landfill problems faced by many cites. Wind generators and small dams can be locally owned and operated. With any form of fuel, the *cogeneration* of heat and electricity substantially improves efficiency. Two-thirds of the energy input into most electric plants is simply wasted as heat. Instead, the heat can be used in industrial processes or in community-level systems. District heating, integrated systems, and the recovery of energy from urban sewage and agricultural residues are best carried out locally.

Decentralized systems offer *flexibility* in adapting to local conditions. Solar sources are diverse and can be matched to local resources and to differing end-use and temperature needs. They typically involve shorter construction times than large installations. In addition, they are *less vulnerable* to sabotage, terrorism, or catastrophic accidents. The stakes are smaller when errors or accidents do occur. Careful design and monitoring for environmental damage may be necessary, but not the elaborate safety precautions and security measures that nuclear plants require. Finally, the costs and the benefits of small-scale systems *tend to fall on the same people*. In the case of large power plants, nearby communities receive much of the pollution and environmental degradation, while most of the benefits go elsewhere; it is not surprising that local opposition to the siting of large plants has been rising. Decentralized systems offer a more just distribution of costs and benefits and the prospect of less vehement community opposition.[61]

Critics of decentralization say that small-scale systems are neither efficient nor socially desirable. Solar components such as photovoltaics will have to be mass-produced to be cheap enough to be widely adopted. Like the auto, solar equipment can be individually owned and decentralized in use, but it can be cheaply produced only with the economics of scale possible in large factories. Moreover, with the existing distribution of economic power it is likely that many forms of solar energy will be controlled by large companies. The social regulation of such companies may be difficult, but it is not impossible. Even decentralized systems require central regulation. A million smoky wood stoves would be no improvement on coal-burning plants when it comes to air pollution.

Even if local self-sufficiency were possible it might not be *equitable*; an urban ghetto or a rural village would receive much poorer electric service than an affluent suburb. By stressing local self-reliance, say their critics, decentralists have neglected the importance of social integration and cooperation for the common good. Most people are more interested in the cost and convenience of energy than in local control; they are willing to pay someone else to deliver energy to them. Critics also fear that renewable sources will not be adequate to meet energy demands; severe shortages would lead to slower economic growth, rationing, and government intervention to allocate scarce supplies. Authoritarian responses to scarcity might leave us with more centralization than we have now.[62]

Furthermore, the correlations between *energy systems* and *social structures* are loose and ambiguous. Solar enthusiasts and nuclear enthusiasts sometimes share the assumption that the right technology, the "technical fix," will solve our social problems. But the social and institutional context in which a technology is deployed is often crucial in determining its ultimate social consequences. Nevertheless, we must acknowledge that some technologies have distinctive potential that can be supported by deliberate social policies. The relationships between scale, efficiency, justice, and participation have to be examined separately for each part of an energy system if we are to understand the trade-offs between local participation and other values.

My own conclusion is that *a mix of small and large systems*, adapted to varied tasks and conditions, is preferable to either type alone. For example, the disperse production of electricity reduces transmission and distribution costs, which constitute half of the consumer's electric bill. But the electric grid offers convenience and reliability in service, and it allows power to be transferred between regions with different peak-load hours or unused capacity. Local sources should therefore be tied into networks wherever possible. Large blocks of electricity for heavy industry and urban areas will probably require central generation. Some photovoltaic installations and some biomass production can be locally controlled, but competition for scarce land may make large solar arrays in remote areas or large plantations of plants or trees for fuel desirable.

But a mix of scales will require a deliberate effort to develop the *untapped potential of small systems*. In the past we have subsidized large-scale technologies. Past investment in such systems has created a momentum for their perpetuation, whereas the constituencies for the small are diffuse and less well organized. The centralization/decentralizadon debate also involves differences in value priorities and in visions of the future, to which we will return in the final chapter.

IV. Conservation

Conservation is the most cost-effective response to energy shortages. Most ways of reducing energy demand are cheaper than increasing supply by an equivalent amount. It costs less to save than to produce a barrel of oil or a kilowatt-hour of electricity. But conservation also furthers every one of the values discussed in this volume. Conservation in industrial nations reduces global inequities in energy consumption. It cuts the waste of the irreplaceable resources that future generations will need. It is essential for the transition to sustainable sources. Conservation measures seldom harm the environment. A dollar spent on conservation is seven times as effective in cutting carbon dioxide emissions as a dollar spent on nuclear power. Reducing oil imports diminishes a major cause of international conflict. We will look particularly at two values that might seem incompatible with reduced energy use: economic development and personal fulfillment. Finally, we examine the distinctive needs and opportunities of the Third World.

1. Energy and Economic Development

In chapter 2, I said that we should seek economic development: selective economic growth that does not jeopardize equitable distribution, resource sustainability or environmental protection. The conservation of energy and other resources can make a major contribution to economic development.

Until the oil embargo of 1973, the graphs of U.S. energy consumption and gross national product rose on similar curves, and it was assumed that demand would continue to rise in a growing economy. Restricting energy growth, it was said, would automatically restrict economic growth. But from 1973 to 1987, U.S. energy consumption actually fell, while the GNP grew by 35 percent.[63] The nations in the international Energy Agency lowered their energy use per unit of GNP by 24 percent from 1973 to 1989.[64] While higher oil prices did initially result in somewhat slower economic growth, the combined effect of various conservation measures showed that, over a longer period, economic growth can be at least partially uncoupled from energy consumption. But since 1988, with oil prices lower, energy use has started to rise again.

Forms of economic growth that are compatible with *rapid reduction in energy consumption* in industrial nations are essential to global justice and the transition to sustainable solar sources. The United States spends 10 percent of its GNP on energy, while Japan spends only 4 percent, but even Japan has barely begun to fulfill the potential for conservation. Four forms of conservation are most promising.

1. Transportation. Transportation fuel comprises two-thirds of U.S. oil use. In response to fuel economy standards introduced by Congress in 1975, the average fuel economy of new cars doubled from 14 miles per gallon (mpg) in 1975 to 28 mpg in 1985, but the standards were subsequently relaxed.[65] The auto industry continued to oppose higher standards, and in early 1992 Congress was still unwilling to require more than the current standard (27.5 mpg average for the new cars produced by any company). Readily available technologies could produce cars with 38 mpg, and the extra cost would be offset by the savings on fuel.[66] The Volvo LPC 2000 gets 81 mpg on highways, and the four-to-five-passenger Toyota AXV prototype achieved 98 mpg on the combined urban/highway test administered by the EPA.[67]

Mass transit and railways are far more efficient than autos and trucks, produce much less carbon dioxide and harmful air emissions, and would reduce the congestion that is paralyzing many cites. Frequent, rapid service with small buses using express lanes will attract urban riders. Electric trolleys and light railway vehicles are much less expensive than underground subway systems, and parking spaces for autos and bicycles can be provided at suburban stops. City centers should be reserved for pedestrians and bicycles. Public transportation also helps low-income families, many of whom do not own cars.[68]

2. *Buildings*. Large savings are possible in commercial and residential heating and cooling. In office buildings, better insulation, thermal reflective glass, more efficient lighting, and the recovery of waste heat from ventilated air can cut energy input in half. For new homes, insulation standards, building codes, and loan requirements could lead to much lower heat losses. Superinsulated homes in Sweden save 89 percent on heating bills and pay for their additional cost in five years. But housing stock turns over slowly; more rapid savings can come from retrofitting existing houses with insulation and weather-stripping, saving up to 50 percent on heating bills. Yet many home owners are reluctant to invest in such improvements unless the payback time is three or four years—a shorter period than they expect in other investments. Renters have little incentive to improve their landlords' houses, and landlords and housing contractors do not pay the energy bills. Some utility companies are taking an active role in home energy audits, subcontracting and guaranteeing the installation of insulation, and arranging loan repayment from the saving in future fuel bills. By helping to control demand, utilities can avoid having to build costly new power plants. But the institutional obstacles to energy conservation in homes can be overcome only by stronger governmental leadership, including housing standards, efficiency ratings, and low interest loans to low-income families.[69]

3. *Industry*. Many companies have already reduced their energy demand substantially. More efficient equipment and processes have been introduced in such energy-intensive industries as steel, aluminum, paper, glass, and chemicals. New techniques have been used for waste heat recovery and for the cascading of processes requiring successively lower temperatures. Process steam can be cogenerated with electricity, at twice the efficiency of separately generated electricity. The recycling of materials usually takes far less energy than primary extraction from raw materials. A shift is also occurring within industry from the energy-intensive processing of basic materials to fabrication, finishing, and high-tech products. Electronic systems use few materials and little energy, and they can be used to monitor and control the flow of materials and energy in other industrial processes.[70]

4. *Electricity*. In the past, low electricity rates were offered to large users, partly to promote sates and partly because of economies in distribution and billing. Today, "inverted rate structures" are proposed to discourage heavy use. "Lifeline rates" would start with a low price for a basic block of electricity for minimal needs per person, with rising rates thereafter. This would offer some help to low-income families and would encourage conservation. Lower off-peak rates would produce some shift in demand away from peak-load periods. For appliances, testing and labeling, and perhaps efficiency standards,

would be helpful. Some air conditioners and refrigerators on the market are twice as efficient as others. Heat pumps can use the same equipment for heating in winter and cooling in summer. Lighting consumes 20 percent of U.S. electricity, and this could be greatly reduced. A 15-watt fluorescent bulb produces the same amount of light as an ordinary 75-watt bulb. It lasts thirteen times as long, more than repaying its higher initial cost; if the electricity is coal generated, each bulb saves a ton of carbon dioxide and twenty pounds of sulfur dioxide emissions during its life.[71]

Apart from conservation and efficiency measures, selective growth requires other *changes in the economy*. The energy-intensive manufacturing sector has been shrinking while the service sector has been growing (including health care, financial services, information services, and education), and this shift can be carried further. Sudden and severe energy shortages do indeed result in economic and social disruption. The 1973 oil embargo led to job layoffs and economic recession; minority groups were laid off first and low-income families were hardest hit. But gradual shifts toward efficiency and services produce a stronger economy that spends less on energy and is less vulnerable to future oil crises or price fluctuations.

Expenditures on energy conservation also create *more employment* than expenditures on energy production. A European Community study found that conservation expenditures produced more jobs than traditional energy investments.[72] A U.S. study concluded that every dollar invested in conservation produced twice as many jobs as a dollar invested in conventional energy industries.[73] Home insulation and public transportation are labor-intensive, and the jobs are well distributed geographically. Higher energy prices usually result in some substitution of labor for energy. The shift to less energy-intensive products will of course decrease jobs in some industries, but the new industries and services that replace them will more than compensate for such losses.

Issues of justice in conservation do require special attention. The paradox is that the poor cannot afford the higher initial costs for energy-efficient homes or appliances, and they end by paying more in the long run in higher utility bills. They live in poorly insulated homes and they spend a much larger fraction of their income on energy than more affluent people do. The poorest tenth of the population spends 34 percent of its income directly for energy, while the richest tenth spends only 2 percent.[74] It is misguided, however, to try to keep energy prices low to protect the poor, for this reduces incentives for conservation. Instead, both financial and energy services should be targeted especially on low-income families: fuel assistance in emergencies only, home insulation subsidy, a revised utility rate structure, greater support for public transportation, and so forth.

Conservation does involve some risks to *health and environment*, but they are relatively small. Raw materials and energy are needed to fabricate insulating materials. Some insulation gives off formaldehyde, which causes respiratory illness. Sealing a house tightly against air leakage allows a buildup of radon gas (a cause of lung cancer) from cement, bricks, or soil in some regions; this can be avoided with air ventilation and a heat exchanger, but at considerable cost.[75] Smaller cars save energy and pollute less, but the fatality rate in accidents is higher. Conservation does entail environmental and health risks, but in most cases these are less than the risks from equivalent energy production. Overall, conservation gets high marks on each of the criteria we have been using.

2. Life-Styles and Personal Fulfillment

Improvements in efficiency allow people to obtain the same goods and service with a lower expenditure of energy. These pragmatic conservation measures would require very little sacrifice and would not harm *the quality of life*. Comparisons of 35 industrial nations have shown no correlation between energy use and a varied set of social indicators (including life expectancy, literacy, unemployment, crime, suicide rates, and environmental quality indexes).[76] Another study showed that Sweden had a GNP per capita close to that of the United States and outranked the U.S. on almost every social indicator but used 40 percent less energy per capita. In Sweden, heavy gasoline taxes, smaller cars, and excellent public transportation (aided by geographical compactness) had produced high transportation efficiency, while commercial and residential use of energy was much less wasteful. Britain came out between Sweden and the United States in energy use and on most of the social indicators.[77]

The conservation measures described above rely on technical changes, economic incentives, and legislated standards, but they would be more effective if accompanied by relatively minor *changes in individual behavior*. Turning thermostats down in winter, turning off unused lights, using public transportation, or recycling glass, paper, and aluminum cans may seem inconsequential, but many small actions add up to significant savings. Educational programs can increase awareness of the importance of conservation and of simple ways to save energy. Psychologists have shown the importance of social reinforcement and group support in behavior change.[78] But the political constituency for conservation is difficult to mobilize because the benefits are diverse, long-run, and widely diffused, whereas well-organized and powerful groups in industry, labor, and government receive immediate benefits from continued dependence on fossil and nuclear fuels.

Changes in life-styles could further reduce energy consumption by altering the goods and services people seek rather than simply providing the same goods and services more efficiently. A consumer society encourages a high demand for material goods, highly processed and packaged foods, and energy-intensive products. During the 1970s, a significant number of young people in North America and Europe were disillusioned with the prevailing materialism and individualism and the stresses of a competitive society. They sought alternative sources of satisfaction in personal growth, human relationships, smaller communities, and greater harmony with nature, and they adopted more frugal life-styles. Some of them joined communes or new religious movements. Others tried to find meaningful work, family life, spiritual growth, and fulfilling activities within traditional institutions.[79] Some of these experiments were short-lived, but others continued in the 1980s, expressing values that are neglected among the dominant goals of industrial societies.

In whatever form they are expressed, *new views of personal fulfillment* can lead to lower levels of resource consumption and energy use. I do not believe that moral exhortation or appeals to austerity or sacrifice will have much influence today. But a revitalization of Western religious traditions could bring new perceptions of the good life and a new recognition of less resource-intensive sources of satisfaction that would alter patterns of consumption in affluent nations. In chapter 9 I will discuss the shift from the prevailing industrial paradigm to a *postindustrial paradigm* more appropriate to an interdependent world with finite resources. But such paradigm shifts occur slowly except in response to severe crises. In the meantime, the practice of individual frugality must be combined with political efforts for effective legislation, economic incentives, and efficient technologies, which are the most promising social paths to energy conservation today.

3. Energy in the Third World

The Third World is highly dependent on *fossil fuels*. The disastrous impact of higher oil prices was mentioned earlier. Oil has played a vital role in transportation, agricultural irrigation, and fertilizer production. Only a few Third World countries have coal deposits, and the release of greenhouse gases makes increased use of coal problematic. Several developing nations have significant natural gas deposits, and others have not yet been explored; these could be very helpful during the next decades, though they would require the construction of pipeline systems. *Nuclear power* has played a negligible role in the South. It is expensive and perpetuates dependence on equipment and exports from the North. A second generation of smaller, passively stable reactors might be useful in urban and industrial centers in the more advanced developing countries, but most areas lack the electrical grids necessary for distributing large blocks of electricity.

Waterpower and *biomass* account for nearly half the primary energy use of the Third World, but fuelwood, the chief source in rural areas, has been used much faster than it has been replaced. We have seen that deforestation without replanting has resulted in severe soil erosion and flooding as well as fuelwood shortages. Cheap *solar technology* would be a great boon to the sun-rich Third World. It would reduce dependence on other nations for expertise and fuel. Solar cookers, solar water pumps, methane digesters, small hydroelectric dams, windmills, and photovoltaic cells would be especially helpful. They would encourage national self-reliance and fit in with local cultures.[80]

Conservation might seem insignificant in developing countries, since the amount of energy that could be saved is so much smaller than that wasted in affluent nations. But in fact conservation is crucial for future prospects in all countries. The Brundtland commission concluded that with strong conservation programs the global energy consumption in 2030 could be only 10 percent higher than in 1980 (rather than growing by a factor of three as in some projections). The report emphasizes the fuelwood crisis, pointing out that an open fire uses eight times the energy of a gas stove of equivalent cooking capacity. It sees promise in biogas, small dams, and solar installations. It advocates incentives for tree planting, community woodlots, and the combination of food and energy production in agroforestry. With careful planning, fast-growing trees could be used efficiently, and replanting would prevent the soil erosion that attended previous fuelwood use.[81]

A report by the World Resources Institute (WRI) concludes that if *efficiency* is strenuously pursued in all countries, global energy demand in 2020 would be only 10 percent higher than in 1980, even with the expected growth in population. Energy use in the North would have to be cut in half, while that in the South would grow, and living standards in the Third World in 2020 could be comparable with those of Western Europe in the midseventies. For $4 billion, a highly efficient wood stove costing $10 could be provided to 400 million rural households in the Third World. Stoves of even higher efficiency would burn biogas from crop and animal residues or producer gas from the partial oxidation of other forms of biomass. The study urges intensive research on better technologies for the conversion of biomass to liquid fuels for transportation. It also advocates the electrification of all villages, using local resources whenever feasible.[82]

The World Resources Institute study looks at energy end use in the framework of a development strategy focused on *basic human needs*. It points out that a quarter of World Bank loans have been for energy but mostly for large projects such as dams or central power plants. "Over 90 percent of energy development aid has gone to building large systems for generating and transmitting electricity.... Less than 1 percent of international aid has been used to improve energy efficiency, and most of this 1 percent has gone to the industrial sector."[83] Such aid has paid for foreign consultants and equipment, benefiting the donors, but it has done little to develop indigenous technical capacities. It has favored cities and heavy industries over rural areas and small-scale technologies. The WRI report advocates self-reliant development, production for local needs, and the expansion of industries producing equipment for agriculture and rural areas rather than for export or the urban elite. It suggests that a shift from materials processing to fabrication and finishing would also reduce energy use and increase employment opportunities.

Some authors hold that developing nations will have to use large-scale electric generation (such as large dams and nuclear and coal-fired plants) if their *electricity demands* continue growing at current rates (7 percent per year, with demand increasing fourfold in twenty years).[84] They hold that developing countries are likely to give industrial growth higher priority than environmental impacts, except where the latter are already serious and obvious (urban respiratory problems, for instance). While some development of such capital-intensive technologies may be necessary, they tend to perpetuate foreign dependency and trade deficits, and the benefits will be short-lived. Third World countries should rather seek to develop their own distinctive renewable sources and seek the transfer of technologies more directly related to basic human needs.

V. Conclusions

By the criteria of evaluation outlined in earlier chapters, the "hard path" of fossil fuel and nuclear expansion is less desirable than the "soft path" of renewable energy and conservation for both industrial and developing nations. Dependence on *imported oil* has been a source of global injustice, international conflict, and environmental damage. Some of the environmental impacts of *coal* can be reduced by improved combustion and emission control technologies, but others, especially the greenhouse effect, are likely to be very serious. *Natural gas* is preferable environmentally and is crucial for the transitional period, but reserves are unevenly distributed and are not indefinitely sustainable.

Nuclear fuels are sustainable for many centuries (especially with breeder reactors) and environmental risks are low in normal operation. But we have seen that economic costs are high, accidents are potentially catastrophic, and uncertainties about radioactive waste disposal are unresolved (though probably resolvable). The risk of diversion of plutonium to nuclear weapons counts against breeders and reprocessing, and all nuclear plants are vulnerable to human errors, institutional failures, and extortion by terrorists. I expressed support for a program of careful, open research on fusion and on smaller, passively stable reactors—but only as forms of insurance in the unlikely event that promising solar sources (especially photovoltaics) and storage methods (such as hydrogen) remain costly despite intensive research and development efforts.

Renewable sources, by contrast, correlate well with all of the values I have defended. They are compatible with justice because they are available to all countries, more evenly distributed than fossil or nuclear fuels, and more readily subject to national self-determination. They reduce threats to world peace from conflicts over oil and from the proliferation of nuclear weapons. They are compatible with participation because they are diverse, predominantly small-scale and decentralized, and amenable to community ownership and local control. They are uniquely sustainable because they do not significantly deplete resources. Their environmental impact on air and water is lower than that of fossil fuels, and problems of land use and soil erosion can be controlled by careful management.

Whatever sources of energy are used, *conservation* can be justified in every nation in terms of all the values we have been discussing. Efficiency research and conservation efforts have had a small role in the budgets of most national governments and international agencies, and yet these measures are essential to economic development and selective growth. A strenuous conservation program is also required if we are to shift a large fraction of total supply from fossil to renewable fuels without highly disruptive energy shortages.

I have argued that the combination of *renewable sources* and *conservation* would not jeopardize economic development in the long run, though it would involve some increased costs and displacements in the short run. Employment opportunities are greater on the "soft path" than on the "hard." Finally, the understanding of personal fulfillment that I have defended does not require ever higher levels of individual consumption in affluent nations but encourages more frugal life-styles that would give additional support to public policies for conserving energy and other resources.

For several decades we will have to use *a mix of "hard" and "soft" technologies*, even as we try to rely increasingly on the latter. Such diversity would allow flexibility in adapting to new developments and to differing local conditions. Keeping diverse options open would hedge our bets and allow creative responses to technological advances, changing economic costs, and new knowledge of environmental impacts—all of which, along with our value priorities, will influence our future policy judgments.

Article Questions

1. Why are fossil fuels used so prevalently?

2. What are the problems of world wide energy accelerated use? Name five.

3. What is the effect of coal on the environment?

4. What effect does burning fossil fuels have on the environment? What is the main way to reduce global warming?

5. What effect could radioactive wastes have on future generations?

6. What are three ethical issues that can be identified in planning for nuclear waste disposal?

7. How does the energy issue relate to the ecological issues of populations and pollution? What are some of your conclusions?

8. What is the correlation between energy consumption reduction and lifestyle?

Energy Options

Energy Dilemma: Once and Future Crisis

Essayist Wendell Berry once observed that, "The kind and quantity of energy we use determine the kind and quality of the life we live." One of the striking things about the kind of life Americans take for granted is that it requires a prodigious amount of energy. When you add up all the energy used in the United States in 1989—for residential purposes, for transportation, and for commercial and industrial uses—it amounts to annual consumption of 327 million BTUs (British thermal units) for every man, woman, and child. That is the equivalent of the energy contained in 2,500 gallons of gasoline per year, or about 7 gallons per day. The United States, which contains just 5 percent of the world's population, consumes 26 percent of the world's energy.

With that power we heat and light homes, schools, and offices, run computers, play night baseball, operate appliances ranging from refrigerators and microwave ovens to VCRs, and drive cars an average of 10,000 miles per year. For the most part, except when faced with gas shortages, brownouts, or sharp hikes in the price of energy, most people don't think about what the options are in meeting energy needs in a way that is safe, sustainable, and relatively inexpensive.

In August 1990, when Saddam Hussein ordered Iraqi troops into Kuwait and announced that Iraq was annexing that nation, he rekindled a debate about energy that had been dormant for ten years. By making Americans painfully aware of our continued dependence on foreign oil, Saddam Hussein may be more successful in the 1990s than President Jimmy Carter was in the late 1970s in pushing the United States toward a reevaluation of its energy needs and how they can be met.

The Persian Gulf crisis, as former President Carter said soon after it erupted, is evidence of "the dismal failure of our country to acknowledge and deal with its energy vulnerability. The hard fact is that we now have no effective national energy policy. We have a choice between the many reasons to do nothing and looking for ways to get the job done."

What's the Problem?

In contrast to the 1970s, when Americans were repeatedly told that global oil resources would soon be depleted, America's energy problem today is not imminent shortages of the materials from which energy is generated. Ninety percent of America's energy is generated by burning fossil fuels, and there is no shortage of them. America's reserves of coal and natural gas are abundant. Oil reserves are abundant, too, although not domestically.

Eventually, of course, world oil resources will be depleted. Right now, however, oil is plentiful and relatively cheap. World oil reserves are nearly twice as large as they were in 1970. In the midst of the Persian Gulf crisis in 1990, Saudi Arabia, the world's biggest oil exporter—with 10 times the reserves of the United States—announced the discovery of new reserves of crude oil that will enable that country to continue pumping oil at the present rate for at least another century.

"In terms of the next few decades," concludes a recent study, *Energy Imperatives for the 1990s*, from the Atlantic Council of the United States, "there does not appear to be a shortage of energy supplies in useful forms at acceptable prices on a worldwide basis."

So what is the problem? In the words of energy expert Daniel Yergin, "the most visible and vexing part of the energy problem" is America's increasing reliance on imported oil. At a time when half of the petroleum used in the United States is imported, there is growing concern that about 70 percent of known world oil reserves available for export are controlled by the politically volatile Persian Gulf nations.

Petroleum provides 40 percent of America's energy needs and more than 90 percent of the fuel for transportation Unless alternatives to imported oil are found, the United States is likely to be increasingly at the mercy of foreign regimes.

If growing dependence on imported oil is one dimension of the energy problem, growing concern about the environmental effects of burning fossil fuels is another. We are at the end of an era of cheap, readily accessible energy sources whose environmental effects most Americans are willing to accept. There is growing concern about the hazards to human health and to the environment that result from burning fossil fuels.

"It has become painfully clear," write energy analysts Christopher Flavin and Rick Piltz, "that the fundamental constraint on energy systems is not scarce resources, but the threat posed by the forms of energy we use to the livability of our nation and the world. Rising use of fossil fuels could make our nation virtually uninhabitable long before reserves of those fuels are depleted."

A third aspect of the energy problem is less visible but no less important. Demand for electricity in the United States—which is generated mainly by coal and nuclear power—has increased over the past few years to the point where shortages are anticipated.

"New technology and higher incomes cause people to use more electricity," says Bruce Humphrey, a strategic planner for the Edison Electric Institute, a group that represents privately owned utilities. "High tech is virtually synonymous with flowing electrons. There is a need for new generating capacity during the 1990s."

According to the Energy Information Administration, U.S. demand for electrical power is expected to grow for the foreseeable future at an annual rate of more than 2 percent per year. At that rate, the United States will need 110 gigawatts of new power capacity by the year 2000. (A gigawatt is 1 billion watts, roughly the amount of power used each year by a large city.)

Currently, however, only 37 gigawatts of new power generating capacity are planned or under construction. Since the lead time for construction of power plants is typically more than 10 years, it is a matter of some urgency to move ahead with plans to meet the nation's growing power needs—or to reduce consumption.

Era of Abundance

The roots of today's energy problem can be traced to the post-World War II years, when a seemingly endless supply of cheap oil and coal fueled rapid economic growth and a rising standard of living. A lot of new things happened in the United States in the two decades following the war, and most of them plugged into wall outlets or required regular infusions of oil.

In 1949, the Esso Oil Company (which a few years later was renamed Exxon) ran magazine ads in which it tied the fortunes of the oil industry to America's rising standard of living. "The better you live," as Esso put it, "the more oil you use."

And so it was. In the 1950s, cheap oil stimulated a new way of life, a "freeway culture" built around the automobile. With the automobile, journalist Marcia Lowe wrote, "the average wage earner could have more horsepower at his or her disposal than royalty had in other times."

Between 1950 and 1972, the number of motor vehicles in the U.S. doubled. There was growing public enthusiasm for bigger, faster cars. The auto industry responded by producing cars that were, on average, about 700 pounds heavier—and, consequently, less fuel efficient than the previous generation of cars.

The new automobile culture was just one reason why demand for petroleum products soared in the postwar period. From the laborsaving machines used in factories to energy-intensive technologies used on the nation's farms, virtually every sector of the economy substituted machines for human labor.

By the 1970s, for example, the celebrated efficiency of American agriculture allowed a single farmer to feed more than 60 people. Less commonly noted was the fact that the petroleum required for tractors, fertilizers, and pesticides means that a gallon of gasoline is needed to produce a bushel of corn.

The nation's energy appetite increased in less obvious ways, too. Consider the American diet. When you shop for groceries, one item you don't see listed among the ingredients of the products you purchase is the energy required to produce and ship them. "The typical mouthful of food," says energy analyst Alan Durning, "travels 1,300 miles from farm field to dinner plate." Transporting food requires energy.

So do prepared foods, which became an increasingly important part of the American diet in the 1950s and 1960s. "Ounce for ounce," says Durning, "getting frozen orange juice to the consumer takes four times the energy of providing fresh oranges. Likewise, potato chip production has four times the energy budget of potatoes."

Because a cornucopia of new household appliances was produced in the postwar years—including dishwashers, electric clothes washers and dryers, and dozens of other laborsaving products—demand for electrical power soared. In the postwar years, use of electricity in the United States increased at an average rate of 8 percent per year.

In all, during the period 1950-1973, American energy consumption more than doubled. At the time, in an era of apparently limitless energy, few people were concerned about America's growing appetite for energy or the environmental costs of generating it.

ENERGY-INTENSIVE NATION

Overall U.S. energy use increased rapidly in the 1950s and 1960s and then levelled off after the 1973 oil shock. Since 1986, energy consumption has risen to record levels.

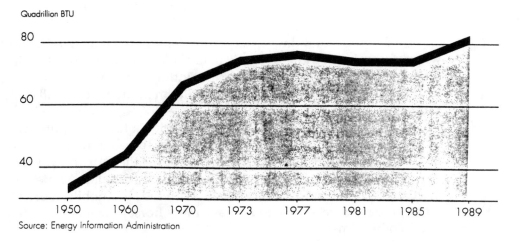

Quadrillion BTU

Source: Energy Information Administration

Creeping Dependence

Because domestic oil production increased year by year during the 1950s and 1960s, the United States was able to meet its own energy needs. But as energy use surged ahead, domestic oil supplies could not keep pace. By 1973, the United States imported almost one-third of its petroleum, most of it from the Middle East.

In the fall of 1973, the United States received the first of several jarring reminders of how vulnerable it had become to suppliers of imported oil. When Arab oil producers increased prices sharply, the price of imported crude oil rose from about $2.50 a barrel to over $10. In 1979, the turmoil that accompanied the Iranian Revolution drove oil prices up sharply a second time—from $13 a barrel to $34. Once again, the United States experienced widespread gas shortages and a recession made more severe by rising fuel prices.

Responding to the oil shocks of the 1970s, three presidents tried to reduce U.S. dependence on imported oil. President Nixon introduced the ill-fated Project Independence. President Ford proposed a National Energy Act. President Carter, who called the energy problem "the greatest domestic challenge our nation will face in our lifetime," proposed a far-reaching national energy plan. But each time an energy plan was proposed, it was greeted by a recalcitrant Congress with months of protracted debate.

The problem was that proposals to develop new power sources impose substantial cost and political pain. "Any comprehensive proposal has something in it for almost everyone to hate," said Eric Zausner, deputy administrator of the Federal Energy Administration in the mid-1970s. "It exacts difficult political costs, including higher prices and environmental impacts. It takes a long time to build oil and gas production facilities, nuclear power plants, or even energy-efficient buildings. Any solution incurs great political costs today that do not provide benefits—in terms of reduced imports—for up to ten years. Long lead times are a politician's nemesis." That may explain why, despite repeated calls for a comprehensive energy strategy in the 1970s, no such plan was agreed on.

Shock Absorbers

Still, the energy problem was widely recognized and progress was achieved on three fronts. As a shock absorber against interruptions of imported oil, the United States created the Strategic Petroleum Reserve, containing 590 million barrels of oil.

The United States also began exploring the feasibility of alternative energy sources. Solar energy and wind power attracted particular attention, and photovoltaic cells (which convert sunlight directly into electricity) showed signs of becoming commercially viable.

By the late 1970s, a dizzying list of energy alternatives was under consideration at the newly created Department of Energy, including alcohol-based fuels, wood-fired power plants, fusion power, tidal power, and the use of waste heat from industrial processes to create energy (a process called cogeneration). Members of Congress proposed tax incentives and other measures to encourage the development of various energy alternatives.

On a third front, Americans began to think about the energy they consumed in their daily lives. Millions of people started to car pool. They bought smaller, more fuel-efficient cars. They examined the energy-efficiency ratings that had begun to appear on appliances. Many Americans also got in the habit of turning off unnecessary lights. Home owners, facing higher heating costs, added insulation to their houses.

Conservation efforts produced striking results. Despite the fact that the American economy grew by more than 40 percent from 1973 to 1986, the amount of power consumed in the United States during that period remained stable.

Market Forces

The 1970s brought a new consciousness about the consumption of energy and dependence on foreign oil. In the 1980s, however, this consciousness faded and energy seemed to disappear as a public issue.

The policies of the Reagan administration were one reason for the change. In an early policy statement, the administration pledged "to minimize federal control and involvement in energy markets." It chose to rely almost exclusively on market forces to determine the supply and demand for energy.

Soon after he took office in 1981, President Reagan instructed the White House staff to dismantle the solar water-heating panels installed by President Carter, an act that symbolized the administration's disinclination to support the fledgling alternative energy business. In 1985, federal tax credits for alternative energy projects were slashed. Fuel economy standards were rolled back for cars and trucks, and federal support for conservation was dramatically reduced.

A second reason for diminishing public concern about energy was the mid-1980s oil glut. Most energy analysts predicted that oil prices would climb during the 1980s, making alternative energy sources such as solar profitable. But just the opposite happened. Because members of the OPEC cartel exported more petroleum than anticipated, the price of oil fell from $30 to less than $15 a barrel. At the same time, the price of natural gas and coal—the nation's other two chief energy sources—also fell. By 1986, the United States was experiencing a glut of low-cost fossil fuels.

Low energy prices were good news for consumers, who saw pump prices drop to their lowest level, in real terms, since 1973. But low fuel prices nipped the alternative energy business in the bud. By 1986, when the price of crude oil fell to $13, there seemed to be no further need to encourage alternatives to fossil fuels. No matter how attractive alternatives such as solar energy or ethanol might be to some consumers, start-up companies that developed them could not make a profit when the price of crude oil was so low. Largely because of the oil glut of the mid-1980s, much of the momentum to develop energy alternatives—including photovoltaic cells and electric-powered vehicles— was lost.

Plentiful supplies of cheap imported oil also knocked many domestic oil producers out of the business. Because domestic oil is more expensive to produce than oil imported from the Middle East, production in the United States reached it lowest level in 25 years by 1989.

Low pump prices conveyed the message that the energy crisis was a thing of the past. Not surprisingly, America's appetite for energy began to grow again. On the same day in August 1988 when the *New York Times* ran a major story on global warming—the threat to the atmosphere posed by carbon emissions from oil and other fossil fuels—the paper's front page carried a story on renewed demand for gas-guzzling "muscle cars." "With fuel cheap," the article concluded, "a fast car has again become a success symbol."

During the 1980s, Americans became less energy conscious at home, too. The federal government's Residential Energy Consumption Survey showed that a typical American household set its winter thermostat a full degree higher in 1987 than in 1984, and the number of households operating air conditioners throughout the summer increased by 40 percent.

Demand for oil in the United States reached 17 million barrels a day by 1989, the highest figure in a decade. The surest sign that many Americans have forgotten the lessons of the oil shocks of the 1970s is that overall U.S. energy consumption in recent years has been growing once again. In 1989, U.S. energy consumption reached a record high—81.3 quadrillion BTUs.

By the late 1980s, the United States was once again deeply dependent on foreign oil. "We fell into a dangerous complacency as oil moved into ample supply and prices tumbled," said Robert D. Hormats, a high-ranking State Department official during the Reagan administration. "We assumed the problems of the 1970s were permanently behind us." In many ways, the Persian Gulf crisis of 1990 was an incident waiting to happen.

The Pollution Problem

While the Persian Gulf crisis reminded the nation of the perils of relying on imported oil, that is just one aspect of the energy problem. Since the 1970s, there has been growing concern about pollution caused by burning fossil fuels, the source of 90 percent of the nation's energy. Three air pollution problems—acid rain, smog, and the greenhouse effect—are all linked to the fossil fuels required to generate the nation's power.

Acid rain is caused by sulfur pumped into the air as coal is burned to generate electricity. Sulfur is carried by the wind, sometimes hundreds of miles, until it falls to the earth as acid rain. Precipitation in the United States is now 5 to 30 times more acidic than it was in preindustrial times. On several Eastern mountains, rainfall acidity is 2,000 times greater than unpolluted rain, or roughly the acidity of lemon juice. This caustic substance is believed to be causing widespread destruction both to forests and to fish life in many regions of the United States and Canada.

Smog is primarily caused by exhaust from cars and trucks. It damages plant life and causes a variety of lung diseases when people are exposed to it for long periods. Since 1970, when Congress passed the Clean Air Act in an effort to reduce air pollutants to acceptable levels, some progress has been made in reducing smog. But in many areas of the country, ozone (one of the chief ingredients of smog) remains unacceptably high. New anti-pollution measures contained in the 1990 revision of the Clean Air Act are a reminder of the seriousness of the problem, as well as the difficulty of solving it while the nation continues to rely on fossil fuels.

Of this trio of air pollution problems associated with the energy we use, global warming has the greatest destructive potential. When burned, coal, oil, and natural gas combine with oxygen to form carbon dioxide, the chief contributor to global warming. As a by-product of producing and using the energy that powers appliances and cars, and heats,

GREENHOUSE EFFECT: CHANGING THE WORLD'S CLIMATE

The concentration of carbon dioxide and other greenhouse gases in the atmosphere has increased by about 25 percent since the start of the industrial revolution. Over the next century, the heat trapped by those gases may profoundly affect world climate. The scenario starts with number #1 . . .

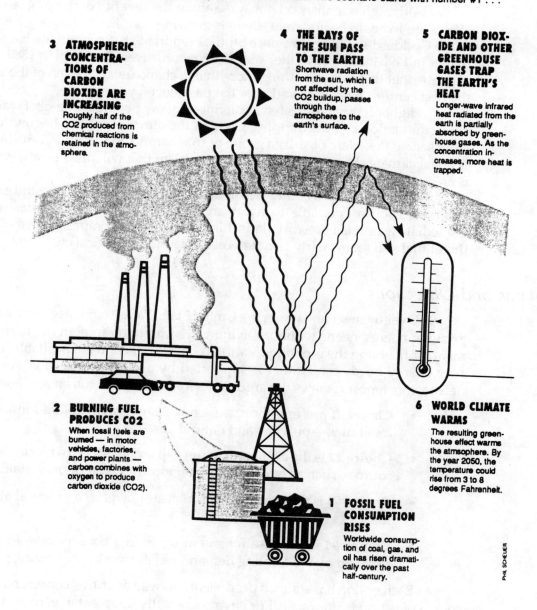

3 ATMOSPHERIC CONCENTRATIONS OF CARBON DIOXIDE ARE INCREASING
Roughly half of the CO2 produced from chemical reactions is retained in the atmosphere.

4 THE RAYS OF THE SUN PASS TO THE EARTH
Shortwave radiation from the sun, which is not affected by the CO2 buildup, passes through the atmosphere to the earth's surface.

5 CARBON DIOXIDE AND OTHER GREENHOUSE GASES TRAP THE EARTH'S HEAT
Longer-wave infrared heat radiated from the earth is partially absorbed by greenhouse gases. As the concentration increases, more heat is trapped.

2 BURNING FUEL PRODUCES CO2
When fossil fuels are burned — in motor vehicles, factories, and power plants — carbon combines with oxygen to produce carbon dioxide (CO2).

6 WORLD CLIMATE WARMS
The resulting greenhouse effect warms the atmosphere. By the year 2050, the temperature could rise from 3 to 8 degrees Fahrenheit.

1 FOSSIL FUEL CONSUMPTION RISES
Worldwide consumption of coal, gas, and oil has risen dramatically over the past half-century.

PHIL SCHEUER

cools, and lights the buildings in which we live and work, two tons of carbon are pumped into the atmosphere each year for every man, woman, and child in the United States. As a result of worldwide fossil fuel use, the amount of carbon dioxide in the atmosphere has increased by 25 percent over the past century and is likely to double over the next century.

Accumulating carbon dioxide in the atmosphere is the chief source of the greenhouse effect, the gradual warming of the earth caused by trapping the sun's energy near the earth's surface. While scientists disagree about whether global warming is already apparent, there is a consensus that rising levels of carbon dioxide in the atmosphere will eventually modify world climate. As a result, the temperature could rise 3 to 8 degrees by the middle of the twenty-first century, causing parched farmland, unprecedented high temperatures, and coastal flooding. Global warming could threaten the habitat of many plants, fish, and wildlife.

Although scientists do not agree about the severity of the problem or just when its effects are likely to be apparent, there is growing concern. In January 1991, climatologists at the Goddard Institute for Space Studies reported that average global temperature was higher in 1990 than in any other year since records were first kept in 1880. Recent evidence suggests that this was something more than a chance event. Seven of the warmest years of the past century have occurred over the past eleven years.

Higher temperatures have convinced many people that global warming caused by an accumulation of heat-trapping gases in the atmosphere has begun. In the words of a letter sent to President Bush by a group of 16 senators soon after the 1990 data were released: "Global climate change is real. It is not a problem that will disappear if we ignore it. There is an increasingly urgent need for policies to address this issue."

The question is whether we should change our energy-using and energy-producing habits as soon as possible to avert an uncertain but possibly catastrophic change. If immediate action is necessary, launching a costly and comprehensive effort to forestall a threat that still seems fairly remote poses a daunting political challenge.

Options and Objections

Over the next few years, the United States faces tough decisions about how to meet growing energy needs without relying increasingly on foreign oil, harming the environment, or hobbling the economy. Various courses of action are available, but no plan about how energy needs can be met is supported by a public consensus. As a framework for debate, this report reviews the arguments for and against four major energy options:

- **Choice #1** presents the case for more aggressive exploration and use of domestic fossil fuels—oil, coal, and natural gas.

- **Choice #2** is the argument for an expanded effort to develop renewable energy sources, such as hydroelectric, windpower, and photovoltaic.

- **Choice #3** is the argument for nuclear power as a practical alternative to fossil fuels.

- **Choice #4** is the case for pursuing energy conservation—solving the energy problem by moderating demand rather than by expanding supplies.

Each option has staunch proponents, as well as critics, convinced that the proposed course of action is impractical or environmentally unacceptable, or that adopting it as an important part of the nation's energy strategy would impose too high a cost.

Pumping Carbon:
Is Global Warming a Clear and Present Danger?

The threat of global warming is one of the chief factors that makes today's energy debate different from the debate of the 1970s. Increasingly, people line up one side or another in the energy debate according to their views on global warming.

Taking Global Warming Seriously

If James Hansen, head of NASA's Goddard Institute, and other scientists predicting global warming are right, the earth is beginning to undergo a fundamental transformation whose consequences will eventually range from parched farmland in the Midwest to coastal cities threatened by rising waters.

As the sea rises because of glacial melting and the thermal expansion of a warmer ocean, we may face a harsh choice: either to abandon low-lying coastal areas in which a substantial fraction of the American population lives, or come increasingly to resemble Holland, where nearly six cents out of every dollar is spent on holding back the sea. That is just the beginning of the list of wrenching dislocations that may result from global warming, which does not take into consideration its worldwide effects.

The seriousness of this threat is reason to take immediate steps to reduce our reliance on oil, coal, and natural gas. Because continuing to rely on fossil fuels for energy jeopardizes the prospects of future generations, those who share this perspective are persuaded that alternatives to fossil fuels must be found.

"The basic value of a sustainable society, and the ecological equivalent of the Golden Rule, is simple," writes Alan Durning. "Each generation should meet its needs without jeopardizing the prospects of future generations."

Rush to Judgment

Many remain unconvinced that rapid action to reduce carbon emissions is necessary. "Drastic measures based on panic should be resisted," says S. Fred Singer, former professor of environmental sciences at the University of Virginia, "until an acceptable scientific base is established."

Even among scientists who accept the greenhouse theory, there is little agreement about likely effects. Patrick Michaels, professor of environmental sciences at the University of Virginia, anticipates that, as the earth gradually heats up, more clouds will form, deflecting sunlight, thus mitigating the warming effect. "The result—warmer nights and cooler, cloudier days—is something we can live with," says Michaels.

Rapid action is ill advised, say those who are skeptical about global warming, because of the huge cost and massive dislocations that would be caused by an ambitious effort to shift to alternative energy sources. Estimates of the expense of shifting energy sources to slow global warming range from several hundred billion dollars to more than three trillion dollars in the United States alone. "Like it or not," says Andrew Solow, a scientist at the Woods Hole Oceanographic Institute in Massachusetts, "the consumption of fossil fuels contributes to our standard of living. Major shifts in our energy policy need better justification than current fears about climate change."

Because the Persian Gulf crisis has drawn attention once again to the energy problem, this is an unusual opportunity for focused discussion on energy options and for decisive public action. Elected officials face important decisions that will affect the nation's energy habits for years to come. The four courses of action presented here provide a map of competing views and a framework for discussion about energy options.

Choice #1 Domestic Sources:
Taking Advantage of America's Fossil Resources

In Texas and Louisiana, hikes in the price of crude oil in 1990 caused by the Iraq crisis provided a shot of adrenalin to this once-bustling center of the U.S. petroleum industry. As the price of crude oil approached $30 per barrel, drilling companies snapped up used extracting equipment that had been selling as scrap iron a few years ago. "No one's happy with the events in the Middle East," says Texas wildcatter Bud Champlin, "but it's going to make for some good activity here."

With crude oil prices higher than they have been since 1982, explorers are going to new depths to locate and tap domestic oil reserves. Since easy-to-tap reserves in shallow water are largely depleted, oilmen are beginning to explore the slopes of the continental shelf, more than 100 miles from land and several thousand feet under water. In coastal waters off Texas and Louisiana, half a dozen major oil companies are engaged in a hunt for reserves that may be four times larger than those found at Alaska's Prudhoe Bay, the last major domestic oil discovery. "Oil at $30 to $40 a barrel is suddenly making every project that boosts domestic supplies look a lot more feasible," says Wayne Dunlap, an offshore technology expert at Texas A&M.

Even if oil prices stay in the $25 to $30 per barrel range for months, however, domestic drillers who got burned by the mid-1980s glut are cautious and not necessarily optimistic about long-term prospects for domestic oil production. In the Permian Basin of West Texas, which for years was the U.S. oil drilling capital, only about 100 rigs were operating in fall 1990—down from 600 a decade before.

To advocates of relying more heavily on domestic fossil fuels for the nation's energy needs, that is the problem. With domestic production down by more than one million barrels per day from 1986 levels and consumption up by the same amount, the United States is rapidly becoming more dependent on imported oil. Since relatively little exploration for domestic oil is currently taking place, the future of American oil production is none too bright.

The nation's dependence on foreign oil, as Interior Secretary Manuel Lujan put it, poses "an issue that Americans will have to deal with sooner or later. Do we want to become increasingly reliant on foreign supplies for oil that this country must have? Or do we want instead to rely on our capacity to safely produce our own?"

Advocates of the first approach to America's energy dilemma are convinced that the U.S. should take immediate measures to achieve a greater measure of energy independence. The most promising way to do that, in their view, is to take advantage of domestic reserves of fossil fuels—not just oil, but also coal, and natural gas.

Fossil fuels are by a wide margin the most important source of America's energy, supplying roughly 90 percent of it. Oil, coal, and natural gas heat our homes and generate electricity, run our cars, and provide power for American industry. Advocates of the first choice are convinced that, for the foreseeable future, there is no realistic and economical alternative to fossil fuels.

In contrast to other, speculative energy sources such as renewables, advocates of this choice point out, fossil fuels are a proven source of power. They are the fuels that our entire infrastructure—factories, homes, and motor vehicles—is designed to use.

Versatile, Powerful, Plentiful

Advocates of this first option point to the fact that substantial reserves of coal, natural gas, and even oil are available domestically, if we take the measures necessary to locate and extract them and put no unnecessary restrictions on their use.

For example, coal deposits can be found beneath 38 of the 50 states. The United States possesses one-quarter of the world's identified coal resources. In sharp contrast to domestic oil production, domestic coal production exceeds U.S. coal consumption. In 1989, the United States exported more than 100 million tons of coal.

The domestic coal industry, proponents of the first option argue, has both the capacity and the available resources to increase production to meet increased demand. Coal, the fuel used to produce 60 percent of the nation's electrical power, could play an even larger role, they say, in America's energy future. In their view, low cost and ready availability make coal-fired generators an increasingly attractive way to meet the need for additional electrical capacity.

The outlook for expanded use of natural gas is also bright, say those who favor this strategy. They note, first of all, that natural gas, which provides about a quarter of America's energy needs, is a versatile fuel. Used to power electrical generators, it can be substituted for either oil or coal. In compressed form, it can be used as a transportation fuel. Compared to coal and oil, natural gas is a clean-burning fossil fuel which emits less carbon monoxide, carbon dioxide, and other hydrocarbons.

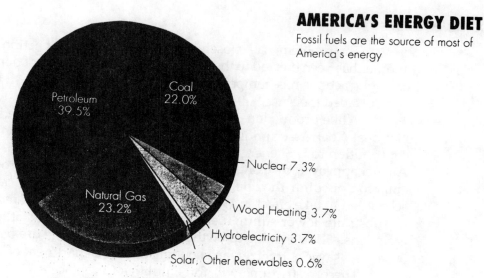

AMERICA'S ENERGY DIET
Fossil fuels are the source of most of America's energy

Petroleum 39.5%
Coal 22.0%
Natural Gas 23.2%
Nuclear 7.3%
Wood Heating 3.7%
Hydroelectricity 3.7%
Solar, Other Renewables 0.6%

Source: Congressional Research Service   July, 1990

Natural gas, like coal, is also readily available. As the Energy Department indicated in its 1990 *Interim Report* on a National Energy Strategy, domestic reserves of natural gas amount to ten times current annual production. In brief, says George H. Lawrence, former president of the American Gas Association, "Ample supplies are available, today and in the future. By using more of its own natural gas supplies, America can reduce its reliance on foreign oil, lower home owners' gas bills, and improve environmental quality."

Extending the Oil Era

Substantial amounts of domestic oil are available, too, say advocates of this strategy—if we are willing to take the measures necessary to explore for it and extract it. In the Middle East, oil can be extracted cheaply because vast pools of it lie just below the desert sands. But, in America, the remaining oil reserves are relatively inaccessible and more expensive to extract.

Nonetheless, America still has large quantities of oil, proponents of fossil fuels argue. Recent studies conducted by the Bureau of Economic Geology at the University of Texas indicate that the U.S. is still rich in untapped oil reserves. According to William L. Fisher, the bureau's director: "Eighty billion barrels of domestic oil could still be produced at a cost of $20 to $25 a barrel. An additional 200 billion barrels could be produced at the somewhat higher price of $25 to $40 per barrel." That is enough, Fisher points out, "to provide stable U.S. production until the middle of the next century."

The essential point, say advocates of this course of action, is to keep in mind how important petroleum is to our economy and our way of life. The United States consumes 17 million barrels of oil per day because petroleum is a reliable and compact form of energy, easily used in many applications.

For these reasons, says James Critchfield, president of Gulf Futures, which engages in energy research: "Extending the life of the oil era remains humanity's best insurance policy against a declining standard of living. We need to hang on to the trapeze we're riding until we get a firm grip on the next trapeze."

Obstacle Course

The problem, say those who favor this course of action, is that one obstacle after another has been erected to the extraction and efficient use of domestic fossil fuels. A series of public actions has hampered exploration for domestic fossil fuels, increased their cost, and curtailed their use.

While production of domestic coal is expected to exceed 1 billion tons in 1990, the National Coal Association is concerned that recent legislation will severely limit coal's contribution to U.S. energy demands in the 1990s and beyond. The legislation, the Clean Air Act approved by Congress in October 1990, imposes two rounds of restrictions on the emission of sulfur dioxide, which contributes to acid rain. Those restrictions, which are scheduled to take effect in 1995 and tighten in the year 2000, require coal-burning utilities to substitute lower-sulfur fuel, or to install scrubbers or other technologies to reduce emissions. "This is going to be the biggest change in the use of coal at utilities in the past 50 years," says Scott Sitzer, an economist at the Department of Energy.

These restrictions will force utilities to replace high-sulfur coal, much of which comes from the Middle West and Appalachia, with low-sulfur coal, which is available mainly in the West. Especially in the Middle West, where many utilities now use high-sulfur coal, higher transportation costs for coal as well as the cost of scrubbers will push up electric rates.

"Since coal is our most abundant domestic energy option," says David Swanson of the Edison Electric Institute, "we cannot afford to write it off or to unduly restrict its expanded use."

Advocates of domestic fossil fuels are convinced that the use of natural gas as a major U.S. energy source has also been hampered by unnecessary restrictions. Natural gas can meet an increasing portion of the nation's energy needs, they say, only if exploration for new sources is permitted and if public permission is granted for the installation of new pipelines. In several regions of the country, especially New England, the lack of sufficient pipelines is a major barrier.

According to industry officials, a government review process that is overly sensitive to environmental concerns has hampered the installation of pipelines needed to transport natural gas. One example, says Nicholas Bush, president of the Natural Gas Supply Association, is a proposed natural gas pipeline from Wyoming to California. "One of the major factors," says Bush, "is watching out for the desert tortoise. Now, I don't want the desert tortoise to be hurt, but we have to find ways to expedite these reviews. We hear Congress and environmentalists talk about how natural gas is the fuel of the future," says Bush. "But we are caught in a moratorium on offshore drilling. Sixty-six percent of the energy from offshore is natural gas."

Environmental concerns that hamper the exploration for natural gas also hamper extraction of domestic oil, say proponents of this choice. Just off the California coastline near Santa Barbara lies what is generally regarded as the last large concentration of untapped oil and gas in the continental United States. More than $2 billion worth of drilling rigs and processing equipment have been installed by 18 oil companies in what was to be a model of environmentally safe coastal drilling. For two years, Chevron and other companies fought for the right to drill a tract of ocean floor leased from the government in 1979. When Chevron tried to install a pipeline to carry the oil from Santa Barbara to its refinery in El Segundo, six municipalities stopped it with a series of lawsuits. Today, the offshore rigs stand idle, a symbol of the vulnerability of U.S. oil to environmental concerns.

Despite substantial reserves of undiscovered oil and natural gas in the Arctic National Wildlife Refuge and other government properties, proponents of domestic exploration note, only 4 percent of the federal government's 2.2 million acres of offshore and onshore lands are currently leased for petroleum exploration. In sharp contrast, Great Britain has leased about half of its offshore acreage, including all the North Sea sites that appear to contain gas and oil. By doing so, Great Britain has escaped its former dependency on imported oil and become an oil exporter.

In the United States, not even the threat to oil supplies posed by the Persian Gulf crisis was sufficient to convince Congress that domestic fuel production should take precedence over environmental concerns such as protecting wilderness areas and coastal waters. In October 1990—two months after Iraq invaded Kuwait—Congress voted to maintain restrictions on vast areas of coastal waters, a decision that provoked sharp responses from the petroleum industry. "It is unwise and shortsighted to put an indefinite hold on petroleum exploration in the most promising areas," said Charles DiBona, president of the American Petroleum Institute.

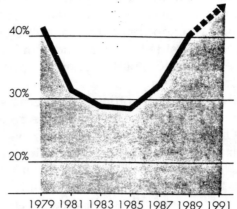

ON THE RISE AGAIN: AMERICA'S DEPENDENCE ON IMPORTED OIL

If imports continue to rise, the U.S. will soon depend on foreign supplies for more than half of its oil.

40%

30%

20%

1979 1981 1983 1985 1987 1989 1991

Source: Energy Information Administration

Cleaner Fossil Fuels

Advocates of this choice argue that much has already been done to limit noxious emissions from coal and oil and that new technologies will go a long way toward alleviating environmental disturbances associated with their use, such as acid rain and smog. In terms of sulfur dioxide emissions, for example, the Energy Department reports that, since the Clean Air Act was passed in 1970, sulfur dioxide emissions from coal-fired power plants have declined by 10 percent, despite a 75 percent increase in coal consumption.

An ambitious Clean Coal Technology Program, jointly funded by government and industry, is also currently working on additional pollution abatement methods. With these technologies, say advocates of clean coal, the United States will be able to burn coal, the most abundant domestic energy resource, in an environmentally acceptable way.

Progress has similarly been made, advocates of domestic fossil fuels point out, in reducing pollution associated with the extraction, transport, and use of oil. Spokesmen for the oil industry maintain that, despite public concern about the environmental hazards of off-shore drilling, it is eminently safe. Between the mid-1970s and 1990, some 5 billion barrels of oil were produced in U.S. waters. Over that period, there were no significant spills at exploratory wells, and only 900 barrels of oil spilled during blowouts at production wells. For more than two decades, exploration and production have taken place on Alaska's north coast at Prudhoe Bay without significant environmental effects.

"Numerous environmental laws ensure that the search for oil in the United States will be carried on with the greatest care," says Charles DiBona. "Today, environmental protection is a part of every oil industry operation and the record is excellent."

Agenda for Public Action

What should be done to take advantage of America's fossil fuel resources, according to advocates of this course of action? With regard to coal, the nation's most abundant fuel source, we should reexamine the environmental cost of burning it cleanly, using current technology, and consider whether existing regulations unnecessarily discourage its use. In addition, publicly funded research efforts to develop clean coal technologies should be expanded.

With regard to oil and natural gas, immediate steps need to be taken to increase domestic production. Since every barrel of domestic oil represents a barrel of oil the United States does not have to import, taking action to develop domestic sources is a matter of urgent importance. "The principal government actions needed to develop our domestic oil and natural gas resources and thus slow the growth in oil imports," said Charles DiBona, in July 1990 testimony to a Senate subcommittee, "are increased leasing of federal lands, tax incentives for domestic petroleum development, and the avoidance of excessive regulatory requirements."

At a time when the most promising areas for oil exploration have been put off limits because of environmental concerns, proponents of this course of action are convinced that the United States must reconsider the implications of locking away the most promising sources of new domestic production.

What Critics Say

The problem with fossil fuels, say critics, is not just our growing dependency on foreign supplies, but the environmental costs—both those that are readily apparent and the long-term effects that scientists are beginning to understand. Fossil fuels are responsible for roughly half of the nation's air pollution, critics note, causing serious problems ranging from smog and acid rain to global warming.

It has long been recognized, critics point out, that coal is an inherently dirty mineral. In London, the burning of coal was barred as early as the thirteenth century because of the smog it causes. Today, we have a fairly accurate understanding of coal's noxious effects. A single, coal-fueled, 1,000-megawatt generating station pours 30 pounds of sulfur dioxide into the air per second, a compound that is linked to lung, heart, and bronchial conditions. It produces as much nitrous oxide—which causes smog and contributes to cancer—as 200,000 cars running simultaneously.

That is just the beginning, say critics, of the list of health hazards of using fossil fuels to generate power. Tallying up the health effects of coal used to generate power in the United States, Petr Beckmann, a professor at the University of Colorado, concludes that it results in 39,000 premature deaths each year.

The environmental ills associated with the extraction and use of oil are equally serious, say critics of this first choice. In March 1989, when the Exxon *Valdez* ran aground after straying off course, 11 million gallons of crude oil spilled into Prince William Sound. To critics, that ruinous spill demonstrated the cost of trying to wrest the remaining oil from remote, environmentally sensitive areas.

Critics point out that even natural gas—the "clean" fossil fuel—is far less benign than is often acknowledged. According to Dean Abrahamson, energy analyst at the University of Minnesota, 2 to 3 percent of the natural gas produced in the United States escapes without being burned. When this happens and natural gas escapes into the

Contested Site:
Balancing Energy Needs And Environmental Concerns

In February 1991, soon after the White House drafted a national energy policy emphasizing expansion of America's domestic oil industry, the Department of the Interior released a report in which it proposed opening thousands of miles of the outer continental shelf for oil and gas exploration.

According to the plan, the government would lease the tracts on the East Coast, in offshore areas running from central New Jersey to southern Georgia; in the eastern part of the Gulf of Mexico; and off the California coast near Santa Barbara. In a proposal that generated heated opposition, the Administration also proposed to open 1.5 million acres of the Arctic National Wildlife Refuge (ANWR) in Alaska for oil exploration.

The wildlife refuge, owned and managed by the Interior Department, runs along the Beaufort Sea in the Northeast corner of Alaska. Virtually untouched by man, this region is one of the country's outstanding wilderness areas, home to caribou, bears, musk oxen, and migrating birds It may also be the site of the largest untapped oil reserve in the United States. The Interior Department believes that some 3.6 billion barrels of oil can be found there, enough to reduce U.S. imports almost 10 percent by the year 2005. So far, oil exploration on the environmentally sensitive coastal plain of ANWR has not been permitted, despite proposals to do so. In hearings held in 1989, members of Congress who favored the Arctic Coastal Oil and Gas Leasing Act argued that production from the region would boost the nation's economy. "It is clearly in the best interests of this nation to look for oil and gas on the coastal plain of ANWR," said Senator J. Bennett Johnson of Louisiana.

At a time when U.S. oil production has fallen to its lowest level in 25 years, say advocates of expanded domestic oil exploration, the coastal region of the Arctic National Wildlife Refuge offers one of the few sites that could significantly add to America's reserves, thus providing the United States with a larger measure of energy independence.

In the words of a 1988 *New York Times* editorial on oil exploration in the Arctic National Wildlife Refuge, "No one wants to ruin a wilderness for small gain. But, in this case, the potential is enormous and the environmental risks are modest. It is hard to see why absolutely pristine preservation of this remote wilderness should take precedence over the nation's energy needs."

Those who are critical of oil exploration in environmentally sensitive areas see the situation in a different light. Robert K. Watson, energy specialist at the Natural Resources Defense Council, says that "We have a 20 percent chance of finding a significant amount of oil there, and a 100 percent chance of trashing one of the environmentally pristine areas of the country."

Even if ANWR lives up to optimistic projections, say those who oppose oil exploration in environmentally sensitive areas, it will do little to overcome America's dependence on imported oil. If 3.2 billion barrels of oil are extracted from the Arctic Refuge over 30 years—the Interior Department's mid range estimate—production from that area will yield only a small fraction of the oil needed to make up for declining domestic oil production elsewhere.

"Further increases in U.S. oil imports," says Worldwatch Institute analyst Christopher Flavin, "are almost guaranteed in the years ahead. Trying to stem this tide with Arctic Refuge Oil is like trying to stop a major fire with a teacup."

atmosphere, it traps solar radiation far more efficiently than carbon dioxide, thus contributing to global warming.

Shortsighted Solution

Trying to solve the energy predicament by exploiting domestic fossil fuels, say critics, is at best a shortsighted solution. We need to recognize, they say, that the United States is just about played out as an oil field. The cheapest oil and natural gas are already gone. Additional fossil fuels will come from smaller, more dispersed fields and from increasingly remote sources. Consequently, it is a virtual certainty that domestic fossil fuels will become more expensive, and that domestic extraction will come at a higher cost to the environment.

Critics of this first strategy argue that the chief danger of stepping up the search for domestic fossil fuels is that it will divert us from developing sensible and sustainable alternatives. Rather than shipping domestic oil past the icebergs of Prince William Sound, we should turn to alternatives such as developing more energy-effficient cars to conserve fuel.

Options such as substituting natural gas for oil and coal need to be understood as stopgaps rather than solutions, say critics, ways to buy time while the United States switches over to new energy sources. The task now is to begin the transition to nonfossil fuels, not to put most of our efforts into extending the fossil fuel era

"There is no question," writes Bill McKibben, "but that we stand at the end of an era—the hundred years' binge on oil, gas, and coal which has given us both the comforts and the predicament of the moment. We must act in every way possible, and immediately. We must substitute, conserve, plant trees, perhaps even swallow our concern over safety and build some nuclear plants. The choice of doing nothing—of continuing to burn ever more oil and coal—is not a choice. It will lead us, if not straight to Hell, then straight to a place with similar temperature."

Choice #2 Remarkable Renewables: Harvesting the Sun's Energy

Fifty miles southeast of San Francisco at the Altamont Pass, motorists on Interstate 580 see an unusual sight. Flanking the highway are some 7,000 metal towers holding 50-foot rotors that are propelled in graceful circles by the wind. At first glance, these wind turbines, an updated version of the windmills that have been used for centuries to pump water and thresh grain, look more like a reminder of energy sources of the past than a solution to the current energy dilemma. To many people, however, wind turbines, like other renewable energy sources that harness an inexhaustible and universally available source of energy, are the wave of the future.

Although the basic design of wind turbines has not changed much over the years, California's wind farms take full advantage of modern technology, including aerospace design and computer controls. The cluster of wind turbines at the Altamont Pass, like similar wind farms in two other California locations, feeds electrical power to utility grids run by Pacific Gas and Electric Company and Southern California Edison. Together, these wind farms generated 2.5 billion kilowatt hours of electricity in 1990, enough power to meet the annual residential needs of one million Californians.

According to Dale Osborn, president of U.S. Windpower, which operates the largest wind turbine facility at Altamont Pass, the facility provides a glimpse of wind power's enormous potential. Wind power, says Osborn, is "a proven, functioning, and ever-increasing economic success."

Wind power is just one of the renewable energy sources that many people regard as the most promising successor to fossil fuels. The renewables also include solar energy, geothermal, and hydropower. What these power sources have in common is that, directly or indirectly, they harness the sun's energy. By taking advantage of air currents stirred up by the atmosphere's warming and cooling, wind turbines convert the sun's energy into electrical power. Photovoltaic cells—the most advanced form of solar energy—convert sunlight directly into electricity. Hydroelectric power uses the water that results from evaporation caused by the sun. When evaporation falls as rain, it flows into rivers and turns generator turbines as it returns to the sea.

Whatever form they take, renewable forms of energy—or renewables, as they are often called—use energy resources that are plentiful, environmentally benign, and naturally replenished. For this reason, says Susan Williams, energy analyst at the Investor Responsibility Research Center in Washington, "Renewable energy technologies have the potential to become the preferred power sources of the twenty-first century."

Meet the Renewables

Although they share a family resemblance in their reliance on the sun, renewable energy sources take quite different forms. The most readily identifiable are solar applications that use the sun's rays directly for such purposes as space heating, hot water heaters, and high-temperature power generators. Such thermal systems employ solar collectors, which concentrate the sun's rays to heat a liquid that drives a turbine generator to produce electricity. These versatile systems can be used in industry as well as homes to generate heat and electrical power. A solar thermal farm in California's Mojave Desert, consisting of 650,000 parabolic mirrors, produces almost 200 megawatts of power for the Los Angeles area, and is planning to triple its capacity.

As advocates of renewables point out, because of technical advances, the cost of energy generated by photovoltaic cells is dropping rapidly. Photovoltaic cells, which are typically no larger than an inch or two, can be used in small clusters to meet modest needs or in huge grids to produce millions of watts. Unlike fossil fuels, which must be extracted from the earth and transported to distant sites where they are used to generate power, solar energy can be collected by cells mounted within a few feet of the appliances they power.

Advocates point out that photovoltaic energy is already economical in sites located at some distance from power grids. Technical advances will soon make it possible to install photovoltaic cells as a roofing surface on homes, and also to build cost effective photovoltaic power stations.

Industry spokesmen point out that energy produced by today's solar thermal and photovoltaic systems is only slightly more expensive than power generated with fossil fuels or by nuclear generators. Over the next decade, more efficient systems are expected to generate power that is competitive with the cost of power produced by conventional means during peak periods. The Solar Energy Research Institute projects that, by the year 2030, photovoltaics could supply half of America's electrical power.

Wind, Wave, and Hydropower

Proponents of renewables are no less enthusiastic about indirect methods of harnessing the sun's energy. One such method is wind farms. Because particularly generous tax incentives spurred their development in California, that is where most of the nation's 17,000 wind turbines can be found. Since the mid-1980s, incentives that spurred the wind boom have been discontinued. But, according to advocates of renewables, California's experiment with wind power shows that this is no pipe dream nor an industry that thrives only with continued public subsidies.

Proponents of renewables note that the cost of producing a kilowatt of wind energy has plummeted from more than $3,000 in 1981 for capital expenditures to an average of $1,000 in 1989, which amounts to seven to nine cents per kilowatt-hour. That makes wind power only slightly more expensive than the cost of power produced by coal-burning generators and less expensive than the power produced by recently completed nuclear plants. According to a 1989 report from California's largest utility, Pacific Gas and Electric, "Wind energy could be a major source of economically competitive energy without any technical breakthroughs."

A second indirect method of harnessing the sun's energy is hydropower, which could also be exploited to a greater extent, say advocates of renewables. For more than a century, hydroelectric dams have been used as a source of electrical power in the United States. Depending on the amount of precipitation, the United States, in recent years, has depended on hydroelectric sources for 10 to 14 percent of its power.

U.S. hydroelectric facilities range from modest sites producing less than one megawatt to huge facilities such as the Grand Coulee Dam in Washington, which generates more than 6,000 megawatts. No matter what their size, hydropower facilities are among the cheapest energy sources. According to proponents of renewables, they are also among the most dependable and environmentally benign.

Untapped Potential: "a Virtual Saudi Arabia Of Wind"

A 1990 Department of Energy (DOE) study concluded that what has worked in California could work for the nation as a whole. The study conducted by Pacific Northwest Laboratories, found that 13 states have at least as much potential for commercial wind farms as California, and that most others contain many sites where wind farms could produce energy at competitive prices.

To produce power efficiently, sites are needed where winds average 16 mph or better at 50 meters above the ground. According to the Department of Energy study, only four states—Alabama, Florida and Mississippi—lack appropriate sites for competitive wind farms.

In the words of Randall Swisher, former executive director of the American Wind Energy Association, the DOE study "establishes the immense potential of wind power to meet America's energy needs." Swisher points out that if appropriate sites in just two states—North Dakota and Texas—were fully developed to take advantage of their potential, wind power from those states alone would replace the energy contained in two billion barrels of oil. Each of those states amounts, in Swisher's words, to "a virtual Saudi Arabia of wind."

Advocates of hydropower acknowledge that sites for huge new dams on the scale of Hoover Dam or Grand Coulee can no longer be found. But sites for small-scale hydropower facilities are still widely available, both here and abroad. In a recent report, the World Energy Conference estimated that the amount of hydropower that could be commercially generated is five times larger than current capacity.

Renewable power sources also include the consumption of wood and other plant matter, referred to as biomass. Before the era of coal burning, biomass—chiefly firewood—was America's principle energy source. In recent years, biomass, which now accounts for about 4 percent of the U.S. energy supply, has experienced something of a comeback

Wood and other forms of plant matter were once simply burned for heat and light. But a variety of more efficient and environmentally benign processes have been devised to take advantage of biomass energy. The most promising methods convert wood and other plant matter into ethanol, a substitute for gasoline refined from crude oil. Methods are also available for extracting other gaseous fuels from agricultural waste products. Proponents of this choice are convinced that, with additional research and development, fuels produced in this way could soon replace fossil fuels in many applications.

The list of renewables also includes two largely untapped resources, wave energy and geothermal power. Just as hydroelectric plants take advantage of river currents, the force of tidal water can be used to produce power. However, the energy of ocean waves is still largely unexploited as a source of commercial power.

Geothermal reservoirs under the earth's surface are another renewable energy source. They have been tapped in some locations for centuries and used for such purposes as therapeutic baths and space heating. This is a largely undeveloped energy source but one, say its advocates, that could generate a significant amount of energy. All that is needed, according to proponents of renewables, is exploration to locate shallow hydrothermal reserves and the installation of pipes to permit steam and hot water to be brought to the surface where they can be used to generate electricity.

Renewable energy sources, says Michael Brower, energy specialist at the Union of Concerned Scientists, were "once considered exotic and impractical. But the technologies for exploiting these resources are becoming increasingly reliable and cost effective in comparison to conventional energy technologies. Some are already widely successful. Others—particularly wind and solar technologies—are now, or soon will be, competitive with fossil fuels in a broad range of applications. Although some technical issues remain to be solved, there appear to be no insurmountable barriers to prevent renewable energy sources from eventually meeting most, if not all, of U.S. and world energy needs."

A Practical Alternative

Despite technological advances that make renewables increasingly viable, advocates are concerned that little is being done to encourage their use as a major energy source. Unless more public initiatives are undertaken, they claim, renewables will languish. Currently, renewables meet only about 7.6 percent of U.S. energy needs. According to recent Department of Energy projections, they are likely to provide only 9.5 percent of U.S. energy supplies in 2000, and 12 percent by 2010. Of that total, hydroelectric power from large dams built years ago is responsible for the largest part.

Proponents of this course of action argue that there are several compelling reasons why renewables should be considered the most promising candidate as the chief energy source for the twenty-first century.

First, despite the misgivings of skeptics, renewables are practical and cost effective. Wind turbines, solar power plants, hydroelectric plants, and geothermal facilities are capable of producing energy at competitive prices. Over the next few years, more efficient photovoltaic cells are likely to produce cheaper electricity than generators fueled by oil or gas.

Further, no technological breakthroughs are needed to make renewables practical. Modest refinements in technologies that are already available will bring the cost of various renewables down to competitive levels. In contrast to nuclear power plants, which typically take six to ten years to build, renewable technologies—most of which are small and modular—can be put into place quickly and updated regularly to take advantage of technical advances.

Most important, say advocates of this choice, is the fact that renewables—unlike fossil fuels—are nonpolluting. And unlike nuclear power, they pose no threat to public safety. Wind turbines, for example, produce no air or water pollution, and even large wind farms do not alter wind or weather conditions. Solar energy and hydropower are also environmentally benign. Thus, shifting to renewables on a significant scale would mitigate serious environmental problems, ranging from acid rain to urban smog. As the threat of global warming becomes more apparent, proponents declare, renewables will become even more attractive.

What's more, unlike nuclear power, which is used only to generate electricity, renewables are capable of supplying all forms of energy used today—heat, electricity, and transportation fuels.

Even the fact that solar and wind power are inherently variable is no impediment to their development, say advocates of this choice. When the sun goes down or the wind stops, all that is needed is a storage or backup system, neither of which, advocates maintain, poses an insurmountable barrier. Hybrid systems using renewables and fossil fuels already provide dependable power. All that is required for the renewables to become fully competitive, say proponents of this choice, is a market large enough to permit economies of scale.

"We can no longer afford to consider these alternatives as the gadgets of hippies and technocrats," says Bruce Piasecki, a professor of energy and environmental management at Rensselaer Polytechnic Institute. "They represent the vanguard of a society more in tune with the limits and rhythms of the earth. With them, we can achieve more sustainable lifestyles."

ENERGY FUNDING: ON THE WRONG TRACK?

Federal funding for renewable energy declined sharply in the 80s but increased slightly in fiscal year 1991.

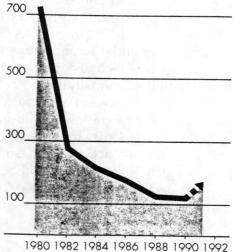

Millions of Dollars

Source: Congressional Research Service

A New Commitment

The chief impediment to the rapid development of renewable energy sources, say advocates, is that over the past decade there has been no public commitment to develop alternatives to fossil fuels, and few incentives to develop solar energy, wind power, and other renewables.

In the wake of the 1970s oil shocks, federal funding for renewable energy research and development rose rapidly, from $75 million in 1975 to more than $720 million in 1980. As a result, old technologies were improved during the 1970s and new ones developed.

But since the oil glut of the 1980s, severe shakeouts have taken place in the renewable energy business. Of the 40 U.S. firms engaged in developing commercial wind power in the early 1980s, fewer than a dozen remain in business and few wind farms are currently being developed. Little drilling is currently under way to locate new sources of geothermal energy.

Although production of photovoltaics has continued, slim profits have prompted various American firms—who held the lead in this emerging industry a decade ago—to sell out to Japanese and European concerns. In 1989, after Atlantic Richfield spent 12 years and $200 million to become the world's leader in solar panels, the division was sold to Siemens, a West German firm. The transaction prompted sharp criticism from American proponents of renewables. "It's a national disgrace," said Republican Representative Claudine Schneider, a member of the House Natural Resources Subcommittee. "There is vast global market potential for renewable energy technology. The U.S. should be in the lead. Instead, we're dragging our feet."

When Congress decided on federal spending commitments in the fiscal 1990 budget, the Department of Energy's renewable energy budget was increased for the first time in a decade. But despite this modest turnaround for the renewable energy business, advocates of this approach fear that American firms will continue to shun renewable energy technologies—no matter how bright their long-term prospects—because they are not as profitable in the short term as fossil fuels.

The promise of renewable energy will not be realized, say advocates of this strategy, unless government takes a strong leadership role. "With strong government leadership and appropriate market incentives," says Michael Brower, "this picture could change dramatically. The share of U.S. energy supplies provided by renewable energy sources could be increased to 15 percent—double the present level—by 2000, resulting in a 5-10 percent reduction in fossil fuel use and carbon emissions. As much as 50 percent of U.S. energy supply could be provided by renewable energy sources by the year 2020."

Most proponents of this course of action agree that increased government funding is essential to encourage an industry on the brink of commercial success. "Renewable energy technologies deserve at least as much support as they received a decade ago—$1 billion annually in 1990 dollars," says Christopher Flavin. "With such a commitment, private investment would increase rapidly and renewable energy sources would begin to make a significant additional contribution to U.S. energy supplies before the 1900s are out."

Other incentives to renewables should also be put in place, say advocates of this course of action. One desirable incentive would be to reinstate tax credits for installing solar panels. Another would be to rewrite electric utility regulations to favor environmentally benign power sources. Moreover, banks should be encouraged to offer favorable lending terms to builders and home owners who install such devices as solar-powered water heaters.

What Critics Say

Few people oppose the development of renewable energy sources. But many are skeptical about claims that solar energy, wind power, and more exotic renewables will soon be able to provide significant amounts of energy at competitive prices.

"Solar power," says Frederick Seitz, former head of the National Academy of Sciences, "seems to be a wonderful idea. Every square yard of sunshine contains about 1,000 watts of inexhaustible energy, free for the taking. The trouble is, the taking *isn't* free. To meet our electrical needs, we'd have to build enough collector plates to cover the state of Delaware."

Critics note that even in the Southwest, which receives more sunlight than other regions of the United States, about three square miles of land are required to collect from solar radiation the energy produced by a standard power station. On cloudy days, at nighttime, or during the short days of winter, the electricity produced by such facilities is sharply diminished. According to critics, wind power is similarly unreliable. Yet utilities must have reliable power, particularly during periods of peak demand. "It's hard to imagine powering twentieth-century industry with sunshine," says Gerald Kraft, an analyst at Charles River Associates. "Maybe we can. Nobody knows."

Even if solar technologies or wind power can provide limited assistance over the next few decades in meeting the nation's electrical power needs, argue the critics, the crux of America's energy problem is the shortage of liquid fuel. Pointing to the primitive state of current efforts to fuel vehicles with renewable power, analysts project that these energy sources are not likely to supplant fossil fuels for transportation purposes for decades to come.

Critics note that other, more exotic renewables, such as harnessing ocean tides or waves or extracting energy from the earth's crust, are even more speculative and unlikely to offer significant amounts of energy soon.

As for hydropower, which currently supplies more renewable energy than all other sources combined, critics argue that it has a limited growth potential. In the United States, most bodies of water that can be profitably dammed and developed for their hydropower potential are already in use. New hydropower projects, the critics maintain, raise serious environmental concerns because of the damage they cause by flooding wildlife habitats and blocking the flow of rivers and streams.

In all, critics conclude that none of the renewable power sources is likely to supplant fossil fuels in the foreseeable future as a major source of U.S. power. In the words of Dr. William Fulkerson, associate director of the Oak Ridge National Laboratory, and director of a recent study of renewables, "You are very quickly struck by the fact that none of them is ready to compete on a large scale with fossil fuels."

Critics of this course of action also question the wisdom of providing large public subsidies for renewable energy projects that are not commercially viable. In the energy field, as elsewhere, say critics, government should let unimpeded markets work. When the government decides to subsidize such questionable ventures as the development of synthetic fuels, says Fereidun Fesharaki, an oil analyst at the East-West Center in Honolulu, it amounts to "taking my tax dollars and subsidizing something uneconomic. It creates industries that do not deserve to be created. When oil rises in price, alternatives will emerge on their own." Over the long run, conclude critics, there is no public benefit in tilting the playing field in favor of any one solution to the energy dilemma.

Choice #3 Atomic Power: A New Era for Nuclear Energy

Since the nuclear era began in the 1940s, people have envisioned a time when atomic fission would provide abundant power from a virtually inexhaustible source, at a cost so low—as early promoters of nuclear power said—that it would be "too cheap to meter." The advantage of nuclear power over fossil fuel was immediately apparent: it produces about 100 million times as much energy per atom as the combustion of carbon, while avoiding its noxious by-products. As the nation's need for electrical power grew in the 1960s and early 1970s, nuclear plants seemed the most promising way to meet that need.

Both in the United States and abroad, the growth of the nuclear power industry has been impressive. By 1989, 428 commercial nuclear energy plants were in operation around the world. More than 100 of them are located in the United States where they produce a total of 3.5 gigawatts, which is about 20 percent of the nation's electrical power. Without those nuclear plants, the U.S. would have to rely to a far greater extent on coal and oil.

Yet despite the sizable contribution nuclear power makes to the nation's energy supply, even proponents of this option acknowledge that the nuclear power industry is in serious trouble. The sharp decline that has taken place over the past decade in the fortunes of the nuclear industry is not hard to explain. On March 28, 1979, a serious accident took place at the Three Mile Island nuclear facility, 10 miles southwest of Harrisburg, Pennsylvania. When a malfunctioning pump caused a breakdown in the cooling system, the reactor overheated, causing a chain of events that came dangerously close to a meltdown. As a result, the public's confidence in the safety of nuclear power was severely shaken. Fears about the hazards of nuclear power were confirmed in April 1986, when the Chernobyl nuclear reactor in the Soviet Ukraine exploded.

By 1988, a Louis Harris poll showed that 61 percent of Americans oppose the construction of additional nuclear plants, while 30 percent are in favor— the reverse of the pattern that polls found a decade earlier. The last order for an American nuclear facility was placed in 1978, the year before Three Mile Island, and subsequently canceled. Since then, plans for 65 additional nuclear plants have been abandoned. Unless additional units are ordered, the role played by nuclear power in meeting the nation's growing needs for energy will diminish over time as the current generation of nuclear plants is retired.

Proponents of this choice argue that a new generation of inherently safe generators is the best way to meet the nation's growing need for electrical power. If stringent operating standards are put into place and if a decision can be reached soon about acceptable sites for nuclear wastes, advocates believe the nuclear option will regain the public acceptance it enjoyed in the 1970s.

"Just as America gave birth to the nuclear technology in the 1940s," said President Bush in a 1989 address to the Nuclear Power Assembly, "we can lead the world into a new era of safe, reliable, economical, and environmentally clean nuclear power in the 1990s. This clean domestic source of power lessens the risk of energy dependence on foreign sources."

Powerful Arguments

Advocates of nuclear power insist that this course of action responds to each of the three aspects of the nation's energy problem. First, it helps to reduce dependency on imported oil. Second, since nuclear power creates no carbon emissions or other air pollutants caused by burning fossil fuels, it offers a cleaner alternative. And, third, since it is a proven source of large amounts of energy, it offers a solution to the problem posed by growing demand for electrical power.

Speaking to the first of those concerns, advocates of nuclear power point out that it is "homegrown" energy. By relying to a greater extent on nuclear plants to generate power, we could ensure a future in which the United States is able to meet its own energy needs. Moreover, advocates note, since supplies of uranium are available in many nations, nuclear power is less threatened than oil supplies by cartels trying to corner the market.

With regard to concern about the environment, advocates of nuclear power are convinced, in the words of scientist John P. Holdren, professor of energy and resources at the University of California, Berkeley, that "nuclear energy is incomparably less disruptive climatologically and ecologically than are fossil fuels."

Because of the nuclear-powered generators currently in use, airborne pollutants are reduced by over 19,000 tons every day. More environmentally dangerous in the long run is the threat of global warming and the shadow it casts over the continued dependence on fossil fuels. Advocates of this power option point out that nuclear power cuts greenhouse gas emissions from utilities by 20 percent.

Indeed, growing concern about global warming caused in large part by carbon emissions from fossil fuels is one of the main reasons for the recent reassessment of nuclear power and its role in the nation's energy future. In the words of Senator Tim Wirth of Colorado, a champion of environmental causes, "Nations that have halted the nuclear option are going to have to reconsider." Evidence of the greenhouse effect, says Wirth, convinced him that the United States has to find a cure for its "nuclear measles."

Other public officials agree with Wirth about the promise of nuclear energy as a means of averting global warming. In 1990, a bipartisan task force of the National Governors' Association urged development of a "new generation of safe nuclear power" as one of the nation's key goals for the 1990s. In the words of former Governor James Thompson, chairman of the task force, "Global warming is a much more serious challenge to life on this earth than the possibility of trouble from nuclear reactors."

Finally, at a time of looming shortages of electrical power in the United States, advocates of this choice argue that nuclear power provides a proven way to generate large quantities of energy. Proponents of this course of action point out that recent brownouts during peak power seasons, especially in the Mid-Atlantic and Northeastern states,

SOURCES OF AMERICA'S ELECTRICAL POWER

September, 1990

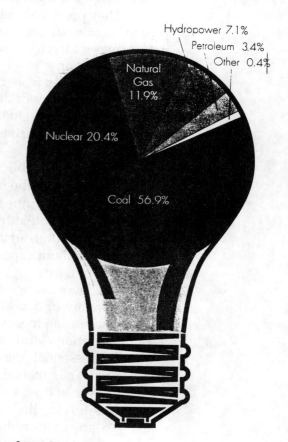

Hydropower 7.1%
Petroleum 3.4%
Other 0.4%
Natural Gas 11.9%
Nuclear 20.4%
Coal 56.9%

Source: Energy Information Administration

may be a harbinger of widespread power shortages. Testifying to the Senate Energy Subcommittee in 1988, former Secretary of Energy James Schlesinger warned that looming shortages of electrical power are a pressing problem, and that they pose a greater threat to the nation's economic health than dependence on imported oil.

Proponents of this choice note that nuclear energy is already the nation's second largest source of electricity, providing enough power to light over half the homes in the United States. Unlike the renewables, nuclear energy is a proven source of large quantities of electrical power and, for this reason, proponents conclude it is the best way to meet growing energy demands.

Because nuclear plants need only small amounts of fuel, they are less vulnerable to shortages than coal- or gas-powered plants. And since uranium supplies are virtually inexhaustible, advocates point out that long-term supplies are secure.

Safer, Smaller, Cheaper

If the promise of nuclear power that is "too cheap to meter" turned out to be unrealistic, proponents of this choice insist that nuclear power can be produced more cheaply than energy from other sources. Spokesmen for the nuclear power industry contend that costs of nuclear-powered energy have risen in recent years mainly because of excessive, counterproductive regulations, and because complicated licensing requirements have delayed the startup of completed plants.

They point to the modest cost of nuclear power in France and Japan, where licensing procedures are streamlined. In France, where nuclear power supplies 70 percent of the nation's electricity, it costs 30 percent less than coal-fired power. In Japan, according to the Ministry of International Trade and Industry, nuclear power is cheaper by a significant margin than power from coal-fired plants or from hydroelectric plants.

"Unless we work to revive the nuclear option," says Representative Michael Bilirakis, member of the House Committee on Energy and Power, "Americans will continue to pay more for expensive electric power and our reliance on foreign energy supplies will be exacerbated."

Contrary to public perception, says Scott Peters, spokesman for the U.S. Council for Energy Awareness, "the nuclear power industry has an excellent track record for safety." Although critics continue to dismiss nuclear power as unsafe, not a single American civilian has been injured or killed as a result of nuclear accidents after more than 2,900 reactor years. Advocates also point out that U.S. naval personnel have traveled 60 million miles on nuclear submarines without experiencing a nuclear accident.

Acknowledging the potential hazards associated with nuclear power, advocates of this choice favor stringent standards for government-certified nuclear plants, as well as careful training of operators and prudent oversight procedures. Key workers should be licensed according to strict government standards, just as U.S. pilots are required to pass Federal Aviation Administration certification procedures.

The essential point, say advocates of this choice, is for the public to recognize that nuclear power is manageable, and not inherently unsafe. They argue that judging the nuclear power industry by what happened at Chernobyl—an appallingly obsolete facility—is like judging the viability of air travel on the basis of the *Hindenburg* dirigible.

"Many of the glittering promises of the first advocates of the nuclear age can come true," writes Lawrence Lidsky, a professor of nuclear engineering at the Massachusetts Institute of Technology. "Nuclear power really does have the potential to be one of the least

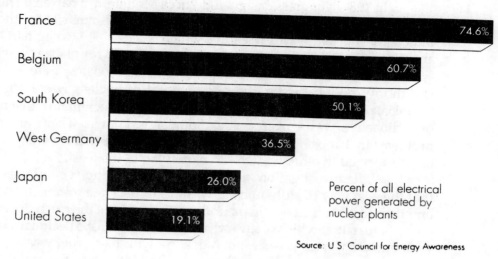

TAKING ADVANTAGE OF NUCLEAR POWER
Other nations derive a greater percentage of their electricity needs from nuclear plants than the U.S.

France   74.6%
Belgium   60.7%
South Korea   50.1%
West Germany 36.5%
Japan   26.0%
United States 19.1%

Percent of all electrical power generated by nuclear plants

Source: U S Council for Energy Awareness

environmentally damaging and most economical sources of power available. The current problems are inherent not in nuclear power, but in the machinery we have devised to exploit it."

Advocates of this choice are enthusiastic about the prospects of a new generation of safer, smaller, and cheaper nuclear generating plants. Most of the nuclear power plants now operating in the United States are watercooled reactors. Like high-strung racing cars, they need constant care to operate properly. If the water that cools these systems is absent for just a few seconds, the super-hot fuel can destroy the metal casing, leading to a meltdown. Because of the complexity of the safety mechanisms required by water-cooled reactors, such reactors are very costly to construct and to operate.

In contrast, a new generation of compact, mid-sized reactors relies on natural processes such as convection and gravity rather than error-prone human caretakers or complicated machinery to prevent overheating and possible meltdown. In a major design breakthrough, these new reactors are far less sensitive to changes in fuel temperature.

An important feature of this new generation of reactors, says Lidsky, is that its safety can be demonstrated to a skeptical public. "Because an inherently safe reactor will survive a worst-case accident without damage," says Lidsky, "it could be licensed much as aircraft are. You could actually try out each reactor and prove it won't melt down. Such license by test is absolutely essential if the American public is ever again to accept nuclear power."

According to industry spokesmen, substantially improved reactors—several of which are already being built by General Electric in Japan—could be on-line and ready to meet America's growing energy needs within ten years.

What About the Wastes?

A critical hurdle for nuclear power, advocates acknowledge, is that a final burial place has to be found for America's radioactive waste. Currently, used fuel rods and other radioactive debris are temporarily stored at the nation's 112 nuclear reactor sites. A repository is needed that will isolate radioactive wastes and prevent them from contaminating the surrounding environment for 10,000 years, by which time radioactive decay will have rendered them harmless.

In 1987, Congress designated Yucca Mountain, a barren terrain of volcanic rock 100 miles northwest of Las Vegas, Nevada, as the candidate site for the nation's most highly radioactive nuclear waste. If testing, which is scheduled to begin in 1991, does not indicate any disqualifying factors, the site may be approved for nuclear waste beginning in 2010.

As proponents of this choice see it, while choosing a site for nuclear waste disposal is a thorny political issue, the safe disposal of nuclear waste poses no insurmountable technical problems. "It is utterly untrue," says Petr Beckmann, "that no method of disposing of radioactive waste from nuclear power is known. There are no major engineering problems in disposing of nuclear wastes in a manner whose safety is unrivaled by any that can be applied to other wastes—in particular, to the fossil fuels."

While investigation of various disposal methods continues, it is generally agreed that the best way to store nuclear waste is to package it in metal and ceramic containers, and then to bury the containers underground where the earth provides shielding.

No matter which of several methods is used, says Beckmann, the problem of dealing with nuclear wastes is easier than dealing with fossil fuel wastes because the volume of nuclear waste is small. Even when solidified into glass or ceramic packages, radioactive waste produced by a large, 1,000-megawatt generator amounts to just two cubic meters per year—a package, as Beckmann points out, "that would comfortably fit under a typical dining room table."

If you put all of the radioactive waste that has been produced over the past 30 years in the United States in one place, Beckmann observes, it would only fill a football field to the depth of five feet. Because nuclear waste comes in small packages, it is a fairly easy technical matter to monitor it and to design reliable storage that will withstand even the most severe assaults.

Advocates recognize that a final problem needs to be resolved—the procedure for licensing nuclear plants. Currently, says Frederick Seitz, former head of the National Academy of Sciences, "the procedure is a nightmare." Even after construction of a nuclear facility is completed, groups that object to a facility can prevent it from starting up. They can insist on costly changes in the facility, or they can delay operation with a series of legal challenges. "The way out of this mess is clear," says Seitz. "Once a go-ahead is given, the utility should be able to build and operate the plant so long as it passes inspection by the Nuclear Regulatory Commission.

"The nuclear industry should not be given carte blanche," concludes Seitz, "but neither should those who would seize on any technicality of the law to destroy it. Risks should be evaluated reasonably, not hysterically."

Faced with growing demands for electrical power and mounting evidence of the hazards of using fossil fuels to generate it, advocates of this choice are persuaded that the nuclear option deserves to be seriously reconsidered. In the words of a 1990 *New York Times* editorial, "The United States cannot afford to wash its hands of an energy option that could prove both competitive and environmentally benign. The nuclear industry is worth reviving."

What Critics Say

The fundamental reason for rejecting the nuclear option, critics reply, is that—despite promises of a new generation of "fail-safe" generators—any process that creates radioactive material poses an unacceptable risk.

The accident at Three Mile Island in 1979 (which prompted a Washington rally of 70,000 anti-nuclear power protestors, some of whom carried signs reading "Hell no, we won't glow") was no isolated incident, critics argue. In the years since then, records kept by the Nuclear Regulatory Commission (NRC) indicate that U.S. nuclear power plants have experienced some 30,000 "mishaps," several dozen of which could have led to even more serious situations than the partial meltdown at Three Mile Island. The NRC estimates that the chances of a "severe core meltdown" occurring over the next 15 years at one of the 112 U.S. nuclear plants is as high as 45 percent.

That, say critics, is too high a risk to take to meet energy needs that can be met in other, safer ways. It is one thing for the government to sanction and regulate a potentially hazardous activity such as air travel, in which disaster causes, at worst, the loss of several hundred lives. It is another thing entirely, as the Chernobyl disaster demonstrated, to encourage an industry in which "mishaps" can cause almost unthinkable harm.

Estimates of the number of deaths directly attributable to the Chernobyl disaster range from 30 to 300. But critics of nuclear power say that only begins to describe its toll to human life and to the environment. According to Ales Adamovich, a prominent author and a deputy in the Soviet Union's parliament, the explosion of the reactor at Chernobyl placed at least 2.5 million people in jeopardy. In downwind areas, says Adamovich, "At least 400,000 people were exposed to such high radiation levels that they ought to have been evacuated. A significant portion of Byelorussia's territory became so contaminated that inhabitants still, four years later, cannot consume the local water, milk fruit, vegetables, or meat. Mothers cannot nurse their babies. And hundreds of children are dying of leukemia."

As a result of fallout, crops grown throughout eastern Europe and as far away as northern Italy were declared unfit for human consumption. In northern Scandinavia, the accident severely disrupted the Lapps, because the reindeer on which the local economy depends were too contaminated with radiation to sell.

Critics note that the Chernobyl disaster caused most Western European nations to rethink the nuclear option. Having witnessed firsthand the destruction caused by radioactive fallout, Sweden—a nation that depends heavily on nuclear power—decided to phase out nuclear power by 2010. A handful of other nations reacted to Chernobyl by announcing their intention either to cancel plans to build additional nuclear facilities or to eschew this option entirely.

PUBLIC OPPOSITION TO NUCLEAR POWER

Public opposition to the building of new nuclear power plants rose dramatically after the 1979 accident at Three Mile Island and has remained at high levels ever since.

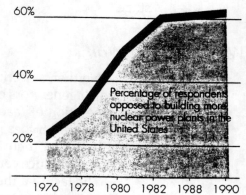

Percentage of respondents opposed to building more nuclear power plants in the United States

Sources: Louis Harris Polls (1976–1988), Research/Strategy/Management and Greenberg/Lake (1990)

Dangerous Leftovers

Disasters such as Chernobyl, say critics of this choice, demonstrate only the most extreme hazards associated with nuclear power. Forty years after the age of nuclear power began in the United States, evidence is accumulating about other hazards, such as the danger posed by the shutdown of nuclear facilities when they reach retirement age. In an August 1989 report, the federal government's General Accounting Office (GAO) used contamination levels at nuclear fuel processing plants as a guide to estimate the contamination likely to be found at commercial nuclear power facilities when they begin to be dismantled in the 1990s. At five facilities, the GAO found dangerously high levels of groundwater contamination and soil contamination.

As critics point out nuclear power has for years attracted the lion's share of federal government research monies for energy alternatives and, in doing so, has diverted attention and funding from other alternatives. Yet despite generous government funding, fundamental problems remain that cast a shadow over the nuclear option, such as the chronic issue of nuclear waste disposal.

"Forty years into the nuclear era," says Russell Peterson, former governor of Delaware and a member of the commission that investigated the Three Mile Island accident, "the world still doesn't have the means to dispose of the highly radioactive waste accumulating at nuclear plants. Each year, about one-third of the used fuel loaded with dangerous fission products is placed in pools of water outside the protection of containment buildings, waiting for a decision on what to do with it—or for some accident or terrorist act to spread it around the countryside."

Soaring costs are another reason this option should be abandoned, say critics. When the nuclear power boom began in the 1960s the projected cost of nuclear power was significantly less than the power produced by oil or coal plants. By the late 1960s, however, it cost twice as much as projected, and the cost of nuclear power has escalated ever since. At plants completed since 1985, the average generating cost is about 12 cents per kilowatt-hour, even before the cost of decommissioning and waste disposal is included. That is about twice as high as the cost of power based on fossil fuels, and it is substantially higher than the cost of some currently available renewable power sources.

"Whether new-generation reactors will be as safe and cheap as their proponents claim," says Christopher Flavin, "is something that only a decade of development and billions of dollars can determine. But the track record of the nuclear industry indicates that policymakers shouldn't place any confidence in cost projections made at such an early stage."

Why We Can't Wait

Neither, say critics, is there any reason to believe that a new generation of "inherently safe" generators can be put into place quickly. Long delays can be expected before a new generation of reactors is proven safe and reliable. A new-generation demonstration plant is, at the very least, years away. Another decade will pass before commercial reactors are on-line, and then it will take years more for enough new plants to be installed to significantly reduce carbon emissions.

The fact that the transition to the new generation of "inherently safe" reactors will require several decades is a critical flaw, say some critics, since immediate action is needed to head off catastrophic warming. Unlike stepped-up energy conservation efforts or expanded use of solar panels and wind power that could make an immediate difference in carbon emissions, a new generation of nuclear reactors will do little or nothing to mitigate global warming for the next 20 years.

"If the lessons of the past decade and a half mean anything for the future," writes Christopher Flavin, "attempts to resuscitate the nuclear option will yield political friction, economic waste, and serious accidents, not a solution to the global warming problem."

Choice #4 Energy Conservation: Doing More with Less

In late summer 1990, oil prices climbed in the wake of the Iraqi invasion of Kuwait and thousands of American troops were being deployed in the Middle East. For President Bush, as for many Americans, it was time for summer vacation. Reports from administration officials about the Middle East situation were accompanied by pictures of the president cruising off the coast near his home at Kennebunkport, Maine, in his 8-miles-per-gallon speedboat, *Fidelity*. Talking to reporters on August 22, the president called on the American public to save energy, saying "I think it is a good time to conserve." But, he added, "That doesn't mean that life screeches to a halt . . . I'm going to keep using my boat."

Some people commented that the president's actions on energy conservation spoke louder than his words. At a time when overall use of energy in the United States is on the rise again, some regarded the president's speedboat as a symbol of the nation's inability to control its appetite for energy and its disinclination to give up energy-intensive habits.

The Persian Gulf crisis, said Alden Meyer, director of the Union of Concerned Scientists energy program, might turn out to have a silver lining if it forces the American public to recognize its addiction to energy. "As Alcoholics Anonymous has proven," said Meyer, "admitting you have a problem is the first step on the road to recovery."

To advocates of a fourth course of action on energy, the fact that Americans use twice as much energy per capita as Western Europeans proves that we have a problem. The fact that Western Europe has been able to achieve a comparable standard of living using far less energy shows that energy use can be substantially reduced.

The most prudent and promising solution to the energy dilemma, in this view, is not to devise new ways to generate more of it. It is, rather, to figure out how to reduce our appetite for energy and how to get more out of less energy.

"The clearest lesson of the last fifteen years," wrote the authors of a recent report from the Natural Resource Defense Council, "is that energy supply can be expanded either by finding more fuel supplies or wasting less of the supplies we already have. For purposes of meeting the needs of a growing economy and population, a kilowatt-hour preserved from waste by an efficient appliance is indistinguishable from a kilowatt-hour delivered to customers by a new power plant. If we see a need for increased supply, we should be weighing our conservation options against our generators, oil fields, and gas wells, and picking the best buys first."

A Strategy That Works

The most compelling argument for energy efficiency, say advocates of this course of action, is that the nation's experience since 1973 proves that it works. "Nothing has so dramatically improved the American energy situation since the early 1970s as energy efficiency," write William Chandler, Howard Geller, and Marc Ledbetter in a 1988 report from the American Council for an Energy-Efficient Economy. "Effficiency has, in effect, cut the nation's annual energy bill by $160 billion. With little fanfare, efficiency improvements have become our most important energy resource. If the nation pursues energy efficiency aggressively, the economy can continue to grow while energy use remains constant or declines."

Since the first oil shock in 1973, energy intensity has been reduced substantially in every sector of American life. Prodded by Corporate Average Fuel Economy (CAFE) standards enacted in 1975, the fuel economy of automobiles driven in the United States has improved by more than a third. The average new car in the United States today is rated at 28 miles per gallon, twice as high as the 1974 average. Improvements in fuel economy of U.S. cars since 1973 save four million barrels of oil per day.

There have also been dramatic improvements in the energy efficiency of American homes and offices, which consume even more energy than transportation. Due to improved lighting, heating, and ventilation systems, observe advocates of conservation, the demand for heating fuel has dropped by 1.2 million barrels of oil per day, which amounts to two-thirds of the oil pumped through the Alaska pipeline. At the same time, rapid advances have taken place in the energy efficiency of home appliances. The 125 million refrigerators and freezers used in American kitchens require the electrical power generated by thirty 1,000 megawatt plants. If those appliances were as inefficient as the refrigerators used in 1975, they would require an additional 20 power plants of that size. Industry has also made notable advances, assisted by federal energy research and development programs, that have speeded the introduction of high-effidency products onto the market.

"All told," says Arthur Rosenfeld, director of the Center for Building Science at the University of California, Berkeley, "savings from improved efficiency in all sectors are enormous. The savings in oil and gas are equivalent to 13 million barrels of oil per day, or half of the production capacity of OPEC. Conservation is saving this country $150 billion per year in energy costs." This improvement in energy efficiency has also been a major factor in mitigating the environmental side effects of burning fossil fuels.

Untapped Potential

For all the steps that have been taken since the 1970s to improve energy efficiency, advocates of this choice are convinced that vast quantities of energy are still wasted in the United States and that major opportunities for energy conservation remain. The fact that Americans use roughly twice as much energy per person compared to the Japanese and the West Germans, say advocates of this choice, shows how far we have to go in becoming energy efficient.

Substantial gains can be made in various areas, they say, such as improving the energy efficiency of homes. While the typical water heater consumes 4,500 to 6,000 kilowatt-hours of electricity, for example, water heaters currently on the market consume only 800 to 1,200 kilowatt-hours.

Advocates of this choice also note that if compact fluorescent bulbs—which use just 16 watts to produce as much illumination as a 60-watt incandescent bulb—were widely used, the energy saved would eliminate the need for 20 standard-sized power plants. In industry, the potential for energy savings is even greater, say advocates of conservation. Substantial gains can be achieved by employing new technologies such as high-efficiency motors and replacing older equipment.

"If all cost-effective conservation measures were taken and the U.S. became as energy efficient as, say, Japan," says Arthur Rosenfeld, "this country would consume half as much energy as it does today and save $220 billion per year." For each kilowatt saved, the nation would be spared the environmental effects of producing that energy.

If fuel efficiency of the average American car were raised from its current level of 19 miles per gallon to 30 miles per gallon, and if Americans cut down on their driving by 25 percent, consumption of oil for cars could be reduced by 50 percent. That, as advocates of this strategy note, would eliminate the need for Middle East oil imports and reduce carbon emissions by almost 300 million tons a year.

Moreover, say advocates of renewed efforts to improve energy efficiency, this strategy has an important advantage over the nuclear option. While a majority of the American public opposes building more nuclear power facilities, there is strong public support for energy efficiency. As indicated by a 1989 poll taken for the Union of Concerned Scientists, a majority of the American public endorses steps to require greater efficiency, as long as they do not cost too much. Eighty-three percent supported a federal fuel-economy standard of 45 miles per gallon, if it results in no more than a $500 increase in the price of a new car.

Waning Enthusiasm

Why, if so compelling a solution is close at hand, don't we take advantage of it to solve the energy dilemma? The problem, say advocates, is that the momentum that built up in the 1970s in favor of energy conservation has been lost. In the words of Lee Schipper, an energy expert at the Lawrence Berkeley Laboratory, Americans have in recent years been "backsliding, using more heat, buying bigger cars, driving more, and in more congested areas."

Since the oil glut of the mid-1980s, proponents of conservation note, consumption of gasoline has been rising, and automobile fuel efficiency has been declining. Responding to carmakers' ads that emphasize performance over efficiency, people are buying bigger cars with more horsepower.

The same pattern, say energy conservationists, is apparent in home energy use. Most Americans are not so inclined today as they were in the 1970s to turn out lights, or pay attention to the energy implications of consumer purchases.

Proponents of this choice acknowledge that various energy-efficiency programs are in place. In many areas of the country, utility companies are engaged in rebate programs to encourage the purchase of efficient appliances and lighting equipment. By 1992, appliance efficiency standards contained in the National Appliance Energy Conservation Act of 1987 will go into effect.

Overall, however, proponents of conservation maintain that, in the absence of high-level support for energy conservation, this option has languished. As former President Jimmy Carter said in August 1990, "Conservation of energy, which I have always believed to be the cornerstone of a workable energy plan, and which other industrial nations have made a continuing focus of national policy and public education, has become an after-thought in the United States."

Top of the Agenda

What, from this perspective, should be done to resolve the energy dilemma? In the words of a recent report from the American Council for an Energy-Efficient Economy, "We urge the United States to place efficiency at the top of its energy agenda. We propose that

A New Generation of Energy-Efficient Cars

One of the main uses of petroleum in the United States today is as fuel for more than 180 million cars and trucks. If those vehicles were replaced with a new generation of more fuel-efficient vehicles, substantial energy savings could be achieved.

Many people insist that currently available technologies could be combined with new developments to significantly improve fuel economy without sacrificing safety, comfort, or affordability. Some features already used on certain models to improve efficiency—such as aerodynamic styling or the use of 4-cylinder, 4-valve engines—could be applied to most vehices. If fuel efficiency were an overriding factor when new cars are designed, the new generation of cars would far exceed the average of 28 miles per gallon for today's new cars.

New developments, such as advanced engine designs, continuously variable transmissions, and the use of composite materials to reduce the weight of vehicles, are being tested. A two-seat prototype car developed by Volvo, the LCP 2000, accelerates from 0-60 miles per hour in just under 11 seconds, but gets 81 miles per gallon in highway driving.

Still, Volvo, like other firms that have developed efficient prototype cars, is not exactly racing to produce this new generation of cars. Referring to the LCP 2000, a Volvo spokesman says "Nobody wants to buy it right now. You don't see a lot of commercials for high fuel economy anymore. That's not what people want to hear."

According to some spokesmen for the auto industry, the high cost of more fuel-efficient cars is a real obstacle. Industry analysts estimate that cars twice as efficient as the current generation will cost $800-$1,000 more to build. Even if consumers anticipate recovering those costs in fuel savings, they are likely to balk at the time of purchase, which explains why manufacturers are less than enthusiastic about manufacturing such cars.

Automakers say they are already taking advantage of current fuel-saving technologies, such as front-wheel drive, fuel injectors, and aerodynamic design. To achieve greater fuel efficiency, automakers say, it will be necessary to manufacture smaller cars, which is not what today's consumers want.

"I don't think it's reasonable to hold that the most mobile society in the world can meet its personal and business transportation needs with a fleet of minicompacts, subcompacts, and compacts," says Thomas H. Hanna, president of the Motor Vehicle Manufacturers Association. "Sales, the barometer of consumer preference, support this. In 1989, cars rated at 50 miles per gallon or better accounted for less than 3 percent of U.S. sales."

the nation set a goal of reducing energy intensity by at least 2.5 percent per year well into the next century. This rate would approximate the efficiency improvements of 1976-1986."

Although the immediate responsibility for energy conservation falls on individuals and on private firms that produce cars, buildings, appliances, and machinery, advocates of this view are convinced that an energy conservation strategy can only go so far if it rests entirely on private sector activity. To be effective, they say, energy efficiency must be pursued simultaneously by a great many people. For this reason, it requires government coordination and commonly shared incentives.

As Marc Ross, a University of Michigan physicist who serves as a consultant to the Energy Department, puts it, "In this country, we have over 80 million households using appliances. We have 100,000 to 200,000 contractors who have to learn how to better insulate houses. It will take government intervention because there are so many players."

In some cases, energy conservationists observe, states are leading the way with energy-efficiency standards. Several years ago, California adopted strict standards for refrigerators—the most energy-intensive appliance in American homes. Coupled with other state-mandated measures, California's benchmarks for home appliances have helped the state achieve efficiency improvements that consistently outstrip progress achieved in the nation as a whole.

An energy plan proposed in January 1991 by Vermont Madeline Kunin shows what states can do to mandate efficiency measures. Among its various measures, the plan calls for low-cost loans to home owners and businesses that make energy-efficient choices, financial incentives to buy more efficient cars, and a reduction of the speed limit from 65 to 55. It also calls for changes that Vermont could not enact on its own, such as raising the fuel efficiency of new cars from the current federal standard of 28 miles per gallon to 40 miles per gallon.

Governor Kunin, who proposed the measures just a few days before the end of her term, refers to the proposed energy-efficiency measures as "harsh medicine." But, she said, such measures are necessary to keep the United States from becoming even more dependent on imported oil and to prevent environmental degradation.

Going After Gas Guzzlers

As illustrated by the Vermont proposal, advocates of energy efficiency favor various actions, beginning with measures to discourage unnecessary driving and to make cars and trucks more fuel efficient.

The fuel efficiency of American cars has improved by about 50 percent since 1973, in no small part because of fuel economy standards enacted by Congress in 1975. Concerned about the fact that, since 1988, many American buyers have chosen bigger cars with more powerful engines, advocates of energy efficiency favor tighter standards to ensure further improvements throughout the 1990s.

One such bill proposed recently in the Senate would raise the average fuel economy of new American cars from its current level of 28 miles per gallon to 40 miles per gallon by the year 2001, which would save nearly 3 million barrels of oil a day. The bill's chief sponsor, Senator Richard Bryan of Nevada, says it would stimulate automakers to develep new engine and transmission technologies and to use lightweight materials.

To encourage consumers to buy the most fuel-efficient cars, energy experts Amory and Hunter Lovins propose widespread adoption of auto "feebates" such as those recently approved in California. This measure is intended to remind consumers of the environmental and national security costs of energy-inefficient cars at the time of purchase. It would impose a tax on those who insist on buying gas guzzlers, and provide rebates to purchasers of smaller, more efficient cars.

As the Lovinses explain, "Rebates for efficient cars should be based on the difference in efficiency between your new car and the old one—which you'd scrap, thus getting the most inefficient cars off the road. That's good for Detroit, for the environment, and for displacing oil from the Persian Gulf sooner."

The fundamental weakness of efforts to encourage more fuel-effcient vehicles, many believe, is that there are few economic incentives to do so. Accordingly, advocates of energy conservation favor higher gasoline taxes as the most direct way to create a larger market for energy-efficient cars. While most industrial countries tax vehicle fuels by $1.50 to $3.00 per gallon, the average tax in the United States—combining state, federal, and local

TAXING SOLUTION

Gasoline taxes are lower in the United States than in other industrialized countries.

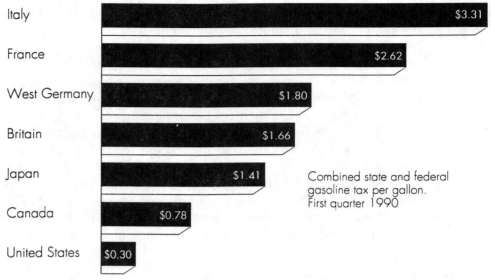

Italy	$3.31
France	$2.62
West Germany	$1.80
Britain	$1.66
Japan	$1.41
Canada	$0.78
United States	$0.30

Combined state and federal gasoline tax per gallon. First quarter 1990

Source: Energy and Resources Branch, United Nations Secretariat

taxes—is only about 30 cents. That, say proponents of energy conservation, sends the wrong signals and offers little incentive for consumers to purchase smaller, more fuel-efficient cars.

Accordingly, advocates of this choice favor raising the federal gasoline tax by about 50 cents per gallon within 5 years. The revenue, they say, should be spent on mass transit and for energy-efficiency programs.

Energy-Saving Decisions

Advocates of this choice would also create new incentives to stimulate more energy-effcient homes and buildings. One of the chief determinants of the nation's energy efficiency, they note, is how well new buildings are constructed. Decisions made when a building is designed and constructed— such as its orientation to the sun, the materials used for construction and insulation, the type of windows installed, the heating plant, and the appliances with which it is equipped—determine how much energy that structure will require over the 50- to 100-year period in which it is used.

Advocates of this solution to the energy dilemma point out that, while manufacturers of air conditioners or refrigerators are required to state their energy efficiency, no such requirement applies to new building construction. Often, because builders are more concerned with keeping construction costs down than with long-term operating costs, the houses they erect are as energy inefficient as some of the worst gas guzzlers on the road.

To remedy the situation, say proponents of this choice, contractors should be required to show that a home is designed according to approved methods of energy conservation before a building permit is issued. Lending institutions should offer incentives to individuals who design and construct buildings that require less energy than the average new home.

"Opportunities abound to improve energy efficiency in the building, transportation, and industrial sectors of the economy," says Senator Timothy Wirth of Colorado. "By using existing energy sources more efficiently, we can reduce pollution, improve our balance of trade, and strengthen national security. We need to squeeze more out of every gallon of gasoline, every chunk of coal, every cubic foot of natural gas."

What Critics Say

While few people oppose energy conservation, many are skeptical about its promise as a solution to the nation's energy dilemma. They doubt that millions of Americans can be persuaded to change their behavior to save substantial amounts of energy. Willett Kempton, anthropologist at Princeton University's Center for Energy and Environmental Studies, has studied energy-related behavior over the past decade. He points out that today, 20 years after energy first became a prominent public issue, "The average American doesn't have a clue what's best to do."

While many people turn off light switches to conserve energy, they don't often think of the things that have the greatest impact on energy consumption, such as turning down water heaters. "A water heater is in the basement," says Kempton. "You don't directly turn it on, it's not bright, it's invisible. But it turns out that the water heater is a major energy user. People tend to be perceptually incorrect about ranking what is important in terms of energy use."

Even the prospect of saving money by changing habits is not enough to prompt most people to save energy, says Kempton. "If you really wanted to save energy and money for lighting your house, you would replace all the light bulbs you use more than four hours a day with the new compact fluorescents." But the initial cost of the bulbs—more than $20—is a deterrent, and they are not as readily available as conventional light bulbs. So, Kempton concludes, "It's a hard sell. How do you convince the public? That is what's going on with energy now, and that's the problem."

Skeptics about energy conservation point to another obstacle, the inefficiency of most homes and cars. Most of today's housing stock, for example, was built at a time when energy was abundant and cheap. Consequently, many structures are poorly insulated. Ill-fitting single-pane windows allow heat to escape. Critics point out that until these houses are eventually replaced, they will remain energy inefficient.

In the words of John Gray, chairman of ERC Environmental and Energy Services, "To cut down on the use of energy to the extent that would preclude having to increase the supply of energy, you would have to rebuild the entire housing, transportation, and commercial infrastructure of the country. That's a two trillion dollar bill. The argument is that silly."

Costly And Unpopular

What should be recognized, say critics, is that the major sources of inefficiency and the ones most readily corrected have already been addressed. Achieving additional gains will be more difficult, and it will require unpopular and increasingly costly measures.

Imposing a much higher gas tax is so politically unpopular, say critics, that it is unlikely to receive much support from elected officials. In any case, not everyone agrees that higher gas taxes will significantly reduce use of petroleum products. "I don't think consumption taxes do much except buy a bigger government," says Theodore Eck, chief economist at the Amoco Corporation. Even if taxes are increased by 50 cents a gallon, he says, the additional cost of driving is small compared with fixed costs such as the car's purchase price. Faced with higher gas taxes, says Eck, "Not too many people are going to hang it up and walk."

Many people object to higher gas taxes because their burden falls disproportionately on the poor, who can least afford to pay more and more often drive older, less fuel-efficient cars.

Critics are also wary about government intrusion in the name of energy efficiency. To conserve energy, some people favor government standards on everything from lighting fixtures and the design of home appliances to the details of home construction. Critics fear that the price of becoming a more energy-efficient society is that government will become increasingly intrusive, telling us what kinds of products can be manufactured, even how our homes will be designed. Every time a decision is removed from the marketplace and given to government, say critics, a few people end up making the decisions and some personal freedom is lost. A far better way to achieve energy efficiency, they conclude, is to allow consumers to choose for themselves.

Energy Futures: Choosing a Framework for Action

After a decade in which oil flowed abundantly and cheaply and energy virtually disappeared from the public agenda, the energy dilemma is once again at center stage in the 1990s. The Persian Gulf crisis is a vivid reminder that the United States has ignored the dangers of relying on imported oil. At the same time, there is growing concern about environmental damage caused by relying on fossil fuels, as well as concern about a looming shortage of electrical power. Prodded by these concerns, elected officials are for the first time in more than a decade focusing on energy, preparing to make critical decisions about how to resolve the dilemma.

As things stand, most of the American public agrees that the nation should have a comprehensive energy policy, a plan for meeting energy needs today and tomorrow. But there are real differences about which option is most promising, which costs we are willing to bear, which risks we are willing to take, and what changes in personal behavior we are willing to make.

What is needed is widespread public debate about how energy needs can be met in a way that is safe, sustainable, and relatively inexpensive—a debate in which all the major alternatives are considered. The goal of this debate is to arrive at a framework for public action.

Costs and Consequences

Faced with rising demands for energy, we seek reliable sources of power at the lowest possible cost to consumers and to the environment. At each step, the discussion should be informed by a realistic assessment of costs associated with each choice.

Some people are convinced that hard choices are unnecessary because a cost-free scientific solution to the energy dilemma is just around the corner. A remarkable announcement in March 1989 by physicists B. Stanley Pons and Martin Fleischmann appeared to signal just such a breakthrough. Pons and Fleischmann announced that, in a simple tabletop experiment, they had created energy by fusing atoms at room temperature.

Palladium rods in a jar of heavy water, they claimed, produce great quantities of heat. Their claim, which attracted worldwide attention, offered the hope of limitless amounts of safe, cheap, non-polluting energy.

After a few tantalizing reports from scientists who claimed to have repeated the experiment with similar results, it became clear that cold fusion is a mirage, the result of experimental error. Within a few months of the original announcement, further research along those lines was largely abandoned.

The prospect of cold fusion is the latest in a series of illusory solutions to the energy dilemma. A few years ago, science writer G. Harry Stine forecast that, in the twenty-first century, orbiting satellites would collect and transmit "enough energy for everybody to do everything," presumably with no undesirable side effects. His vision reflects a characteristically American faith that science will produce a technical fix for every problem, making it unnecessary to choose among flawed options.

In the real world, however, we are faced with a choice among less-than-perfect options, each of which imposes certain costs. Some environmentalists, for example, object to California's wind turbines—one of the cleaner energy sources—on the grounds that they kill several dozen hawks each year. You may regard that as a small price to pay for a significant amount of power. Still, it needs to be factored into the discussion and weighed against the cost of other choices.

But acknowledging that certain costs are associated with each option is quite a different thing from saying that, because all power sources cause some environmental damage, we should assume those effects are equal. In an important respect, the energy debate consists of comparing costs and deciding which of them we are prepared to accept as the price of maintaining an energy-intensive life-style.

Four Choices

One option is to continue to rely heavily on fossil fuels, if we are willing to put up with the environmental pollution they cause. By opening up coastal areas for oil exploration, permitting exploration in environmentally sensitive areas such as the Alaska National Wildlife Refuge, expanding natural gas pipelines, and developing new ways to burn coal more cleanly, the United States could extend the era of fossil fuels until well into the next century. This is an attractive option because it requires no fundamental change in energy-using habits.

If the environmental pollution associated with fossil fuels is unacceptable, we could make a serious commitment to develop renewables as the source of a large fraction of the nation's power. Renewables are relatively clean, but they are also unproven and somewhat uncertain as a major power source. Switching over to them as a major energy source would require a large investment, both public and private.

Alternatively, in light of the national security costs and environmental consequences of relying on fossil fuels, we could choose to rely more heavily on nuclear power. A major effort could be made to develop a new generation of safer reactors. "If a broad consensus supported a revival of the nuclear option, faster licensing procedures could be devised and satisfactory burial sites for radioactive wastes could no doubt be found.

Nuclear power is a proven source of large quantities of electrical energy, an alternative that causes neither smog nor acid rain and adds no carbon to the atmosphere. The question is whether we are willing to live with the possibililty —however remote—of accidents like Three Mile Island and Chernobyl, the vulnerability of nuclear plants to terrorists and saboteurs, and the production of radioactive wastes that must be guarded for millenia.

A final option is to resolve the energy dilemma not by embarking on a major effort to produce more power but by stepping up efforts to reduce demand. Conservation is an attractive option because it involves no hazards—other than the possibility that, by over-estimating its potential, we may encounter serious energy shortages.

The success of the conservation strategy depends, in large part, on the public's willingness to give up old habits and become far more energy conscious in our day-to-day behavior. Its success depends, too, on our willingness to accept various public measures, ranging from higher gas taxes to restrictions on the vehicles we drive, the appliances we use, and the design of the buildings in which we work and live.

The central questions in the energy debate are clear:

- Should various measures be taken to use domestic fossil fuels more extensively, such as exploring and extracting oil from environmentally sensitive areas?

- Should a serious effort be made to develop renewable energy sources, even if many such technologies are unproven?

- Should a public commitment be made to develop a new generation of reactors to provide nuclear energy, despite the hazards of radioactivity?

- To reduce or eliminate the need for additional energy sources, should public measures be put in place to encourage greater energy efficiency, such as raising gas taxes significantly and requiring more energy-efficient homes, motor vehicles, and appliances?

- Finally, as a hedge against global warming, whose effects may be catastrophic but cannot be precisely predicted, is it prudent to take immediate steps to move away from our dependence on fossil fuels?

Public Actions

At several points in the past, the United States has made a transition from one energy source to another. Since the middle of the nineteenth century, the nation's power sources have shifted from wind, wood, hydropower, and whale oil to coal— and more recently to oil and natural gas. At each step, new energy sources were cheaper, cleaner, more conven-ient, and more abundant. Each shift took place as a result of market forces, not public decisions.

The transition we face today is different in two respects. The options we face are *not* necessarily superior to older energy sources in every respect. If they were, there would be no hard choice to make. If we deal with the hazards of fossil fuels by moving toward nuclear power or renewables, energy from such sources may be more expensive. If we choose the conservation strategy, it will cause a certain amount of personal inconvenience. A public consensus about energy futures is needed, in part, to overcome resistance to the cost and inconvenience of new energy strategies.

The transition we face today is different in another respect, too. It requires a public decision and the commitment of substantial public resources. In response to the threat of global warming and other environmental effects of fossil fuel consumption, individuals can adjust their behavior by driving less, car pooling, installing solar cells on the roof. But, writes Bill McKibben, "A purely personal effort is, of course, just a gesture. Simply driving less won't matter, except as a statement, a way to get other people to drive less." The problem, says McKibben, is that "most people have to be persuaded, and persuaded quickly, to change."

However much individuals can do, a resolution of the energy dilemma requires public deliberation and public action. What is important now is for the American public to join the energy debate, and try to reach a common understanding about how to meet the nation's energy needs throughout the 1990s and into the twenty-first century.

For Further Reading

For useful analyses of the energy issue, see Walter A. Rosenbaum's *Energy, Politics, and Public Policy* (Washington, D.C.: Congressional Quarterly Press, 1981) and Martin Melosi's *Coping with Abundance* (Philadelphia: Temple University Press, 1985). The September 1990 issue of *Scientific American*, which is devoted entirely to the energy issue, takes a broad look at the problem and examines various alternatives.

Daniel Yergin's *The Prize: The Epic Quest for Oil, Money, and Power* (New York: Simon and Schuster, 1990) provides a compelling historical account of the rise of the "hydrocarbon society," and an astute analysis of why energy— particularly oil—has been at the basis of so much of this century's political conflict. The American Petroleum Institute's *Domestic Petroleum Production and National Security* (Washington, D.C.: American Petroleum Institute, 1986) argues that increased domestic fossil fuel production is necessary in order to limit dependence on foreign nations.

On the effects of carbon emissions and various ways of responding to global warming, see Michael Oppenheimer and Robert H. Boyle, Dead Heat: The Race Against the Greenhouse Effect (New York Basic Books, 1990). Bill McKibben's *The End of Nature* (New York: Random House, 1989) is a compelling and broadly informed essay about carbon emissions, how they are changing the natural world, and what responses are appropriate in dealing with them. On strategies for slowing global warming, see Christopher Flavin's *Slowing Global Warming* (Washington, D.C.: Worldwatch Institute, 1989).

For a lucid description of renewable energy sources and their promise, see *Sustainable Energy* by Christopher Flavin and Rick Piltz with Chris Nichols (Washington, D.C.: Renew America, 1989). On the same topic, two recent Worldwatch Institute reports are also recommended, Cynthia Pollock Shea's *Renewable Energy: Today's Contribution, Tomorrow's Promise* (Washington, D.C.: Worldwatch Institute, 1988), and *Beyond the Petroleum Age: Designing a Solar Economy* by Christopher Flavin and Nicholas Lensse (Washington, D.C.: Worldwatch Institute, 1990). *Cool Energy* (Cambridge, Massachusetts: Union of Concerned Scientists, 1990), a report by Michael Brower, explores the potential of various renewable energy sources to reduce the threat of global warming.

The U.S. Council for Energy Awareness makes the case for nuclear power in *Nuclear Electricity and Energy Independence* (Washington, D.C.: U.S. Council for Energy Awareness, 1988). In the September 1990 issue of *Scientific American*, Wolf Hafele examines the nuclear option, and concludes that nuclear power "must play a significant role in a sustainable future." For a rebuttal on nuclear power, see Christopher Flavin's *Reassessing Nuclear Power The Fallout from Chernobyl* (Washington, D.C.: Worldwatch Institute, 1987).

On energy conservation, see *Energy Efficiency: A New Agenda* by William U. Chandler, Howard S. Geller, and Marc R. Ledbetter (Washington, D.C.: American Council for an Energy-Efficient Economy, 1988). On the outlook for the efficiency strategy, see *Building on Success: The Age of Energy Efficiency* (Washington, D.C.: Worldwatch Institute, 1988), a report by Christopher Flavin and Alan Durning.

Acknowledgments

We would like to express our appreciation to the people who helped choose this year's topics and took part in discussions about how they should be approached. Once again, David Mathews and Daniel Yankelovich provided both support and guidance. Our colleagues John Doble, Jean Johnson, Jon Rye Kinghorn, Robert Kingston, Suzanne Morse, Patrick Scully, Jeffrey Tuchman, and Deborah Wadsworth played a valuable role in refining the framework and clarifying the presentation.

Finally, our thanks to Margaret Kriz at the *National Journal* and to Christopher Flavin and his colleagues at the Worldwatch Institute, who provided advice as we prepared the manuscript.

Article Questions

1. What are some significant other alternative fuels? How much of a future role will these fuels play?

2. What is the future of solar power? What are the obstacles? What are some of the pros and cons in using nuclear power?

3. Can nuclear power be a safe alternative source? Explain your reasoning.

4. How much effect can conservation have on energy use?

5. What can be a designed plan for sustainable energy use?

Dismantling the Doomsday Machine

Harold Feiveson and Frank von Hippel

The huge nuclear arsenals of the United States and Soviet Union were built on a fantastic illusion—that nuclear explosives could be used for military purposes by the thousands without destroying modern civilization. Only such an illusion can account for the accumulation of more than 10,000 long-range strategic nuclear warheads and 10,000 tactical nuclear warheads by each country, with a combined destructive power greater than that of 150,000 Hiroshima bombs.

The principal mission of these oversized strategic forces—to target each other—led to exaggerated fears about the possibility of surprise attacks. This in turn led both sides to place large numbers of nuclear weapons on hair-trigger alert and to disperse authority to launch attacks among large numbers of people, thus heightening the danger of accidental nuclear war. The superpowers' preoccupation with mutual nuclear threats also distracted them from the growing dangers of nuclear-weapons proliferation.

The end of the Cold War offers an unprecedented opportunity for the United States and the former Soviet republics, principally Russia, to begin to cooperatively dismantle the largest part of this Doomsday Machine. As a first step, the arsenals could be cut deeply and quickly to about 1,000 warheads on each side.

By making such deep cuts, the superpowers would acknowledge an important reality: that nuclear weapons are useless as war-fighting instruments. A 1,000-warhead arsenal would be plenty destructive enough to hold the other side hostage, but far too small to mount a large attack on the other's nuclear forces. If both sides cut their nuclear forces to such levels, therefore, neither will feel as much pressure to strike first if a conflict arises. It will become easier to move away from the hair-trigger, "use them or lose them" postures that undermine the stability of the present strategic balance.

The deep cuts would increase the legitimacy of U.S. and Russian efforts to stop the international proliferation of nuclear weapons. They should make it easier to achieve a universal ban on the further production of fissile materials not subject to international safeguards. This ban could cap the arsenals of the middle nuclear powers (Britain, France, and China) and of the "threshold" nuclear-weapons states (Israel, India, and Pakistan). Deep cuts in Russia's nuclear forces, along with similar cuts in its conventional forces, would also help ensure that Kazakhstan and Ukraine stick to their decisions to become non-nuclear states.

A 1,000-warhead force would be consistent with the criteria offered in a recent study commissioned by Air Force Gen. Lee Butler, director of U.S. strategic targeting. The study concluded that in the post-Cold War era, the United States should retain a long-range nuclear force at least as large as that of the Commonwealth of Independent States (CIS) and larger than the forces of Britain, France, and China combined. Thus, for whatever it is worth, the United States would retain its "superpower" status. Finally, a recent study by the Congressional Budget Office shows that a 1,000-warhead force would cost billions of dollars per year less than the nuclear arsenal that would remain after the more modest reductions already agreed upon in the Strategic Arms Reductions Treaty (START).

A Landslide of Disarmament

The reduction of the superpower nuclear arsenals has already begun. Since the failed Moscow coup last August, a series of reciprocated unilateral initiatives have added up to what Russian President Boris Yeltsin recently described as a "landslide of disarmament." Both countries have already agreed to either dismantle or place in storage almost all tactical nuclear weapons. START will cut their strategic arsenals by thousands of warheads each, and they are negotiating still deeper strategic reductions.

President Bush started the landslide in September by announcing that the United States would denuclearize all Navy ships and submarines except those carrying long-range ballistic missiles, and withdraw from Europe all short-range nuclear missiles and artillery shells. (Fighter-bomber aircraft stationed in Europe, however, will still have available some 700 nuclear bombs.) The United States will destroy more than 3,000 tactical nuclear warheads as a result of President Bush's decision.

Then-president Gorbachev responded with parallel decisions whose implementation went forward despite his fall from power. In December, in Alma Ata, Kazakhstan, the leaders of the CIS agreed that all tactical nuclear warheads would be moved to Russia by July 1, 1992, where they would be dismantled under joint supervision. As of the end of January, Belarus and Ukraine were reportedly the only republics other than Russia that still had tactical nuclear weapons on their soil, and the withdrawals from those republics were ahead of schedule. Gorbachev's decision is expected to result in the destruction of between 10,000 and 20,000 tactical nuclear warheads.

In January, President Bush shifted the focus to strategic reductions by renewing his proposal that all multiple-warhead intercontinental ballistic missiles (ICBMs) be eliminated. This time, however, he acknowledged that the CIS has a much larger fraction of its strategic warheads on multiple-warhead ICBMs than does the United States. In compensation, he offered to reduce by one-third the number of warheads on submarine-launched ballistic missiles and to shift a "substantial fraction" of U.S. long-range bombers to non-nuclear missions. According to Gen. Colin Powell, chairman of the Joint Chiefs of Staff, this would leave the United States with 4,700 strategic warheads—down considerably from the 9,000 warheads expected to remain in the U.S. arsenal after the START reductions.

Yeltsin, who became chief nuclear policymaker after the Soviet Union dissolved, responded that Russia would reduce its strategic arsenals to START levels in three years instead of the seven stipulated in the treaty, and he proposed still deeper cuts to about 2,500 strategic warheads each.

In the meantime, Belarus, Kazakhstan, and Ukraine had all agreed that the strategic nuclear weapons on their territories would remain under central control and declared their intentions to become non-nuclear weapons states and to abide by the Non-Proliferation Treaty. Belarus and Ukraine declared that they would become nuclear-weapons free within the seven-year reduction period laid out in the START treaty. Kazakhstan has vacillated about making the same commitment, but acceptance of President Bush's proposal to eliminate multiple-warhead ICBMs would eliminate all the long-range missiles based in Kazakhstan.

Presidents Bush and Yeltsin further announced that they would halt the development and production of almost all new nuclear weapons. The only continuing U.S. nuclear "modernization" program is completion of the last 6 of 18 Trident submarines and their associated Trident II missiles. However, production of the Trident II's 475-kiloton, "silo-killing" warheads will be halted and the missiles fitted instead with 100-kiloton warheads from retired Trident I missiles.

In parallel with the initiatives to mothball most tactical nuclear weapons, both the United States and Soviet Union have reduced the alert levels of their strategic Forces. In September, President Bush ended the three-decade U.S. practice of keeping a fraction of its strategic bombers loaded with nuclear bombs and ready to take off within minutes of warning of a Soviet attack missile. President Gorbachev, in turn, ordered Soviet SS-24 rail-mobile ICBMs kept in their bases. (Soviet bombers had never been kept on alert in the U.S. fashion.). Also, the ICBMs in the Ukraine and Kazakhstan have reportedly been disabled in a manner that would take considerable time to reverse.

In February, Yeltsin proposed that the alert levels of the U.S. and Russian nuclear forces be reduced to zero by keeping all ballistic-missile submarines in port, storing warheads separately from bombers and missiles, and putting an international agency in charge of monitoring the warhead storage sites.

Taking weapons off alert makes perfect sense and greatly reduces the danger of accidental or unauthorized launch. However, both sides need to continue to maintain some forces capable of "riding out" a nuclear attack. Therefore, at least a few ballistic-missile submarines, equipped with stringent protections against unauthorized use, should remain at sea. These subs should have orders to stay safely hidden and await instructions from the surviving political leadership in the event of a nuclear attack.

Traditionally, the principal ambition of the Soviet Union was to achieve nuclear "parity" with the United States. However, the current political leadership of Russia seems to realize—as have Britain, France, and China in the past—that a less-than-equal nuclear force can provide an adequate deterrent. Russian Foreign Minister Andrei Kozyrev stated recently that "the renewed Russia sees no need in maintaining parity and does not want to have as many weapons as the United States or any other power."

In addition, some defense analysts argue that economic pressure will force Russia to make deeper cuts than the United States. However, it is widely believed in Russia that eliminating excess nuclear weapons will, in the short term at least, be more costly than keeping them. It does not cost much to maintain an IBM in a missile silo. Furthermore, statements by President Yeltsin and some Russian military leaders suggest that the historic concern about parity is far from politically dead. Trying to persuade Russia to accept unequal cuts might therefore slow or halt the reduction process. In any case, there is no obvious reason why the United States should not cut at least as deeply as Russia does, or that each should not go down to at least the level of 1,000 warheads.

A 1,000-Warhead Arsenal

In designing the 1,000-warhead force, we have made two general assumptions: First, it is unlikely that either country will want to eliminate entirely any leg of the strategic triad. Submarines are able to hide under the ocean and survive a nuclear attack. ICBMs are more vulnerable but it would take a huge attack to even partially destroy a force of a few hundred silo-based missiles. Bomber forces are the most versatile—they can carry either conventional or nuclear weapons and, unlike missiles, can be called back.

Second, in making radical reductions in nuclear forces, both countries should cut the concentrations of warheads on missiles and bombers. The reasoning is that with only a few nuclear "eggs," it would be important not to have too many in any single "basket." Otherwise, a 1,000-warhead force might appear vulnerable to attack—and it is its ensured survivability that makes the small nuclear force work.

The ICBM component of the U.S. force, for example, could consist of 248 Minuteman III missiles "downloaded," as President Bush has already proposed, from three warheads apiece to one. The obvious candidate for the Russian ICBM is the single-warhead, mobile SS-25, of which approximately 300 were deployed as of the end of 1991. Roughly this number could remain in a 1,000-warhead force. However, mobile missiles depend upon dispersal for survivability, and such dispersal creates troubling security problems. A missile on a truck is not as safe from hijack as one in a silo. Russia may therefore wish to consider placing these single-warhead missiles in some of the silos that will be left empty as a result of the elimination of multiple-warhead ICBMs.

The potential for too many eggs in a basket is even more pronounced with submarines than with land-based missiles. Just two Trident submarines, each equipped as today with two dozen, eight-warhead missiles, would carry almost 40 percent of a 1,000-warhead force. But two submarines cannot ensure robust survivability. If the United States wanted to keep all of its planned Trident submarines, it could download their missiles to a single warhead each, for a total force of 432 warheads. Or the same number of warheads could be carried on a smaller number of submarines with partially downloaded missiles. Russia could similarly download as many as 440 missiles on 25 of its most modern submarines.

To reduce concerns that the stripped-down missiles might be reloaded, the extra warheads should be destroyed in a verified manner. Also, the "buses" that currently direct the warheads of multiple-warhead missiles to their different targets should be eliminated, and tests simulating release of more than the reduced number of warheads banned, as stipulated in the START treaty.

The remaining 320 U.S. warheads could be carried by 40 long-range bombers, each carrying its maximum internal load of eight cruise missiles. The United States would presumably use B-1 bombers for this purpose and either retire its B-52s or convert them into conventional bombers. Russia could similarly complete its 1,000-warhead force with some of its long-range bombers carrying their maximum internal loads of six cruise missiles each. Surplus cruise missiles would be destroyed, as would pylons that would enable aircraft to carry cruise missiles externally. As today, the bombers would be kept off alert, with their nuclear weapons in storage nearby.

No plausible cheating or breakout from these 1,000-warhead limits could threaten either country's ability to retaliate. In the U.S. case, with current at-sea rates, two-thirds of the Trident submarines would be hidden in the sea at any one time. These subs would carry a total of 288 warheads, each with an average destructive power equal to seven Hiroshima bombs. In addition, at least 50 ICBMs, each carrying a warhead with eight times the destructive power of the Hiroshima bomb, could be expected to survive even a worst-case attack. These surviving warheads would contain a huge destructive potential and constitute a more than adequate deterrent.

Critics of proposals like ours sometimes assert that a drastically pared-down nuclear force would be incapable of a large "counterforce" attack on the enemy's military. These critics maintain that this would leave a country with only one option for retaliation: the "immoral" one of attacking cities. But a small arsenal does not necessitate attacks on cities. Even after being hit by a nuclear attack, a country with 1,000-warhead arsenal would still have hundreds of surviving warheads, and it would always have the option of retaliating with some of them against military targets. And in any case, massive attacks on military targets would kill so many civilians that distinctions between counterforce and counter-city attacks become nearly meaningless. The deterrent strategy associated with a 1,000-warhead force would therefore be no less moral than the counterforce strategies around which today's forces are designed.

The Bush administration has proposed deploying strategic defenses to protect against accidental launches of up to 200 CIS warheads and against Third World missile attacks. But any defensive shield that could guard against 200 warheads would also raise doubts about the effectiveness of the retaliatory attack by a 1,000-warhead force. Thus any strategic defense system could make deep cuts impossible to achieve.

Other ways to provide similar protection would not conflict with deep cuts. For example, "command-destruct" devices would make it possible to destroy accidentally launched missiles with a coded radio command. As for Third World nuclear threats, the principal focus should be on stopping nuclear proliferation— especially since such nations would probably use methods other than long-range ballistic missiles to deliver a warhead.

Supervised Safeguards

The arrangements agreed to under START could easily be adapted to verify deeper reductions of bombers, ballistic missiles, and their launchers. The United States and Russia should, however, go beyond START to verify disposal of excess warheads. Verified warhead elimination would reduce concerns about the possibilities of a breakout from a deep-cuts agreement. Even after warhead dismantlement, the recovered fissile materials (plutonium and highly-enriched uranium) must be effectively safeguarded. The technical basis for such an arrangement has been worked out in some detail in a five-year collaborative research project by the Federation of American Scientists and CIS technical experts.

Since dismantling of more than 10,000 warheads by each country will take years, verification should begin by making sure that the warheads to be dismantled are stored at declared locations in sealed and tagged containers. At this stage and throughout the warhead dismantlement process, the United States and Russia would verify each others' commitments. After the fissile materials are removed from the warheads and changed into shapes that no longer reveal any clues on warhead design, the International Atomic Energy Agency could take over as the principal safeguarding authority.

(A more comprehensive scheme would verify not only what warheads were destroyed but also which were kept. It would include declarations of the numbers, types, and locations of all nuclear warheads and the total quantities of fissile materials in the warheads and weapon-complex stockpiles. President Yeltsin recently proposed that all five acknowledged nuclear-weapon states make such declarations.)

When warheads are delivered to the dismantlement facility, the verifying party would check that the tags and seals were intact and that the neutron and gamma radiation emanating from the container matched the warhead's declared identity. The perimeter of the dismantlement facility would also be monitored to ensure that all fissile material removed from the facility is placed under international safeguards.

Dismantling warheads and safeguarding their contents should logically be coupled with a halt in any further production of enriched uranium and plutonium. A permanent ban on such production would require the verified shutdown of all military plutonium production facilities and international safeguards on all civilian facilities that contain or could produce significant quantities of fissile materials. The obligation to submit to such safeguards has already been accepted by the approximately 140 non-nuclear-weapons states that have signed the Non-Proliferation Treaty. But while the Russian government has made clear its willingness to accept these arrangements, the Bush administration wants to retain the option of reusing in weapons all fissile material recovered from dismantled nuclear warheads and even to produce new fissile material for this purpose.

This position is extraordinarily shortsighted. If the United States would forgo the reuse of the fissile materials recovered from warheads that are not to be replaced—thereby "locking in" the U.S. force reductions—Russia would forgo future weapons use of several times more material. Moreover, the world would become a substantially safer place because there would be internationally supervised safeguards against diversion of surplus nuclear warheads and fissile materials by subnational groups.

A U.S.-Russia agreement to permanently end the production of fissile weapons material would have another benefit as well: it would strengthen the legitimacy of U.S. efforts to persuade Israel, India, and Pakistan to halt their production of unsafeguarded fissile materials. Convincing these countries and Britain, France, and China to join in a cutoff would establish the basis for a worldwide ban.

Just Say No to Testing

As a natural complement to a universal halt of fissile weapons materials, the United States and Russia should agree to a comprehensive nuclear weapons test ban (CTB).

In the past, proponents of a CTB have focused on stopping the development of new generations of potentially destabilizing warheads. But the end of the Cold War has largely ended this area of competition, and today the strongest arguments for a CTB relate to efforts to halt nuclear proliferation.

The Non-Proliferation Treaty must be renewed in 1995, and, in light of the Iraq experience, it must be strengthened to provide greater assurances that countries are fulfilling their commitments to forgo nuclear weapons. However, a large number of non-nuclear states made it clear at the 1990 Treaty Review Conference that they will not support a strengthened Non-Proliferation Treaty without a commitment to a test ban.

The Soviet and successor governments have advocated a comprehensive test ban since August 1985, when Gorbachev initiated a unilateral test moratorium that lasted 18 months. Soviet testing halted again in October 1989 when a local citizen movement permanently shut down the main test site in Kazakhstan. The Soviets (and CIS) have conducted only one test since then, on the Arctic island of Novaya Zemlya, in October 1990.

This test generated so much public outrage that a formal testing moratorium was declared until October 1992. But the Reagan and Bush administrations have adamantly argued that U.S. testing must continue, principally to develop safer warhead designs.

Nuclear weapons can be made virtually immune to an accidental nuclear explosion without changes that require testing. The principal other hazard is that the chemical explosive in a warhead might detonate accidentally, creating a fine aerosol of plutonium oxide, a potent carcinogen. Almost all the warhead types that the United States plans to keep in its arsenal contain a chemical explosive that cannot be detonated by a fire, the impact of an airplane crash, or even a bullet.

Replacements will be needed for the two or three warhead designs that do not contain such insensitive high explosives. But according to a congressionally commissioned analysis by Ray Kidder, a former nuclear weapons designer at Lawrence Livermore, development of replacement designs that contain insensitive high explosives could be completed before 1995 with fewer than 10 tests.

Some have proposed a new generation of "inherently safe" warhead designs. The plutonium core would be kept inside an armored shell, separate from the chemical explosive until the warhead was armed. But a program to develop such designs would cost billions of dollars and require testing to continue well past 1995. The small residual dangers do not justify such a costly effort.

Eventually, if democracy becomes firmly rooted in Russia and finally reaches China, nuclear deterrence between the current nuclear weapon states will become as irrelevant as it is now to the relationships between the United States, Britain, and France. Under these circumstances, still further cuts would be possible—to levels constrained primarily by the need to guard against the risk of a rogue nation acquiring nuclear weapons.

How low should we go? One criterion suggested by Herbert York, a former director of Livermore, is that nuclear forces should be cut to such a level that no single person or group could produce damage substantially worse than an all-out conventional war such as World War II. By this standard, the arsenals of the nuclear-weapon states might each retain up to about 100 strategic warheads, with Britain and France perhaps sharing a "European" force.

The nuclear forces of some or all of the members of the U.N. Security Council might then be placed under a joint command. Individual countries could reserve the right to unilateral action in response to a nuclear threat against itself—just as Britain now subordinates its nuclear submarines to NATO except in case of "supreme national emergency."

Further in the future, we hope it will be possible to eliminate nuclear weapons entirely. The alternative—accepting nuclear weapons as a permanent part of the military arsenals of certain nations—would in the long term fatally undermine the effort to control proliferation, since there is no universally acceptable prescription for dividing nations into nuclear-weapons haves and have nots.

The possibility of a nuclear-weapons-free world is just beginning to be taken seriously again. The resulting debate will be complex, challenging us to examine our deepest assumptions about international relations. The United States and Russia could take a major step by reducing their arsenals to 1,000 warheads without stretching too far the currently accepted standards on stability and verifiability. After they take such a step, all nuclear states will be better positioned to explore together how to proceed with further reductions.

Article Questions

1. Conceptually, what is meant by the term Doomsday machine?

2. Give two examples of how the doomsday machine is being dismantled. Explain each example.

3. What does the statement "Furthermore, statements by President Yeltsin and some Russian military leaders suggest that the historic concern about parity is far from politically dead" mean?

4. Do you feel that reducing the number of warheads to 1,000 is reasonable? Explain your answer.

Beyond the Gulf Crisis: An Energy Strategy for the '90s

Christopher Flavin

President Bush has demonstrated that the U.S. commitment to protect Persian Gulf oil is more than rhetorical. He has not yet done the same regarding our domestic energy policy, which continues to founder in a sea of rhetoric nearly devoid of clear goals or programs. While the United States has spent more then a decade preparing its troops to fight a desert war in the Persian Gulf, it has allowed its oil imports to rise so high that U.S. vulnerability to events in this politically unstable region has been greatly increased.

Deputy Secretary of Energy W. Henson Moore explained the administration's perspective in early 1990 when he wrote, "We anticipate a decade of relative stability" in world oil markets. He attempted to sum up the Bush energy policy but did not even mention the problem of rising U.S. oil imports. The Energy Department was apparently no better prepared than the rest of the administration, which was providing Saddam Hussein with high-tech weapons only weeks before his tanks overran Kuwait.

The United States and the Persian Gulf

Even without Saddam Hussein, the world oil situation has been deteriorating steadily in recent years. The Middle East's share of the world oil market is rising at more than one million barrels per day each year, the world is again as dependent on the Persian Gulf as it was in 1980. Indeed, since 1980, the Middle East's share of world oil reserves has risen from 59 percent to 68 percent. Meanwhile, production in the United States and the Soviet Union, the two largest producers, is falling. Contrary to Secretary Moore's conclusions, steep oil price hikes during the '90s are a virtual certainty, even without Saddam Hussein's assistance.

OPEC is not only back in the driver's seat, but is increasingly dominated by the major Persian Gulf producers, such as Saudi Arabia and Iraq. One-fifth of global reserves are now under Iraq's direct control, and over one-half are in the immediate area of the Persian Gulf. Before this crisis, the major Middle Eastern producers still had three million barrels per day worth of spare capacity, most of which is now being used to help weather the embargo of Iraq and Kuwait. But current trends would eliminate all that reserve by the mid-'90s, leaving almost no reserve margins in case of future political upheavals.

The United States bears considerable responsibility for the deterioration in the world oil picture. Throughout the '80s, the Reagan Administration sought to eliminate virtually every government program aimed at reducing oil dependence. It has now been over a decade since the Congress passed significant legislation to reduce U.S. oil consumption. The Bush Administration has eased back on the rhetoric, but is in most respects carrying on with a Reagan-like energy policy. The short-run response to the Persian Gulf crisis is similarly weak. Drivers are exhorted to pump up their tires, and local officials are encouraged to scrap environmental limits in order to save a few thousand barrels of oil.

President Bush has failed to project a vision of the country's energy future or to make the tough political choices that are needed. As a former oil company executive, he waxes enthusiastic about oil drilling in several of the country's valuable protected areas. But the oil in question is by all accounts minimal; pursuit of that oil is a feeble attempt to resurrect a policy that has failed on its own terms. This policy can be redirected when the Department of Energy delivers its National Energy Strategy to the President in December. Unfortunately, it is not yet even clear whether the administration has embraced the obvious goal of reducing U.S. oil imports. To carry through on that goal, the United States would need to develop a convincing way to improve the energy efficiency of the U.S. economy—particularly of the motor vehicles that now account for nearly two-thirds of U.S. oil consumption. Improved efficiency is far and away the quickest and most cost-effective means of reducing oil dependence. It would also boost the nation's economic competitiveness and strengthen its environmental health.

The U.S. Oil Outlook

From the mid-'70s until 1986, the U.S. energy situation improved considerably, under the dual influence of high oil prices and an array of policies designed to do everything from weatherizing buildings to commercializing alcohol fuels. As a result, the U.S. economy has grown by 50 percent since 1973, while energy use has increased by less than 7 percent. The U.S. economy is nearly 30 percent more energy-efficient than it was in 1973, which has made it possible to cut the national fuel bill by $150 billion annually. U.S. oil imports fell from a high of nearly nine million barrels per day in 1978 to just five million barrels per day in 1985.

During the past five years, U.S. oil consumption has risen rapidly, and import dependence has again grown to nearly nine million barrels per day. The American Petroleum Institute, the National Petroleum Council, and the U.S. Department of Energy have all released major studies that point with alarm to these trends and argue that U.S. economic health and national security will be threatened by the forces now at work.

The decline in domestic U.S. oil production is a major factor in this deterioration. As the world's pioneering oil producer, the United States has already heavily exploited its oil reserves and has a reserves-to-production ratio of just nine years, far lower than the 100-plus years available to most Persian Gulf producers. The heavy investments that went into U.S. oil exploration a decade ago delayed the decline in production that began in 1971.

However, even when prices were at their zenith, U.S. oil production in the lower forty-eight states was still 20 percent below its peak level. Today it is 35 percent below its peak. Meanwhile, oil from Alaska's North Slope, which temporarily compensated for declines elsewhere, peaked at about two million barrels per day in 1988 and has declined by over 12 percent since then.

Far from being a victim of world oil market fluctuations, the U.S. oil industry benefited from the OPEC-led price increases of the '70s. These high prices temporarily misled U.S. oil producers into thinking they could still compete with low-cost Middle Eastern oil. To the contrary, U.S. oil production will inevitably decline. Interior Department figures show that of the country's thirteen largest oil fields, seven are at least 80 percent depleted.

As finding oil in the United States has become more difficult, the amount of oil discovered per foot of exploratory well has fallen to less than half the rate that prevailed in the early '70s. The average U.S. oil well yields just fourteen barrels of oil, compared to 2,500 barrels in Saudi Arabia. As oil becomes more difficult to find and extract, average U.S. oil extraction costs have reached at least five times those in the Middle East. The U.S. industry can no longer compete at the world price. The 1.6 million barrel per day decline in U.S. oil production since 1985 is among the steepest ever recorded, but it is only the beginning of a downward trend. The Department of Energy's *Annual Energy Outlook* projects that crude oil production in the lower forty-eight states will fall from 6.12 million barrels per day in 1988 to 4.9 million barrels per day in 2000 at crude oil prices of $28 per barrel.

While domestic production was falling, consumption was up 10 percent between 1985 and 1989. By 1989, imports made up 42 percent of consumption. In three of the first seven months of 1990, the United States imported more oil than it produced. The cumulative decline in oil and natural gas liquids production in the continental United States and Alaska could increase U.S. dependence on oil imports to 75 percent by the year 2000.

In short, the United States no longer has an abundant, low-cost energy resource that can substitute for other economic weaknesses. Indeed, in the future the U.S. energy picture is likely to grow closer to that of Europe and Japan, which lack cheap domestic energy sources and yet have been able to develop economies that function well in a high energy cost environment. The United States uses around twice as much oil per unit of GNP and per person as do the European nations.

Oil Supply Options

Still, the inclination of the oil industry and the Bush Administration is to deal with the country's energy problems by pursuing the increasingly difficult goal of expanding the country's oil output. Given the declining U.S. oil resource base, this is an uphill battle. The agenda of the oil companies centers on opening up pristine areas in Alaska and off the coast of California for drilling. While these projects would undoubtedly boost oil company profits, they would hardly alter the country's dangerous level of oil dependence. The Arctic Refuge is an example. Damage to the ecology of the Refuge is virtually guaranteed. At the same time, the Interior Department's official figures show that the chances are against finding enough oil to be extracted. In the recent past, oil companies have estimated much higher success rates for Alaska and offshore oil projects, invested hundreds of millions of dollars in their development, and come up completely dry.

The Interior Department's 1987 report, *Arctic National Wildlife Refuge, Alaska, Coastal Plain Resource Assessment*, calls attention to the belief that, "the 1902 acre area is currently the unexplored area in the United States with the greatest potential to contain giant and supergiant fields"—a statement that reflects not the oil riches of the Refuge but the meager oil exploration prospects now remaining in the United States. The Interior Department's mid-range estimate of the Arctic Refuge resource is only 3.2 billion barrels. That is about as much oil as the United States consumes every six months, or far less than one percent of worldwide ultimately recoverable oil resources. This is an important figure because it is the overall world supply/demand balance that determines oil prices. Even when global supplies are tight, price will not be appreciably affected by the small amounts of Arctic National Wildlife Refuge oil.

The Department of the Interior also focuses at some length on the presumed economic benefits of 3.2 billion barrels of oil, estimated at $79.4 billion (undiscounted). This figure looks impressive, but the United States currently has an *annual* energy bill of over $400 billion; these revenues spread over a thirty-year period would be less than one percent of the annual national energy bill. Moreover, this oil would still have to be paid for by consumers; the benefits to the economy and job creation would be limited. If 3.2 billion barrels of oil are extracted from the Arctic Refuge over thirty years, as estimated by the Interior Department, then production will average 290,000 barrels per day. This would restore only a fraction of the oil production the United States is projected to lose by the turn of the century—the earliest that this new oil could be made available. Oil thought to be available in offshore California fields is even smaller in magnitude.

Since 1985, U.S. oil imports have risen by over three million barrels per day, or ten times the projected yield of Arctic Refuge oil. Further increases in U.S. oil imports are, as the Department of Energy points out, almost guaranteed in the years ahead. Trying to stem this tide with Arctic Refuge oil is like trying to stop a major fire with a teacup.

Even in the unlikely event that oil is extracted from the Arctic Refuge, this "success" would have an almost imperceptible impact on the U.S. energy situation. U.S. oil import dependence would at best be lowered by a few percentage points for a limited period of time, delaying by less than a year the major energy adjustments the United States must make. Indeed, there is something pathetic about the world's first major oil producer desperately sucking oil out of a national treasure to maintain wasteful practices that our industrial competitors are abandoning.

Even if continuing to expand fossil fuel consumption could achieve the economic goals claimed, it would undermine our environmental future. Fossil fuels are the main source of air pollution now choking rural areas and cities alike. In addition, rising levels of carbon dioxide and other gases are irrevocably altering the world's climate, and according to scientists could make the world warmer fifty years from now than at any time in human history.

The main cause of this phenomenon is fossil fuel consumption, which adds six billion tons of carbon to the atmosphere each year, more than one tone for each person on the planet. Although there is now evidence that global temperatures have already begun to rise, the implications of such a warming are fully understood. They could well include serious disruptions in agriculture and the flooding of densely populated coastal areas. In response, several governments have begun to develop energy policies aimed at reducing emissions of greenhouse gases. As the Netherlands, Denmark, and Japan all recognize, improved energy efficiency will have to play the largest role in reducing carbon dioxide output over the next two decades, and this can only occur with active government intervention. Fortuitously, these policies will also help to reduce oil consumption.

A Failed Energy Policy

From the mid-'70s until the mid-'80s, the United States was well on the road to easing its oil dependence. Oil imports had fallen to just one-third of consumption as energy efficiency improved throughout the economy. These gains were in part a result of higher energy prices, but they were also induced by a series of successful energy policies. While synthetic fuels projects collapsed and nuclear research programs led nowhere, other policies led to notable gains. These include energy price deregulation, energy conservation and renewable energy tax credits, minimum efficiency standards for cars and appliances, home weatherization programs, federal and state utility reforms, and federal funding of research and development on energy-efficient and renewable energy technologies.

The improved energy efficiency of the U.S. economy since 1973 has saved the equivalent of 5 billion barrels of oil in 1989, or 14.5 million barrels per day. This is fifty times the potential contribution from the Arctic Refuge, and studies indicate that energy efficiency's contribution could be doubled to the equivalent of more than 20 million barrels of oil per day by 2000. President Reagan entered office determined to eviscerate most of these programs, claiming that energy was a matter for the private sector, not for public policy. Initially, he sought to abolish the Department of Energy and then appointed a dentist to be his first Secretary of Energy. Even the solar collectors atop the White House were torn down. Congress saved the Department and resisted many of his policies, but President Reagan eventually got most of what he wanted. By the late '80s, most of the tax credits for energy conservation and renewable energy sources had expired. And federal budgets for key areas of energy research and development had been cut by 80 percent.

The $194 million being spent on all energy efficiency research and development in 1990 is equivalent to about four days' worth of spending on the U.S. military forces now in the Persian Gulf. Nearly 70 percent of the Department of Energy's budget goes to nuclear weapons production and cleanup. The remaining federal energy budget continues to be dominated by spending on fossil fuels and a host of nuclear technologies that have virtually no chance of making a contribution during the next few decades.

The Reagan Administration and Congress also permitted automobile fuel economy standards to lapse at the level achieved in 1986. For several years, the administration even provided the auto industry with exemptions to the standards already in place. As a consequence, new cars rolling off Detroit's assembly lines in 1989 were actually less efficient than those of the previous year. This is a costly reversal. Automobiles are at the root of U.S. oil dependence. Some 43 percent of the country's oil is now used in automobiles. Another 20 percent is used in other forms of transportation such as air travel and trucking. If average fuel economy were just seven miles per gallon higher, we would be importing two million fewer barrels of oil each day, and be in a much better position to withstand the effects of the embargo in Iraq.

Reaching Oil Dependence

While President Bush used the words "energy conservation" as U.S. troops were on their way to the Persian Gulf, in a year and a half in office he has not proposed any significant policies to reduce dependence on imported oil. The steady rise in U.S. oil imports during the Reagan Administration has continued during the Bush presidency.

Christopher Flavin

Means are available to reverse this trend. We can make our cars, buildings, and industries far more fuel-efficient than they are today. And we can gradually develop clean renewable fuels to run our vehicles. The record of the recent past demonstrates the enormous potential of energy efficiency. Keeping up with our Japanese and European competitors requires continued efforts to improve efficiency and cut national energy bills.

The first step in this direction would be for the United States to develop a "least cost energy plan" that would fairly weigh all new sources of energy supply and conservation, and consider various energy policies on the basis of their ability to achieve national goals. Recent experiences and numerous analytical studies show that improved energy efficiency is the fastest and least expensive means of reducing dependence on foreign oil. Simply raising new car fuel economy from the current average of 27 miles per gallon to 40 miles per gallon would reduce U.S. oil consumption by 2.8 million barrels per day by the year 2005. This is nearly ten times the rate of extraction that the Department of Interior thinks is possible from the Arctic National Wildlife Refuge.

The automotive technologies to accomplish these goals are at hand. Prototype vehicles that run over 70 miles per gallon have been developed, though they have not yet reached the marketplace. These include improved engines, more efficient transmissions, and greater use of lightweight synthetic materials. The projected additional cost for a 40-mile-per-gallon car is $500, according to Marc Ledbetter of the American Council for an Energy-Efficient Economy. This sum would be more than offset by gasoline savings of over $2,000 during the life of a typical car. Overall, such technologies can save gasoline at a cost of about 43 cents per gallon or one-third the current retail price.

Strong programs are also needed to continue the energy efficient revolution that began to sweep U.S. buildings in the '70s and '80s. These programs can greatly reduce the use of natural gas, freeing up gas to replace oil in other sectors. However, in recent years, the federal government has provided little support for those who are considering reducing their household or office energy consumption. This year the Bush Administration recommended an 85 percent cut in federal grants in this area. Energy efficiency improvements that have occurred so far only scratch at the potential to develop new energy-efficient technologies. Refrigerators, air conditioners, lights, and buildings can all be powered at a fraction of their current energy requirements.

The past decade's efficiency improvements were driven largely by high energy prices which have since fallen. Moreover, the government has yet to address seriously the market imperfections that cause underinvestment in energy efficiency. Without energy policy reforms, the efficiency potential will not be realized, and oil imports will remain high. One strategy that has been effectively employed in New England is to encourage utilities to invest hundreds of millions of dollars in improved energy efficiency by rewarding them with high rates of return on those investments.

Beyond Oil

Ultimately, freeing the world of oil dependence will mean harnessing the world's abundant reserves of renewable energy resources such as solar, wind, and biomass energy. None of these offers an immediate large-scale alternative to liquid petroleum, but over the coming decades they can begin to form the basis of a non-fossil-fuel transportation system.

While steady progress has occurred in many of the technologies to harness these resources, it has been slowed by low oil prices and declining federal budgets. The U.S.

government spends a pittance on all of these technologies combined—$138 million annually or one-fifth the estimated cost of a B-2 bomber. Nonetheless, a host of renewable energy technologies have made it to the commercial market, producing power from wind turbines, solar power plants, and geothermal facilities at competitive prices. California, which is the hotbed of this activity, has 17,000 wind turbines in place and gets over 40 percent of its electricity from renewable energy sources. Renewable energy has greatly reduced California's consumption of oil and natural gas. These results stem not just from California's abundant resources but from a concerted state effort to encourage renewable energy development.

Renewable energy technologies deserve at least as much support as they received a decade ago—$1 billion annually in 1990 dollars. With such a commitment, private investment would itself increase rapidly, and renewable energy sources would begin to make a significant additional contribution to U.S. energy supplies before the '90s were out.

Using renewable energy for transportation will require substantial investments in delivery, storage, and combustion systems. Electric vehicles, for example, can run on electricity coming from any source. General Motors, Fiat, and other companies already have such vehicles under development. Even more promising is the prospect of nonpolluting hydrogen cars. Hydrogen can be produced directly from water, using solar or other renewable energy sources. The hydrogen can then be moved around the country by pipeline and stored in large tanks.

It will take time to develop a hydrogen-based transportation system, but Germany already has an integrated national program to develop all aspects of a hydrogen-powered transport system—to be centered around massive solar installations in southern Europe and northern Africa. Involved in the program are research institutes, pipeline companies, engineering firms, and the automobile industry. Mercedes Benz and BMW already have prototype hydrogen-powered cars.

Towards a National Energy Strategy

The concerted German effort highlights a major weakness of U.S. energy policy. It has no clear goals, resources are scattered over miscellaneous technologies, and funding is guided by today's shortsighted industrial interests rather than by a strategic view of the country's energy future. If we continue in this direction, we will not only sacrifice our national security and environment, but the economy as well. The Germans and Japanese, for example, are now outspending us on key solar technologies that are likely to become major competitive industries in the future.

The coming months will be a window of opportunity for U.S. energy policymaking, which is often driven by crisis. Not only is there the chance to consider important new legislation, but President Bush is scheduled to unveil a National Energy Strategy that has been underway for more than a year. With the dangerous implications of our lack of an energy policy now clearly demonstrated, the National Strategy provides an opportunity to implement a plan to reduce oil dependence and improve energy efficiency. Steps to improve automobile fuel economy, to boost energy efficiency research and development budgets, and to reinstate programs encouraging home weatherization, are among the policy steps that would help curb our dependence on the Persian Gulf.

Unfortunately, Secretary of Energy James Watkins now appears to be retreating from the notion he voiced a year ago of a strong, comprehensive energy strategy. Rather, the Secretary has spoken recently of lists of options to be delivered to the President in December, at which point they may well be eviscerated by White House political advisors and lobbyists form the energy and auto industries. Meanwhile, just this September, the Bush Administration successfully defeated the most effective short-run policy—legislation before the U.S. Senate that would have raised U.S. new car fuel economy to 40 miles per gallon by the year 2000.

The United States can no longer afford to lurch from one oil crisis to another. The stakes will only grow as the Middle East's share of the world oil market continues to increase in the years ahead. The technology is available to end this explosive cycle. With American lives now on the line and with tens of billions of dollars likely to be spent in the Gulf in the next year alone, it is high time we got serious about "energy security."

Article Questions

1. Why was the Gulf war fought?

   a. To liberate Kuwait

   b. To maintain cheaper supply of oil

   c. President Bush wanted to Punish President Saddam Hussain

   d. All of above

   Explain your answer with facts and opinions.

2. What energy policies were formulated by Reagan and Bush administrations to reduce U.S dependence on foreign oil?

3. During the 1980's, did Congress pass any legislation to encourage oil consumption and oil dependence? Explain your answer.

4. Compare the U.S oil strategies for the following eras:

   a. 1960's

   b. 1970's

   c. 1980's

   d. 1990's

5. How can the United States avoid future oil crisis and potential oil wars? List and explain three ways.

Discussion Questions

1. Do you think that nuclear energy is a clean source of energy? Support your response with facts.

2. What might be the consequences of a major accident at a nuclear power plant?

3. Considering the potential risks involved with nuclear technology, and the past experiences at Three Mile Island and Chernobyl, the worldwide development of new nuclear plants should be stopped. Do you agree? Explain your answer.

4. A number of developing countries are constructing nuclear power plants for their growing energy needs. Due to scarce resources for the majority of the developing countries, the nuclear energy appears to be the best viable solution to their exponential increase in the demand for energy. The developed countries are trying to prevent the transfer of nuclear technology to Third World countries. Should Third World nations be denied the access to nuclear technology? Support your answer. What alternate sources would you recommend?

CHAPTER THREE
ECOLOGY

The Grim Payback Of Greed

By Alan Durning

      Early in the age of affluence that followed World War II, an American retailing analyst named Victor Lebow proclaimed that an enormously productive economy "demands that we make consumption our way of life... We need things consumed, burned up, worn out, replaced and discarded at an ever increasing rate.

      Americans have responded to Mr. Lebow's call, and much of the world has followed. The average person today is four-and-a-half times richer than were his great-grandparents at the turn of the century. That new global wealth is not evenly spread among the Earth's people, however. One billion live in unprecedented luxury; one billion live in destitution.

      Overconsumption by the world's fortunate is an environmental problem unmatched in severity by anything but perhaps population growth. Their surging exploitation of resources threatens to exhaust or inalterably disfigure forests, soils, water, air and climate.

      Of course the opposite of overcompensation—poverty—is no solution either to environmental or human problems. Dispossessed peasants slash-and-burn their way into the rain forests of Latin America, and hungry nomads turn their herds out onto fragile African rangeland, reducing it to desert.

If environmental destruction results when people have either too little or too much, we are left to wonder how much is enough. What level of consumption can the Earth support? When does having more cease to add appreciably to human satisfaction?

The consuming society: Skyrocketing consumption is the hallmark of our era. The trend is visible in statistics for almost any per capita indicator. Worldwide, since mid-century the intake of copper, energy, meat, steel and wood has approximately doubled; car ownership and cement consumption have quadrupled; plastic use has quintupled; aluminum consumption has grown sevenfold; and air travel has multiplied 32 times.

Moneyed regions account for the largest waves of consumption since 1950. In the United States, the world's premier consuming society, on average people today own twice as many cars, drive two-and-a-half times as far, use 21 times as much plastic and travel 25 times as far by air as did their parents in 1950. Air conditioning has spread from 15 percent of households in 1960 to 64 percent in 1987, and color televisions from 1 to 93 percent. Microwave ovens and video cassette recorders found their way into almost two-thirds of American homes during the eighties alone.

The eighties were a period of marked extravagance in the United States; not since the Roaring Twenties had conspicuous consumption been so lauded. Between 1978 and 1987, sales of Jaguar automobiles increased eightfold, and the average age of first-time fur-coat buyers fell from 50 to 26. The select club of American millionaires more than doubled its membership from 600,000 to 1.5 million over the decade, while the number of American billionaires reached 58 by 1990.

Japan and Western Europe have displayed parallel trends. Per person, the Japanese of today consume more than four times as much aluminum, almost five times as much energy and 25 times as much steel as people in Japan did in 1950. They also own four times as many cars and eat nearly twice as much meat. In 1972 one million Japanese traveled abroad; in 1990, the number was expected to top ten million. As in the United States, the eighties were a particularly consumerist decade in Japan, with sales of BMW automobiles rising tenfold.

Like the Japanese, West European's consumption levels are only one notch below Americans'. Taken together, France, West Germany and the United Kingdom almost doubled their per capita use of steel, more than doubled their intake of cement and aluminum and tripled their paper consumption since mid-century. Just in the first half of the eighties, per capita consumption of frozen prepared meals—with their excessive packaging—rose more than 30 percent in every West European country except Finland; in Switzerland, the jump was 180 percent.

The cost of wealth: Long before all the world's people could achieve the American dream, however, the planet would be laid waste. Those in the wealthiest fifth of humanity are responsible for the lion's share of the damage humans have caused to common global resources. They have built more than 99 percent of the world's nuclear warheads. Their appetite for wood is a driving force behind destruction of the tropical rain forest and the resulting extinction of countless species. Over the past century, their economies have pumped out two-thirds of the greenhouse gases that threaten the Earth's climate, and each year their energy use releases perhaps three-fourths of the sulfur and nitrogen oxides that cause acid rain. Their industries generate most of the world's hazardous chemical wastes, and their air conditioners, aerosol sprays and factories release almost 90 percent of the chlorofluorocarbons that destroy the Earth's protective ozone layer. Clearly, even 1 billion profligate consumers are too much for the Earth.

Beyond the environmental costs of acquisitiveness, some perplexing findings of social scientists throw doubt on the wisdom of high consumption as a personal and national goal: Rich societies have had little success in turning consumption into fulfillment. A landmark study in 1974, for instance, revealed that Nigerians, Filipinos, Panamanians, Yugoslavians, Japanese, Israelis and West Germans all ranked themselves near the middle of a happiness scale. Confounding any attempt to correlate affluence and happiness, poor Cubans and rich Americans were both found to be considerably happier than the norm, and citizens of India and the Dominican Republic, less so. As Oxford psychologist Michael Argyle writes, "There is very little difference in the levels of reported happiness found in rich and very poor countries."

As measured in constant dollars, the world's people have consumed as many goods and services since 1950 as all previous generations put together. Since 1940, Americans alone have used up as large a share of the Earth's mineral resources as did everyone before them combined. If the effectiveness of that consumption in providing personal fulfillment is questionable, perhaps environmental concerns can help us redefine our goals.

In search of sufficiency: Some guidance on what the Earth can sustain emerges from an examination of current consumption patterns around the world. For three of the most ecologically important types of consumption—transportation, diet and use of raw materials—the world's people are distributed unevenly over a vast range. Those at the bottom fall below the "too little" line, while those at the top, in what could be called the cars-meat-and-disposable class, consume too much.

About 1 billion people do most of their traveling, aside from the occasional donkey or bus ride, on foot, many of them never going more than 100 kilometers from their birthplaces. Unable to get to jobs easily, attend school or bring their complaints before government offices, they are severely hindered by the lack of transportation options.

The massive middle class of the world, numbering some 3 billion, travels by bus and bicycle. Kilometer for kilometer, bikes are cheaper than any other vehicles, costing less that $100 new in most of the Third World and requiring no fuel.

The world's automobile class is relatively small: Only 8 percent of humans, about 400 million people, own cars. Their cars are directly responsible for an estimated 13 percent of carbon dioxide emissions from fossil fuels worldwide, along with air pollution, acid rain and a quarter-million traffic fatalities a year.

The global food consumption ladder has three rungs, as well. At the bottom, the world's 630 million poorest people are unable to provide themselves with a healthful diet, according to World Bank estimates.

On the next rung, the 3.4 billion grain-eaters of the world's middle class get enough calories and plenty of plant-based protein, giving them the most-healthful basic diet of the world's people. They typically receive less than 20 percent of their calories from fat, a level low enough to protect them from the consequences of excessive dietary fat.

The top of the ladder is populated by the meat-eaters, those who obtain close to 40 percent of their calories from fat. These 1.25 billion people eat three times as much fat per person as the remaining 4 billion, mostly because they eat so much red meat. The meat class pays the price of its diet in high death rates from the so-called diseases of affluence—heart disease, stroke and certain types of cancer.

The Earth also pays for the high-fat diet. Indirectly, the meat-eating quarter of humanity consumes nearly 40 percent of the world's grain—grain that fattens the livestock they eat. Meat production is behind a substantial share of the environmental strains induced by the present global agricultural system, from soil erosion to overpumping of underground water.

In raw material consumption, the same pattern emerges. About 1 billion rural people subsist on biomass collected from the immediate environment. Most of what they use each day—about a half-kilogram of grain, 1 kilogram of fuelwood, and fodder for their animals—could be self-replenishing renewable resources. Unfortunately, because these people are often pushed by landlessness and population growth into fragile unproductive ecosystems, their minimal needs are not always met.

These materially destitute billion are part of a larger group that lacks many of the benefits provided by modest use of nonrenewable resources—particularly durable things like radios, refrigerators, water pipes, high-quality tools, and carts with lightweight wheels and ball bearings. More than 2 billion people live in countries where per capita consumption of steel, the most basic modern material, falls below 50 kilograms a year. In those same countries, per capita energy use—a fairly good indirect indicator of overall use of materials—is lower than 20 gigajoules per year (compared to 280 gigajoules in the United States).

Roughly 1.5 billion people live in the middle class of materials' use. Providing each of them with durable goods every year uses between 50 and 150 kilograms of steel and 20-50 gigajoules of energy.

At the top of the heap is the throwaway class, which uses raw materials extravagantly. A typical resident of the industrialized fourth of the world uses 15 times as much paper, 10 times as much steel and 12 times as much fuel as a Third World resident. The extreme case is the United States, where the average person consumes most of his own weight in basic materials each day—18 kilograms of petroleum and coal, 13 kilograms of other minerals, 12 kilograms of farm products and 9 kilograms of forest products, or about 115 pounds total.

In the throwaway economy, packaging becomes an end in itself, disposables proliferate and durability suffers. Four percent of consumer expenditures on goods in the United States goes for packaging—$225 a year. Likewise, the Japanese use 30 million disposable single-roll cameras each year, and the British dump 2.5 billion diapers. Americans toss away 180 million razors annually, enough paper and plastic plates and cups to feed the world a picnic six times a year and enough aluminum cans to make 6,000 DC-10 airplanes.

In transportation, diet and use of raw materials as consumption rises on the economic scale. so does waste—both of resources and of health. Yet despite arguments in favor of modest consumption, few people who can afford high consumption levels opt to live simply. What prompts us, then, to consume so much?

The cultivation of needs: "The avarice of mankind is insatiable," wrote Aristotle 23 centuries ago, describing the way that as each of our desires is satisfied, a new one seems to appear in its place. That observation, on which all of economic theory is based, provides the most obvious answer to the question of why people never seem satisfied with what they have. If our wants are insatiable, there is simply no such thing as enough.

Much confirms this view of human nature. The Roman philosopher Lucretius wrote a century before Christ: "We have lost our taste for acorns. So [too] we have abandoned those couches littered with herbage and heaped with leaves. So the wearing of wild beasts' skins has gone out of fashion.... Skins yesterday, purple and gold today—such are the baubles that embitter human life with resentment."

Nearly 2,000 years later, Russian novelist Leo Tolstoy echoed Lucretius: "Seek among men. from beggar to millionaire, on who is contented with his lot, and you will not find one such in a thousand.... Today we must buy an overcoat and galoshes, tomorrow, a watch and a chain: the next day we must install ourselves in an apartment with a sofa and a bronze lamp; then we must have carpets and velvet gowns: then a house, horses and carriages, paintings and decorations."

What distinguishes modern consuming habits from those of interest to Lucretius and Tolstoy, some would say, is simply that we are much richer than our ancestors and consequently have more ruinous effects on nature. There is no doubt a great deal of truth in that view, but there is also reason to believe that certain forces in the modern world encourage people to act on their consumption desires as rarely before.

The search for social status in massive and anonymous societies, omnipresent advertising messages, a shopping culture that edges out nonconsuming alternatives, government biases favoring consumption and the spread of the commercial market into most aspects of private life—all these things nurture the acquisitive desires that everyone has. Can we, as individuals and as citizens, act to confront these forces?

A culture of permanence: When Moses came down from Mount Sinai, he could count the rules of ethical behavior on the fingers of his two hands. In the complex global economy of the late twentieth century, in which the simple act of turning on a light sends greenhouse gases up into the atmosphere, the rules for ecologically sustainable living run into the hundreds.

The basic value of a sustainable society, though, the ecological equivalent of the Golden Rule, is simple: Each generation should meet its needs without jeopardizing the prospects of future generations to meet their own needs.

What is lacking is the thorough practical knowledge—at each level of society—of what living by that principle means. For individuals, the decision to live a life of sufficiency—to find their own answer to the question "How much is enough?"—is to begin a highly personal process. The goal is to put consumption in its proper place among the many sources of fulfillment and to find ways of living within the means of the Earth. One great inspiration in this quest is the body of human wisdom passed down over the ages.

Materialism was denounced by all the sages, from Buddha to Muhammad. These religious founders, observed historian Arnold Toynbee, "all said with one voice that if we made material wealth our paramount aim, this would lead to disaster." The Christian Bible echoes most of human wisdom when it asks, "What shall it profit a man if he shall gain the whole world and lose his soul?"

For those people experimenting with voluntary simplicity, the goal is not ascetic self-denial. What they are after is personal fulfillment: they just do not think consuming more is likely to provide it.

Still, shifting emphasis from material to nonmaterial satisfaction is hardly easy: It means trying both to curb personal appetites and to resist the tide of external forces encouraging consumption.

Many people find simpler living offers rewards all its own. They say life can become more deliberate as well as spontaneous, and even gain an unadorned elegance. Others describe the way simpler technologies add unexpected qualities to life.

Realistically, however, voluntary simplicity is unlikely to gain ground rapidly against the onslaught of consumerist values. The call for a simpler life has been perennial through the history of North America, from the Puritans of Massachusetts Bay to the back-to-the-landers of the 1970s. None of these movements ever gained more than a slim minority of adherents.

It would be naive to believe that entire populations will suddenly experience a moral awakening, renouncing greed, envy and avarice. What can be hoped for is a gradual weakening of the consumerist ethos of affluent societies. The challenge before humanity is to bring environmental matters under cultural controls. and the goal of creating a sustainable culture—a culture of permanence—is a task that will occupy several generations.

Alan Durning

The ultimate fulfillment: In many ways, we might be happier with less. Maybe Henry David Thoreau had it right when he scribbled in his notebook beside Walden Pond. "A man is rich in proportion to the things he can afford to let alone."

For the luckiest among us, a human lifetime on Earth encompasses perhaps a hundred trips around the Sun. The sense of fulfillment received on that journey—regardless of a person's religious faith—has to do with the timeless virtues of discipline, hope, allegiance to principle and character. Consumption itself has little part in the playful camaraderie that inspires the young, the bonds of love and friendship that nourish adults, the golden memories that sustain the elderly. The very things that make life worth living, that give depth and bounty to human existence, are infinitely sustainable.

Article Questions

1. How much richer are Americans than at the turn of the century?

2. What is another major cause (other than consumption) of severe environmental problems?

3. What two groups are most destructive to the environment? Give two examples from each of the groups.

4. Name three statistics of the industrialized countries' (1/5 world population) destruction of global resources.

5. Give some evidence that refutes the idea of consumerism as an avenue for happiness.

6. Which world class of people do the least damage to the environment? Give three examples.

7. Why do the industrialized nations keep accelerating their consumerism?

8. What can be done to curb this exponential consumerism?

9. Explain briefly the major points in the "Payback of Greed." What did you learn from this article?

10. Define the consuming society. Do you think that this will continue to be a problem in the next few decades? Why? Why not?

11. How has wealth effected ecological issues? Does materialism create ecological concerns? How?

12. What is the ultimate fulfillment?

13. How can the payback of greed be stopped?

Can Superfund Get on Track?

Karen Schmidt

Fourteen years ago, the future of 140 miles of Montana's Clark Fork River looked as bleak as any science fiction writer could have imagined. Forming the largest polluted area in the nation, some 50,000 acres of the river corridor were littered with arsenic, copper, zinc, cadmium and lead. Heavy rains swept these toxic metals into the river and periodically killed massive numbers of fish. Toxic dust denuded a forest where otters, deer, elk and osprey once lived, leaving it a barren moonscape. The cause? More than a century of extensive and poorly regulated mining and smelting activity.

Then came Superfund, formally known as the federal Comprehensive Environmental Response, Compensation and Liability Act (CERCLA)—an ambitious plan to finance the cleanup of the nation's most hazardous abandoned dumps. Now, the Clark Fork region comprises four separate Superfund sites. Companies testing waste-treatment strategies have sprouted around Butte, Montana, and more than $100 million worth of cleanup is underway. Tailings are being scooped from stream banks in Butte, tainted soil is being removed from the town of Anaconda, and a clean new drinking-water system is operating in Milltown.

But for all that, surprisingly little has changed. The hazardous material still abounds, and people and wildlife are still suffering from the pollution. As residents who live near Clark Fork can attest, cleaning up is hard to do. Here, on a grand scale, can be found the pitfalls of Superfund—variations of themes playing at most of the country's Superfund sites, including a history of lawsuits upon lawsuits, cases of poor management and confusion about how best to proceed. As for finances, most of the millions spent in the Clark Fork area, as at other sites, have gone until recently to solving legal disputes and conducting preliminary studies, while the pollution persists.

Locations of Superfund Sites

Suburban:
39.3 percent

Urban:
18.4 percent

Rural:
42 percent

This year, as Superfund makes its way through reauthorization in Congress, just about everyone involved is voicing dissatisfaction—government officials, industry representatives and environmental organizations alike. Even President Clinton has said flatly, "Superfund has been a disaster."

It was not supposed to be this way. Recalls Congressman Al Swift (Democrat, Washington), chairman of the subcommittee on Transportation and Hazardous Materials, "Superfund was passed in 1980 to address what many believed to be a serious, but relatively limited, problem. The EPA was instructed to find the worst hazardous sites, known as the National Priority List (NPL). Most believed that cleaning up a site was relatively inexpensive and involved removing containers or scraping a few inches of soil off the ground."

Now, legislators envision the Superfund program as lasting for decades. So far, 221 long-term cleanups have been completed and 55 have been removed from the list. But the National Priority List now names more than 1,192 sites and is expected to continue expanding. To clean up the sites presently on the list will cost more than $28 billion, EPA estimates.

This year, Congress will try to identify Superfund's successes, diagnose its ills and come up with a corrective prescription: amendments to the law, changes in EPA administration or the much more unlikely creation of a new kind of public works program.

At the heart of the legislation is the protection of both human health and natural resources. At Superfund sites, EPA evaluates public health threats. One example is the exposure of Milltown residents to metals in their drinking water. However, the law assigns the duty of defending natural resources to other federal agencies, states and Native

American groups. For example, the state of Montana is assessing how toxic pollution around Clark Fork has harmed wildlife and water resources. The state is suing ARCO, the multinational giant responsible for the site's cleanup, and hopes to one day coordinate a plan for revitalizing the ecosystem.

Congress must also decide how much money to authorize EPA for funding enforcement of the law. The agency orders companies that contributed to the pollution to pay for a site's restoration. When EPA can find no responsible party, it draws money out of the "Superfund," a trust fund of taxes collected for the most part from the chemical and petroleum industries.

The question of the law's fairness is also generating considerable debate. Industry says it forces big companies to pay too much—in the form of taxes, defensive litigation and clean-up costs. "We're not fighting the polluter-pays concept," says Morton Mullins, Vice President of Regulatory Affairs for the Chemical Manufacturers Association (CMA). "But we're against the polluter paying and paying and paying."

CMA, the American Insurance Association (AIA) and other industry groups are urging Congress to convert Superfund to a public works program funded by taxpayers—or, at the very least, to overhaul the rules for determining who pays. Industries blame the current rules for gumming up the works with too many lawsuits (which they themselves often initiate). As the AIA explains in its Superfund briefing book, companies "challenge EPA clean-up decisions

The Nation's Mounting Mess

As of September 30, 1993, 37,537 potential-hazardous-waste sites had been identified for EPA's review under the Superfund program.

Of those, 26,913 had been evaluated (selected for Superfund action, deferred to other programs or designated as not requiring action) and 10,624 sites were still waiting for evaluation.

EPA expects to add 1,200 sites to its review list every year.

As of December 1993, 1,192 sites were on the Superfund National Priorities List (NPL) of the nation's worst hazardous dumps.

Of those sites, 221 were "construction complete," meaning all pumps and other clean-up devices were in place.

Fifty-five sites have been cleaned up and deleted from the NPL list since 1980.

So far, Superfund cleanups have taken an average of 11 years from initial site studies to reach "construction complete" status.

About 17 percent of Superfund sites are municipal landfills.

More than 4,800 existing sites may be eligible for Superfund listing.

throughout the investigation and remediation process in order to protect themselves."

Environmentalists believe the law's mandate to collect funds whenever possible from polluters, called "joint and several liability," is the best solution—and the least likely to further burden taxpayers. But that still leaves the way EPA administers the program. "This program has become bureaucratized to the nth degree," says Erik Olsen of the Natural Resources Defense Council.

Despite the criticism and the dire statistics, so far the nation has no better solutions for cleaning toxic dumps. Fortunately, Superfund's very existence has lit a fire under companies to reduce waste. From 1987 to 1991, the chemical industry cut releases of toxic chemicals to the environment by 35 percent, largely in response to Superfund. Says CMA's Mullins, "The threat of liability strengthens the commitment to pollution prevention."

Referring to the tragic toxic dump in a residential area that first provided the impetus for Superfund, EPA Administrator Carol Browner has credited the program with saving "thousands of communities all over the United States from becoming Love Canals." Under Superfund, EPA has responded to 3,300 emergencies that involved safely removing chemical dangers such as leaky drums of hazardous waste and radioactive medical materials improperly stored in urban warehouses.

Until the act passed in 1980, the poisoned Montana region and hundreds of other sites had little or no hope of reclamation. In a sense, the first Superfund cleanups have been pioneer projects. Site managers at Clark Fork had to develop their own safety standards for lead in soil, for example, because no general federal guidelines were in place. Says Robert Fox, EPA's Clark Fork Superfund coordinator, "We've had to break new ground in many areas."

Indeed, the future of Superfund may well depend on whether the program can learn from the lessons of these pioneer sites. Take the case of New Bedford, Massachusetts. From the mid-1940s to 1978, factories that manufactured electrical capacitors spewed tons of wastes laden with polychlorinated biphenyls, or PCBs, into the town's picturesque harbor. The cancer-causing chemical has settled in sediments and entered the food chain. As a result, fiddler crabs have declined in number and soft shell clams are not reproducing well. One study found that the PCB levels were highly toxic to some members of all major groups of organisms. In 1979, the Massachusetts Department of Public Health banned fishing and seafood harvests from the harbor, but that hasn't stopped the tides from transporting PCBs ever farther into the ecosystem.

Today, New Bedford residents are inhaling small, but not insignificant amounts of PCBs, says Gayle Garman, EPA's sixth and current project manager for the site. The chemical evaporates from the harbor and is carried by the ocean breeze. EPA posted danger signs a decade ago near the most heavily contaminated area, a 5-acre zone called the "hot spot," which contains an estimated 120 tons of PCBs. But people still catch fish there and teenagers drink Cokes on the banks.

After New Bedford harbor joined the Superfund list in 1982, EPA took eight years and $25 million to identify a relatively safe way to remove the "hot spot" sediment without dispersing more PCBs. In 1990, the agency made its recommendation: Carefully dredge the sediment, pump it directly onshore and incinerate it in New Bedford.

As engineers prepare to run a trial burn this spring, they face bitter local resistance to the plan. Though the goal is a permanent reduction in risk, during the four-month burn there will be a slight increase in risk of exposure to emissions of toxics such as dioxin. "This is a Catch-22 situation," laments Jackie Duckworth, a young mother who lives near the harbor. "We can't let the PCBs sit there, but it's dangerous to take them out." Angry local citizens and members of Congress have demanded that an allegedly safer (but untested) technology for burning hazardous waste, called EcoLogic, be tried. According to EPA, the risks associated with the burn are very small, and the EcoLogic option would further delay the cleanup by several years.

As for the harbor's wildlife, the National Marine Fisheries Service (NMFS) emerged victorious from one of the first resource damage cases ever filed. The landmark case, which took 10 tortuous years, should now pave the way for other resource damage claims, says Thomas Bigford, chief of NMFS's Habitat and Resource Protection Division in Gloucester, Mass. To restore New Bedford's wetlands and marine environment, however, could take another 13 to 20 years, he estimates.

In a very different setting, downtown Pensacola, Florida, is marred by two Superfund sites and a third one waiting to join the list. At that last site, the Escambia Treating Company, the low-income minority community has been critical of the emergency action taken there. A local group called Citizens Against Toxic Exposure complains that the opinions of residents have not been respected by federal officials. President Margaret Williams quips, "When EPA talked to us, they acted like they were doing us a favor by cleaning up a site." Tillman McAdams, EPA North Florida site assessment manager, points out that the agency has removed the immediate threat to the town's drinking water. "We're working as hard as we can to address the problem," he says. "That's our job."

The Human Factor

Human exposure to releases from hazardous-waste sites has been documented at about 40 percent of Superfund sites; exposure could occur at another 40 percent.

About 2 percent of Superfund sites present an imminent and urgent public-health hazard.

The most common pathway by which people are exposed to contaminants: groundwater.

Numbers of self-reported community-health problems at 1,607 hazardous waste sites:
Cancer: 1,335
Reproductive defects/disorders: 428
Lung and respiratory disease: 173
Neurotoxic disorders: 155
Liver dysfunction: 141
Kidney dysfunction: 96

An estimated 72 million Americans reside within 4 miles of a Superfund NPL site—and about 4.4 million people live within 1 mile of a Superfund site.

Every year, this country produces 275 million tons of hazardous waste, which adds up to 1,900 pounds per year per person.

The top ten Superfund hazardous substances: lead, arsenic, mercury, vinyl chloride, benzene, cadmium, polychlorinated biphenyls, chloroform, benzo(a)pyrene, trichloroethylene.

Ten Worst Toxic Dumps

The following list represents a sort of triage: EPA scores possible hazardous sites according to their potential impact on human health and the environment. Using those scores, the agency determines which sites are eligible for the Superfund program. This list of the top-ten sites with the highest scores, compiled from the most recent data available, dates from October 1992. Once on the National Priorities List, a site goes through far more extensive and costly studies that might find a hazardous spot much more or less dangerous than when it was initially assessed.

Site	What Made The Waste	Main Contaminants
Big River Tailings Desloge, Missouri	Mining	Lead, cadmium, zinc
Lipari Landfill Pitman, New Jersey	Municipal wastes	Household and industrial chemical wastes
McCormick & Baxter Creosoting Co. Stockton, California	Treatment of utility poles and railroad ties with creosote	PCBs, arsenic, chromium, copper
Tybouts Corner Landfill New Castle Co., Delaware	Municipal and industrial wastes	Various inorganic and organic chemicals
Helen Kramer Landfill Mantua Township, New Jersey	Municipal, industrial and hospital wastes	Insecticides, heavy metals
Industri-Plex Woburn, Massachusetts	Manufacture of chemicals such as arsenic and insecticides for textile industry	Industrial byproducts and wastes
Price Landfill Pleasantville, New Jersey	Industrial chemical waste disposal	Heavy metals
Pearl Harbor Naval Complex Pearl Harbor, Hawaii	Naval military base	Pesticides, PCBs, solvents, waste oil
Pollution Abatement Services Oswego, New York	Chemical waste incineration facility	Heavy metals, volatile organic compounds (VOCs), PCBs, mixed hydrocarbons, waste oil
Hanford Nuclear Reservation 200 and 300 Areas Benton Co., Washington	Plutonium production for nuclear weapons	Radioactive and hazardous wastes, PCBs, VOCs

Across town, several thousand people live within a mile of one of the two listed Superfund sites, American Creosote Works, where a plant once treated telephone poles with wood preservatives. After years of dumping creosote, which contains cancer-causing hydrocarbons, and a compound called pentachlorophenol (PCP), which degrades to toxic dioxin, the company declared bankruptcy. The money for cleanup now comes from the federal Superfund pot and the state of Florida.

In 1983, EPA took emergency action there to reduce the community's potential exposure to the chemicals. Workers drained contaminated lagoons, dried the toxic sludge and then capped it with a layer of impermeable clay. Now, ten years and five project managers later, the "temporarily" capped piles still sit on a lot bigger than a city block. According to Mark Fite, EPA's project manager for the site, cleanup has been slow because federal and state agencies have had to reach agreement every step of the way. "It's not technical problems that are slowing things down here," he says. So far, a plan has been approved for treating the site's groundwater contamination. Plans are still on the drawing board for treating the 100,000 cubic yards of toxic sludge and soil.

States with the Most Superfund Sites	
New Jersey	109
Pennsylvania	99
California	95
New York	85
Michigan	76
Florida	55
Washington	55
Minnesota	41
Wisconsin	40
Illinois	37
Ohio	36
Indiana	33
Massachusetts	31
Texas	30
South Carolina	24

Suburbs too have their share of Superfund sites. In Southern California, a 145-acre unlined gravel pit in Monterey Park began in 1948 to accept all kinds of industrial and residential wastes. When the Operating Industries, Inc., (OII) landfill closed in 1984, houses had been built next to the resulting pile. In places it was 300 feet deep, garbage rotting along with a toxic brew of more than 300 million gallons of hazardous liquids. When the site joined the Superfund list in 1986, toxic vapors and liquids were migrating toward neighborhoods, and the steep slopes of this poisonous mountain—which now had the Pomona Freeway cutting through it—threatened to give way.

Since EPA took emergency action to stabilize the slopes, 180 companies that contributed to the dump have settled with the agency and are now leading the cleanup. They're working toward controlling the spread of the hazardous liquids, the landfill gas and the groundwater contamination. Engineers have nearly finished their design for a huge multilayer cap that will cover the site. Although cleanup has moved along at a good pace, the OII landfill will require decades of monitoring and maintenance, according to Roy Herzig, an EPA project manager.

Cleanup often requires that level of attention. Along with that difficult lesson has come a greater understanding of the magnitude of the tasks at hand. One hundred kinds of chemical pollutants exist in various combinations and mixtures at Superfund sites. The substances are poisoning settings as diverse as mountain streambeds, coastal harbors, urban blocks and suburban neighborhoods. And yet only a limited number of technologies can be counted as ready tools for cleaning up the contamination.

For destroying toxic materials, only incinerations has a proven record of effectiveness and high standards for safety. But even though it may be the only option available for treating highly concentrated and hazardous substances, incineration has become unpopular, as EPA's Garman has found in New Bedford with residents who fear the slight risk of exposure to toxic emissions. "I'm concerned that because of politics we may lose this technology," says Garman, an environmental engineer. "We need it in our bag of tricks to clean up the environmental messes out there."

One promising new alternative for treating some contaminated soils is bioremediation, an inexpensive strategy in which microorganisms break down certain toxic chemicals into harmless substances. However, bioremediation has yet to be critically evaluated and refined for use in the field. So far, the technique does not appear to work on metals, highly concentrated chemical wastes or complex mixtures of toxic substances. At the American Creosote site in Pensacola, bioremediation failed to detoxify the sludge. Although the organisms readily digested the simpler organic chemicals in the mixture, EPA found that the microbes did not degrade more than 30 percent of the carcinogenic compounds.

Another lesson comes from the program's sometimes poor administration, which EPA has been working to improve. After studies found that three of every five African Americans and Hispanic Americans live near toxic dumps and that Superfund sites in minority areas took as much as 42 percent longer to clean up, the agency opened an Office of Environmental Equity in November 1992. In June 1993, EPA also outlined a model for accelerating Superfund cleanups. The plan calls for a single comprehensive assessment of a site and "cookbook" remedies for certain common and well-studied contamination problems, such as wood-preserving chemicals in soil.

The agency is also rounding up more polluters these days. According to Bruce Diamond, director of EPA's Office of Waste Programs Enforcement, EPA now gets companies to pay for more than two-thirds of Superfund cleanups—double the rate five years ago, when the majority of projects drew from the trust fund.

Fixing Superfund, however, may take more than vigorous enforcement and other administrative improvements at EPA. "We've acknowledged that administrative changes are not enough; the law will probably be changed," says Timothy Fields, director of EPA's Superfund Revitalization Office.

EPA Administrator Carol Browner has said she is committed to the law's polluter-pays principle but has expressed interest in changing other parts of the legislation. She may, for example, propose that Congress require EPA to actively involve communities early during cleanups and set national clean-up standards.

Though Congress hopes to set the federal program on a new and accelerated course, streamlining Superfund, like reclaiming toxic dumps, won't be easy. Adding and removing clauses to the already dense and complex law could even slow cleanups at first as site managers adjust to the changes.

Even so, cleanups are finally gaining momentum at many sites, including Clark Fork. There, ARCO and the community of Anaconda are preparing to build a world-class golf course where a mountain of toxic tailings once stood. And negotiations between ARCO and the state of Montana on restoration of the ecosystem are wrapping up. Some day, maybe everyone involved with Superfund will be able to agree with D. Henry Elsen, EPA's Clark Fork legal coordinator, who says, "The Superfund horror stories are mostly from years past."

Making Superfund Better:
The NWF Perspective

The National Wildlife Federation is working to ensure that the country does the best possible job of protecting both human health and the environment in the effort to clean up our worst hazardous-waste sites. Those are already the twin goals of Superfund, but NWF recommends they can be strengthened in the following ways when Congress takes on the law's reauthorization in 1994.

Maintain joint and several liability. This provision, now in effect, ensures that the polluter and not the taxpayer pays for the cleanups. Because it means that any one of a number of potentially responsible parties can be held liable for the entire amount of the clean-up cost, many companies want to change this part of the law. But the alternatives all mean that taxes would fund more of the work, and NWF is concerned that without joint and several liability, in the end there simply would not be enough tax revenues to pay for needed cleanups.

Involve local communities and governments in cleanups. Affected communities should be kept well informed of clean-up progress, and they should have more of a chance to give input into decisions. "They are not now involved in any meaningful form," says NWF legislative representative Patricia Williams. "Usually clean-up decisions are made by the time affected communities know about them." Early community input would be especially useful for helping decide acceptable levels of risk at individual sites and for making future land-use decisions that would help steer technical experts when exploring remedies.

Provide funding for natural resource damage assessments. The law now contradicts itself on this point, in one place providing for such assessments and in another taking it back. Information about ecological damage and status of wildlife at individual sites is essential to making informed decisions about cleanup strategies designed to protect the environment as well as human health.

Direct the U.S. Army Corps of Engineers to help with cleanups. The Corps is now involved in only a handful of Superfund cleanups on a somewhat ad hoc basis. A formal arrangement could help speed up the work and keep costs down by reducing reliance on outside contractors, which have in many cases mismanaged contracts and proceeded more slowly than they originally promised.

Consider land use, potential treatments and available technology when deciding how clean a Superfund site should be. Future use of a site should be a factor in deciding clean-up levels, which are now assumed always to be quite strict. Meeting those standards can be extremely expensive and in some cases not necessary. The money in those cases might be better spent. "This goes back to the idea of the affected community," says Williams. "It can tell you the uses of the site and what's best for the town." Industrial sites, for example, may not require the same standards as residential or rural sites. For example, at the Industri-Plex site in Woburn, Massachusetts, one alternative is to cover soil containing toxic heavy metals with uncontaminated soil, and then to contain and completely isolate it all within or under the structures of a new commuter train station. Removing the toxic soil completely would create far more hazard and expense.

If you would like to stay informed on Superfund issues, write: Department number PS75F003, National Wildlife Federation, 1400 Sixteenth Street NW, Washington, D.C. 20036-2266.

Article Questions

1. In five sentences describe the content of this article.

2. What is litigation soup? What is Superfund? What are Superfund funds?

3. What is the most common pathway by which people are exposed to contaminants?

4. How many tons of hazardous waste is produced in America each year?

5. How many pounds of hazardous waste is produced by individuals in America each year?

6. List five of the top ten superfund hazardous substances. Explain why they are dangerous.

7. Where would you *not* want to live because of the presence of toxic dumps?

8. List three ways to make superfund better.

EVs: On the Road Again

Gil Andrews Pratt

It was 1976, and air-polluting, gas-guzzling American cars were under fire. Congress was toughening pollution laws. The OPEC-induced oil embargo remained fixed in the public's mind. Newly elected president Jimmy Carter was preaching energy independence. The watchword was alternatives—alternative energy sources, alternative fuels, and alternative vehicles.

Riding this wave, the U.S. Department of Energy announced the Near Term Electric Vehicle (NTEV) program—an ambitious plan to quickly develop a practical electric car. Instead of a gasoline tank, the NTEV's car would carry a pack of rechargeable batteries. Instead of an internal-combustion engine, an electric motor would be used. When driven short daily distances by commuters, an electric car could be recharged overnight, to the delight of power companies with excess off-peak capacity. Fossil fuels had earned a bad reputation in 1976, and electric cars, which did not directly burn fossil fuels, seemed a wonderful alternative. The adoption of electric cars and nuclear power, which was then expected to provide ever-increasing fractions of the nation's electricity, together promised to lessen both air pollution and our dependence on imported oil.

At the time, the target of a practical electric vehicle seemed very close. In fact, after a short, optimistic feasibility study, DOE leaders told NTEV engineers to immediately begin the design and construction of two prototypes. It was fully expected that within five years these prototypes would serve as direct inspiration for the nation's automobile manufacturers.

Alas, it was not to be. Fifteen years later, the objectives of the NTEV program seem quixotic. Without question, important research was accomplished. The two prototypes were completed. But by the time the program ended in 1981, it had failed to even approach its goal of developing an economically viable electric vehicle. Many members of the NTEV program were discouraged, and the electric vehicle was relegated to the status of a "far-out idea."

The NTEV program did not fail because of weak technical work, inadequate funding, or bad management. Rather, it was the immature state of several key technologies that led to economic, performance, and reliability handicaps that were simply too great to overcome. Electric motors were inefficient, electronic devices needed to control the motors were unreliable, and batteries couldn't store enough energy to propel the cars very far.

Today, however, renewed interest in electric vehicles is spreading rapidly. Almost every major automaker plans to introduce a model for sale within five years, and many small companies have been started to capitalize on the trend. The federal government is strongly supporting a new research effort—the U.S. Advanced Battery Consortium—in cooperation with the Big Three automakers to improve batteries for electric vehicles. The California legislature, in an effort to combat smog in Los Angeles, has passed a law requiring that by 1998, 2 percent of any company's in-state sales must be "zero-emission vehicles," meaning electric cars; by 2003, at least 10 percent of sales must meet that standard. The first electric car dealership has just opened in Hollywood. And most impressively, the nation's largest automaker, General Motors, has committed a factory to producing what the company claims will be the world's most advanced electric vehicle, the Impact.

Has a new generation of engineers forgotten the real-world lessons of the NTEV program? Not quite. Over the past 15 years much of the technology required to build electric vehicles—in particular, the motors and electronics—has been maturing. Batteries have gotten better too, although in that department engineers aren't out of the woods.

More Desirable Than Ever

Several forces have triggered the resurgence of electric vehicles. As in 1976, most important are the cars' energy efficiency and ability to reduce pollution.

Today's electric-vehicle motors are about 90 percent efficient, and battery packs are about 80 percent efficient. Upstream of the vehicle, of course, lies a power plant; electricity produced by fossil fuels is delivered to the average urban household at an efficiency of about 32 percent. Multiplying the three numbers yields an urban fuel-to-wheel efficiency of about 23 percent. While this is a bit poorer than the efficiency of a high mileage gasoline car traveling on the highway, a direct comparison of gasoline and electric vehicles of the same weight and size shows that the latter do save energy in urban driving, their intended use.

In 1989, the Electric Power Research Institute (EPRI) compared nearly-identical minivans converted to run on electricity (see the chart on the previous page). This analysis showed that in urban use the electric vans required only 60 to 75 percent of the energy consumed by their gasoline counterparts. This study took into account all energy consumption, for both electric and gasoline vehicles, from the oil well to the road. More recent measurements made by the California Air Resources Board show that the urban energy consumption of the Force, a converted Geo Metro made by Solectria Corp. in Waltham, Mass., is about 63 percent that of a gasoline Metro. And GM's Impact, engineered from the ground up as a flashy, high-performance electric sports car, is much more efficient than any of the others because of its lightweight, highly aerodynamic body and special low-rolling-resistance tires.

If used exclusively for highway travel, electric cars offer no advantage. But because they are intended primarily for urban areas, where frequent stops and starts burn excessive fuel in conventional cars, the energy advantage of electric vehicles in cities is significant.

Another factor favoring electric vehicles is energy flexibility. The U.S. transportation sector depends almost exclusively on crude oil; in 1989, oil accounted for 97 percent of transportation energy consumption. As became clear during the oil shortages of the 1970s, this near-total dependence is a real vulnerability.

Electricity, by contrast, can be produced from a wide variety of sources. Any move to decouple transportation from oil, even without improvements in overall efficiency, yields great benefits in the ability to switch to other energy sources should crude oil fall into short supply. Electric vehicles help diversify the country's energy mix.

Whether electric vehicles achieve their second major goal—reducing air pollution—depends on what takes place at local power plants. Although electric vehicles generate no air pollution, the same cannot be said of the plants that must generate electricity to recharge the cars' batteries. Because most of the power plants that supply the Los Angeles basin are located outside the region, the displacement of emissions alone will reduce smog there. But from a national point of view, what matters is the total pollution created, regardless of the source.

The type and amount of pollution generated by a utility depends on the sophistication of its pollution controls and on its mix of "dirty" plants, such as those fueled by coal, and "clean" plants, such as hydroelectric generators. As with energy comparisons, to see if electric cars are cleaner than gasoline vehicles of the same size and weight, analysts must take into account all sources of pollution from the oil well to the road.

EPRI performed such a study in 1989 for the Los Angeles area and the entire United States. Because a small fraction of the power used in Southern California is generated by burning coal (much of it comes from natural gas and hydroelectric plants), the study showed that the use of electric vehicles will significantly reduce regional levels of hydrocarbons, nitrogen oxides, and carbon monoxide. But the situation is less clear for the rest of the country, where the burning of coal is far more common. The EPRI study showed that levels of volatile organic compounds, carbon monoxide, and carbon dioxide across the nation would be lower but that concentrations of sulfur dioxide and nitrogen oxides would be higher. This translates into a lower contribution to global warming and less smog but more acid rain.

As was true for energy consumption, however, electric vehicles provide more flexibility in improving air quality. Emissions from gasoline engines have steadily declined, but with computerized carburation and advanced pollution controls already in place, further improvements are becoming harder to realize. Utilities, on the other hand, can still make great strides; greater use of environmentally friendly energy sources and better pollution controls can bring down emissions dramatically. Indeed, utilities will be forced in this direction by federal legislation requiring significant reductions in sulfur dioxide and nitrogen oxides in the coming decade.

Better Technology for Better Cars

Electric vehicles also offer the advantage of being more reliable. Containing three primary components—an electric motor, a motor controller, and a battery pack— the electric vehicle's "power train" is simpler than the engine, transmission, exhaust, and fuel-injection systems of present-day cars. Modern electric motors have only one moving part and no delicate mechanical controls. There are fewer fluid systems, there's no oil to buy or change, and no muffler to replace. Electric cars, then, should require less maintenance and be easier to repair.

Gil Andrews Pratt

The big headache involves the battery pack. In 1980, the large-lot manufacturing cost of the lead-acid battery pack designed for the NTEV program was estimated at $1,470, with a predicted lifetime of 30,000 miles. Most electric-vehicle makers, including General Motors, estimate similar numbers today (battery cost has fallen, but inflation has risen). Lower maintenance costs would somewhat offset the expense of new batteries, but the requirement is still a disincentive to buyers.

Still, electric-vehicle technology has improved enough so that a viable car can be made today. Though there was only scattered work on electric vehicles in the 1980s, the key technologies advanced for other reasons, especially the surge in demand for better industrial motors and high-power electronics.

The electric motors used in the NTEV prototypes and others of the era were heavy and difficult to cool. They were inefficient, put out little power, and required too much maintenance. Modern motors have gotten lighter, more reliable, and more powerful. Internal energy losses and friction have been reduced, and cooling systems are more effective.

The electronics needed for motor control have also improved since the 1970s, driven largely by advances in industrial-automation technology. The job of an electric motor controller is to efficiently deliver the proper amount of current to the car's motor and to transform the fixed voltage provided by batteries into the variable voltage that the motor requires. In the late 1970s, technology for accomplishing this task was primitive, inefficient, unreliable, and expensive, contributing greatly to the NTEV's problems.

The power semiconductors and design methodologies used for motor control improved dramatically in the 1980s, as integrated circuits replaced systems made with discrete components. Widespread demand in the industrial-automation market drove down cost. These advances have enabled electric-vehicle engineers to make sophisticated, highly reliable motor-control circuits at modest expense: a mass-produced electric automobile's motor controller might cost $1,000 today. In the days of the NTEV, such designs couldn't be bought at any price.

Another technical improvement that is important but less apparent has also occurred since the time of the NTEV. Lighter, stronger alloys and composite materials, and better designs for crash-resistance, have cut the weight of cars significantly. Although consumers were worried about the safety of smaller, lighter cars when they were first widely introduced in the late 1970s, numerous studies have since proven them safe, and the public has come to accept them. The recent inclusion of air bags in many models has further enhanced the safety of small vehicles. Because every pound that can be shed extends the range of electric vehicles, lower weight is critical to performance and is a major factor in their present viability.

Batteries: The Achilles' Heel

So far the electric car looks pretty good, but there's a catch—the batteries. Though better than in the late 1970s, batteries still cannot store nearly as much energy, or generate as much power, as internal combustion engines. They also have a limited lifetime and take a long time to recharge.

Two measures can be used to compare batteries and conventional engines. The first, power density, indicates the amount of power per kilogram of battery weight that can be extracted from a battery. Insufficient power density reduces a vehicle's acceleration and ability to climb hills, and slows recharge time. The second, energy density, measures the amount of electrical energy that can be stored in each kilogram of battery. Low energy density translates into reduced range between recharges.

A simultaneous analysis of power density and energy density shows the huge advantage of internal combustion engines over batteries (*see the chart to the right*). Modern engines have a power density of about 400 watts per kilogram, and an energy density well above 200 watt-hours per kilogram. The figures for batteries are dismal: conventional lead-acid batteries, have a power density of less than 100 watts per kilogram and an energy density of less than 40 watt-hours per kilogram.

The advanced lead-acid batteries used in GM's Impact are better, but still fall far short of engines. Other, more experimental batteries—such as lithium, sodium-sulfur, nickel-zinc, and nickel-iron—have better power and energy densities than lead-acid, but they may not be practical for mass-produced electric cars because they are either more expensive, less reliable, harder to maintain, or in some cases dangerous (because their contents are toxic).

Although the power density of batteries is low compared with engines, it is good enough for typical driving. GM, for example, is using lead-acid batteries with a power density of 200 watts per kilogram, yet the Impact has an exhilarating acceleration of 0-to-60 miles per hour in just 8 seconds—better than many sports cars. The Impact proves that even lead-acid batteries have enough power density for responsive driving if they are used in a lightweight, aerodynamic vehicle fitted with low-friction tires and efficient motors and controls.

Low power density, however, in combination with the modest electric power delivered to households, does slow the rate at which batteries can be recharged. It generally takes 6 to 8 hours to recharge fully depleted lead-acid car batteries. Compared with a two-minute gasoline fill-up, this delay seems cumbersome indeed.

Energy density, too, remains a problem. The best electric vehicles go only 120 miles or so before the batteries are fully depleted. Although the typical American commutes only about 20 miles a day, this limitation is both a practical and a psychological nuisance.

The low energy density and long recharge time of conventional batteries has convinced many electric vehicle developers to target cars for fleet use. Most fleet vehicles travel short distances along identical routes every day and are not used at night, allowing plenty of time for recharging. The economics of electric cars also favors fleet owners, who can invest more money than most individuals in the original vehicle and battery replacements if they can realize long-term savings in maintenance and energy costs. Nevertheless, many commuters also take short, identical routes every day to work, and the commuting car is often not used for other purposes. This commuter market is substantial and will be another likely target of the large auto companies that plan to sell electric cars.

To improve range, some carmakers are experimenting with hybrid vehicles—electric cars that also have a small gasoline engine or fuel cell on board. (Fuel cells, used for many years in the space program, convert chemical fuel into electricity at up to 50 percent efficiency with no moving parts.) The idea is to use battery power when driving in the city, then switch to the engine or fuel cell on the highway; such a setup can easily extend vehicle range by 100 miles or more. In addition, excess power from the engine or fuel cell can be used to recharge the batteries while the car is cruising on the highway.

Several automakers, including GM, Volkswagen, Audi, Mercedes-Benz, and the British-Swedish consortium Clean Air Transport, are working on internal-combustion hybrids, even though they are more complex, less reliable, and more costly than electric cars. Prospects for hybrids that use fuel cells are better. A modern fuel cell powerful enough to propel a 2,200 pound car on a typical commute is roughly the size of a bread box.

Gil Andrews Pratt

However, the cell requires a fuel-storage system, and here the technology still has a long way to go. The most economical fuel cells consume hydrogen, which demands heavy and expensive equipment for storage. At present, metal hydrides seem to be the best storage technology, and they yield higher energy densities than are available from most batteries.

Pioneering Commuters

Designers of the Near Term Electric Vehicle program, in their written words, anticipated that "the electric car resulting from this program is to be suitable for future production at a cost comparable to conventional (internal combustion engine) autos." But they did not appreciate the gravity of the point. The program's final report in 1980 conceded that a bare-bones electric vehicle could be produced in quantities of 300,000 a year for $8,520, compared with the $5,300 price tag for an equivalent gasoline vehicle (in this case, a 1980 Chrysler Horizon TC-3).

Why would a consumer pay 60 percent more for a vehicle with half the range, worse performance, and far more "fill up" nuisance than a conventional car? The obvious answer is that no one would. Despite interesting technical work, the NTEV's most important goal, that of economic viability, was not met.

Since that time, changes in perspectives combined with technological advances have made electric vehicles more attractive. Pollution and global warming are considered much more threatening problems than in the 1970s. Modern electric vehicles are more efficient, better performing, more reliable, and cost less. And the public now accepts lightweight vehicles as safe to drive. But until a battery breakthrough occurs, the range of electric cars is unlikely to be substantially extended.

Nevertheless, General Motors expects people will buy the Impact. The automaker's optimism is based on something never considered by the NTEV program: the car is fun to drive! By designing a sporty electric, GM has added the psychological value of high performance to the electric vehicle's balance sheet of perceived worth. Present gasoline models demonstrate that many drivers are willing to spend $10,000 extra for the thrill of driving to work in a sports car. Though GM won't discuss price, auto analysts have said the Impact will cost between $20,000 and $30,000, which is in line with other high-perform-ance cars.

Although the sports car market is not as large as that of standard models, it can still yield production economies, particularly with modern, small-scale, flexible manufacturing. As more cars are sold, the price will come down. And, for the environmentally conscious, there is added incentive for buying electric sports cars: they need no longer worry about having fun at the earth's expense. The impact is both powerful and environmentally friendly.

Other measures, such as tax credits or pollution penalties, would help make electric cars more competitive. The development of infrastructure would hasten consumer accep-tance: for fast charging, most households would require a modified electrical hookup; and placement of chargers at company parking lots and public garages would roughly double the lifetime of a commuter car's batteries by preventing them from being deeply discharged (batteries last longer if they are only moderately depleted between charges). For this system to work, though, debit-card or electronic-funds transfer systems would be needed to bill customers who use the charging stations. Ready availability of replacement parts, a network of shops that can change battery packs, and mechanics trained to fix electric cars would also be necessary.

In California at least, where electric cars will be mandated by law, all these measures are being developed by local utilities and municipalities in conjunction with carmakers. A few experimental charging stations have been set up in Los Angeles, and the city is considering economic incentives such as credits for local buyers. And California is not alone. Several other states, including New York, have also passed laws requiring carmakers to include electric vehicles in their local product lines.

Realizing the promise of the fleet and commuter markets—both well into the millions—thus seems closer, albeit still not around the corner. In the meantime, although electric cars cost a little more, the pioneering commuters who drive them will work a little harder for the privilege, and we'll all breathe a little easier.

Article Questions

1. How much energy does the electric car expend in comparison to its counterpart according to recent studies?

2. The electric car was developed in the 1970's with a five year prediction of wide-scale market distribution. Why didn't this happen?

3. What has changed to support the development of the electric vehicle?

4. What are some of the specific advantages of the electric car?

5. What are some of the disadvantages of the electric car?

6. Does the electric car reduce pollution? What are some of the pro and con arguments?

7. What are some of the problems with battery technology?

8. What are the advantages of the hybrid engine?

9. Although not discussed in the article, how do you think we can safely dispose of a high volume of used batteries from the electric car technology? Is there an ecological safe approach being considered?

10. Discuss what you think about ecological mandates such as California and possibly New York requiring the use of electric cars. Relate this to our US psychology of capitalism, freedom, and individualism. How do such mandates begin to change national psychologies and address global issues? How do such mandates begin to prepare us for the 21st Century? Relate to 21st Century needs.

Discussion Questions

1. Ecology. What does this term mean to you? How has the media presented the concept of Ecology? Do you believe that the media's concept of ecology is right? Explain your answer with statistics or theory.

2. What does ecology mean to future generations? What is your perception of rivers, trees, atmosphere, and water conditions in the year 2035?

3. List 10 solutions to the ecology problems that we face today.

4. List ten interesting concepts or statistics that you found in this chapter. Do you believe that these are true? Why? Explain your answer.

5. Define the following:

   a. Global warming

   b. Green house effect

   c. CFCs

   d. Biodiversity

   e. Fission

   f. Fossil fuel

   g. Genetic engineering

   h. Third world

   i. Telecommuting

   j. Fusion

   k. Ethics

   l. Acid rain

   m. Biomass

   n. Hydroelectric

   o. Radioactive

   p. Hazardous waste

   q. DNA

CHAPTER FOUR
POPULATION

Population Growth

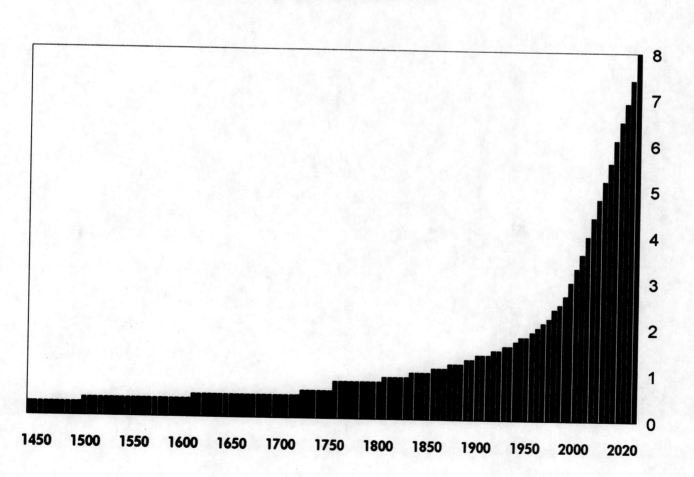

Putting the Bite on Planet Earth

Don Hinrichsen

Each year, about 90 million new people join the human race. This is roughly equivalent to adding three Canadas or another Mexico to the world annually, a rate of growth that will swell human numbers from today's 5.6 billion to about 8.5 billion by 2025.

These figures represent the fastest growth in human numbers ever recorded and raise many vital economic and environmental questions. Is our species reproducing so quickly that we are outpacing the Earth's ability to house and feed us? Is our demand for natural resources destroying the habitats that give us life? If 40 million acres of tropical forest—an area equivalent to twice the size of Austria—are being destroyed or grossly degraded every year, as satellite maps show, how will that affect us? If 27,000 species become extinct yearly because of human development, as some scientists believe, what will that mean for us? If nearly 2 billion people already lack adequate drinking water, a number likely to increase to 3.6 billion by the year 2000, how can all of us hope to survive?

The answers are hardly easy and go beyond simple demographics, since population works in conjunction with other factors to determine our total impact on resources. Modern technologies and improved efficiency in the use of resources can help to stretch the availability of limited resources. Consumption levels also exert considerable impact on our resource base. Population pressures work in conjunction with these other factors to determine, to a large extent, our *total* impact on resources.

For example, although everyone contributes to resource waste, the world's bottom-billion poorest and top-billion richest do most of the environmental damage. Poverty compels the world's 1.2 billion bottom-most poor to misuse their environment and ravage resources, while lack of access to better technologies, credit, education, healthcare and family-planning condemns them to subsistence patterns that offer little chance for concern about their environment. This contrasts with the richest 1.3 billion, who exploit and consume disproportionate amounts of resources and generate disproportionate quantities of waste.

One example is energy consumption. Whereas the average Bangladeshi consumes commercial energy equivalent to three barrels of oil yearly, each American consumes an average of 55 barrels. Population growth in Bangladesh, one of the poorest nations, increased energy use there in 1990 by the equivalent of 8.7 million barrels, while U.S. population growth in the same year increased energy use by 110 million barrels. Of course, the U.S. population of 250 million is more than twice the size of the Bangladeshi population of 113 million, but even if the consumption figures are adjusted for the difference in size, the slower growing U.S. population shill increases its energy consumption six or seven times faster yearly than does the more rapidly growing Bangladeshi population.

In the future, the effects of population growth on natural resources will vary locally because growth occurs unevenly across the globe. Over the course of the 1990s, the Third World's population is likely to balloon by more than 900 million, while the population of the developed world will add a mere 56 million. Asia, with 3.4 billion people today, will have 3.7 billion by the turn of the century; Africa's population will increase from 700 million to 867 million; and Latin America's from 470 million to 538 million. By the year 2000, the Third World's total population is expected to be nearly 5 billion; only 1.3 billion people will reside in industrialized countries.

The United Nations estimates that world population will near 11.2 billion by 2100. However, this figure is based on the assumption that growth rates will drop. If present rates continue, world population will stand at 10 billion by 2030 and 40 billion by 2110.

The United Nations Population Fund estimates that to achieve the 11.2 billion projection, the number of couples using family planning services—such as modern contraceptives—in the developing world will have to rise to 567 million by the year 2000 and to 1.2 billion by 2025. In sub-Saharan Africa this means a 10-fold increase by 2025 in the number of people who use family planning. If these measures do not succeed, human population growth could blast the 11.2 billion figure clear out of the ball park.

Perhaps the most ominous aspect of today's unprecedented growth is its persistence despite falling annual population growth rates everywhere except in parts of Africa, the Middle East and South Asia. Annual global population growth stands at 1.6 percent, down from 2 percent in the early 1970s. Similarly, the total fertility rate (the average number of children a woman is likely to have) has dropped from a global average of six only three decades ago to slightly more than three today.

Population continues to grow because of tremendous demographic momentum. China's annual growth rate, for example, is only 1.2 percent. However, the country's huge population base—1.2 billion people—translates this relatively small rate of growth into a net increase in China's population of around 15 million yearly. Clearly, any attempt to slow population growth is a decades-long process affected by advances in medicine, extended life spans and reduced infant, child and maternal mortality.

The following pages survey the effects of human population growth on a wide range of natural resources.

Plants and Animals: The Shrinking Ark

Biologists have catalogued 1.7 million species and cannot even estimate how many species remain to be documented. The total could be 5 million, 30 million or even more. Yet, we are driving thousands of species yearly to extinction through thoughtless destruction of habitat.

A survey conducted recently in Australia, Asia and the Americas by the International Union for Conservation of Nature and Natural Resources—The World Conservation Union (IUCN) found that loss of living space affected 76 percent of all mammal species.

Expansion of settlements threatened 56 percent of mammal species, while expansion of ranching affected 33 percent. Logging and plantations affected 26 percent.

IUCN has declared human population growth the number one cause of extinctions. The 10 nations with the worst habitat destruction house an average of 189 people per square kilometer (250 acres), while the 10 that retain the most original habitat stand at only 29 people per square kilometer.

Future population growth poses a serious threat to wildlife habitat. Every new person needs space for housing, food, travel, work and other needs. Human needs vary widely from place to place, but a UN survey found that the average person requires about 0.056 hectares (a hectare is a standard unit of land measurement equal to about 2.47 acres) of nonfarm land for daily living. To this must be added land for food production. This varies with land quality and available technologies, but each newborn person probably will need at least 0.2 hectare of cropland unless food production per acre increases in the years ahead. This will require the conversion of more and more wildland into cropland. In East Asia, for example, the amount of irrigated, high-yield corpland per person is already near the 0.2 hectare limit.

UN consultant and author Paul Harrison estimates, very conservatively, that each new person will need at least a quarter of a hectare. Thus, every billion people that we add to the planet in the years ahead will require 250 million hectares more of agricultural

HUMAN NUMBERS

The crowd swells

Population density varies by region but is a deceptive factor. Many nations, from Europe to Africa, expand their land bases by importing food.

31 Oceania

130 Former U.S.S.R.

169 South America

184 North and Central America

People per 1,000 hectares

1,054 Europe

1,140 Asia

217 Africa

403 World

Data compiled for International Wildlife by Banson, Inc.

- Average yearly increase in human numbers between 1950 and 1990: 70 million

- Projected average yearly increase in human numbers for the next 40 years: 90 million

- Total world human population today: 5.6 billion

- Projected population in 2100 assuming reduced fertility: 11.2 billion

- Projected population in 2100 at current rate of fertility: 40 billion

- Percentage of total world population today living in developing nations: 78

Don Hinrichsen

land. Most of this land will have to come from what is currently wildlife habitat. The UN's projected population of 11.2 billion by 2100 would require creation of roughly 20 million square kilometers (8 million sq. mi.) of new corpland—equivalent to more than 80 percent of all forest and woodland in developing countries today.

Conversion of natural habitat for human use can even reduce the value of remaining wild areas for wildlife. When development chops wild lands into fragments, native species often decline simply because the small remnants do not meet their biological needs. For example, studies of U.S. forest birds indicate that species that prefer to nest in forest interiors are more subject to predation and lay fewer eggs when habitat fragmentation forces them to nest along forest edges. A study in southern California indicated that most canyons lose about half of native bird species dependent on chaparral habitat within 20 to 40 years after the canyons become isolated by development, even though the chaparral brush remains. Biologist William Newmark's 1987 study of 14 Canadian and U.S. national parks showed that 13 of the parks had lost some of their mammal species, at least in part because the animals could not adapt to confinement within parks surrounded by developed land.

Habitat loss in North America and in Latin American tropics has caused declines in many bird species that migrate between those regions. The Breeding Bird Survey, a volunteer group that tabulates nesting birds each June, found that 70 percent of neotropical migrant species monitored in the eastern United States declined from 1978 to 1987. So did 69 percent of monitored neotropical migrants that nest in prairie regions. Declining species include such familiar songbirds as veeries, wood thrushes, blackpoll warblers and rose-breasted grosbeaks. As human population growth continues to push development into wild areas, fragmentation will increase and its effects on wildlife survival will intensify.

Land Loss: A Food Crisis

Land degradation, a global problem, is becoming acute in much of the developing world. Population pressures and inappropriate farming practices contribute to soil impoverishment and erosion, rampant deforestation, overgrazing of common lands and misuse of agrochemicals.

Worldwide, an estimated 1.2 billion hectares, an area about the size of China and India combined, have lost much of their agricultural productivity since 1945. Every year, farmers abandon about 70,000 square kilometers (27,000 sq. mi.) of farmland because soils are too degraded for crops.

Drylands, including grasslands that provide rich pastures for livestock, have been hardest hit. Although not as extensive as once thought, desertification—the ecological destruction that turns productive land into deserts—still threatens the Middle East and parts of Africa and Asia.

Because of land degradation, large portions of the Sahel, including Burkina Faso, Chad, Mali, Mauritania, Niger and Senegal, can no longer feed their people. Although annual fluctuations in rainfall may interrupt the trend of cropland loss, the Sahel could suffer agricultural collapse within a decade. Sahelian croplands, as presently farmed, can support a maximum of 36 million people. In 1990 the rural population stood at an estimated 32 million and will exceed 40 million by the end of the decade even if annual population growth slows from the current 3 percent to 2 percent.

Since 1961, food production has matched world population growth in all developing regions except sub-Saharan Africa. In the early 1980s, the UN Food and Agriculture

Organization (FAO) predicted that more than half of all developing nations examined in its study of carrying capacity (62 out of 115) may be unable to feed their projected populations by 2000 using current farming technology. Most of the 62 countries probably will be able to feed less than half of their projected proplations without expensive food imports.

As a direct result of population growth, especially in developing nations, the average amount of cropland per person is projected to decline from 0.28 hectares in 1990 to 0.17 by 2025.

Three factors will determine whether food production can equal population growth:

1. *New Croplands.* Currently, the amount of new land put into production each year may equal the amount taken out of production for various reasons, such as erosion, salt deposits and waterlogging. Thus, the net annual gain in arable land, despite widespread habitat destruction to create it, may be zero.

2. *New Water Sources.* Agricultural demand for water is expected to double between 1970 and 2000. Already more than 70 percent of water withdrawals from rivers, underground reservoirs and other sources go to crop irrigation.

3. *Agrochemical Use.* Pesticides and fertilizers are boosting crop yields. However, in many areas agrochemicals are too expensive to use, while in other areas they are overused to prop up falling yields. Agrochemicals can pose health hazards, creating another expense for developing nations.

Forest: The Vanishing World

The quest for more crop and grazing land has sealed the fate of much of the world's tropical forests. Between 1971 and 1986, arable land expanded by 59 million hectares, while forests shrank by at least 125 million hectares. However, consultant Harrison estimates that during the same period, land used for settlements, roads, industries, office buildings and other development expanded by more than 30 million hectares as a result of growth in urban centers, reducing the amount of arable land in surrounding areas. Consequently, the amount of natural habitat wiped out to produce the 59-million-hectare net in arable land may have exceeded 100 million hectares.

When both agricultural and nonagricultural needs are taken into account, human population growth may be responsible for as much as 80 percent of the loss of forest cover worldwide. Asia produces the highest rate of loss, 1.2 percent a year. Latin America loses 0.9 percent yearly and Africa 0.8 percent.

If current trends continue, most tropical forests will soon be destroyed or damaged beyond recovery. Of the 76 countries that presently encompass tropical forests, only four—Brazil, Guyana, Papua New Guinea and Zaire—are likely to retain major undamaged tracts by 2010, less than a generation away.

Population pressure contributes to deforestation not only because of increased demand for cropland and living space but also because of increased demand for fuelwood, on which half of the world's people depend for heating and cooking. The majority of sub-Saharan Africa's population is dependent on fuelwood: 82 percent of all Nigerians, 70 percent of Kenyans, 80 percent of all Malagasies, 74 percent of Ghanaians, 93 percent of Ethiopians, 90 percent of Somalians and 81 percent of Sudanese.

Don Hinrichsen

By 1990, 100 million Third World residents lacked sufficient fuelwood to meet minimum daily energy requirements, and close to 1.3 billion were consuming wood faster than forest growth could replenish it. On average, consumption outpaces supply by 30 percent in sub-Saharan Africa as a whole, by 70 percent in the Sudan and India, by 150 percent in Ethiopia and by 200 percent in Niger. If present trends continue, FAO predicts, another 1 billion people will be faced with critical fuelwood shortages by the end of the decade. Already, growing rings of desolation—land denuded for fuelwood or building materials—surround many African cities, such as Ouagadougou in Burkina Faso, Niamey in Niger and Dakar in Senegal. By 2000, the World Bank estimates, half to three-quarters of all West Africa's fuelwood consumption will be burned in towns and cities.

According to the World Bank, remedying the fuelwood shortage will require planting 55 million hectares—an area nearly twice the size of Italy—with fast-growing trees at a rate of 2.7 million hectares a year, five times the present annual rate of 555,000 hectares.

Troubled Oceans: Disappearing Resources

Population and development pressures have been mounting in coastal areas world-wide for the past 30 years, triggering widespread resource degradation. Coastal fisheries are overexploited in much of Asia, Africa and parts of Latin America. In some cases—as in the Philippines, Indonesia, Malaysia, China, Japan, India, the west coast of South America, the Mediterranean and the Caribbean—economically important fisheries have collapsed or are in severe decline. "Nearly all Asian waters within 15 kilometers of land are considered overfished," says Ed Gomez, director of the Marine Science Institute at the University of the Philippines in Manila.

Overfishing is not the sole cause of these declines. Mangroves and coral reefs—critical nurseries for many marine species and among the most productive of all ecosystems—are being plundered in the name of development.

In 1990, a UN advisory panel, the Group of Experts on the Scientific Aspects of Marine Pollution (GESAMP), reported that coastal pollution worldwide has grown worse over the decade of the 1980s. Experts pointed to an overload of nutrients—mainly nitrogen and phosphorus from untreated or partially treated sewage, agricultural runoff and erosion—as the most serious coastal pollution problem. Human activities may be responsible for as much as 35 million metric tons of nitrogen and up to 3.75 million metric tons of phosphorus flowing into coastal waters every year. Even such huge amounts could be dissolved in the open ocean, but most of the pollution stays in shallow coastal waters where it causes massive algal blooms and depletes oxygen levels, harming marine life near the shores.

Although the world still possesses an estimated 240,000 square kilometers (93,000 sq. mi.) of mangrove swamps—coastal forests that serve as breeding grounds and nurseries for many commercially important fish and shellfish species—this represents only about half the original amount. Clear-cutting for timber, fuelwood and wood chips; conversion to fish and shellfish ponds; and expansion of urban areas and croplands have claimed millions of hectares globally. For example, of the Philippine's original mangrove area—estimated at 500,000 to 1 million hectares—only 100,000 hectares remain; 80 to 90 percent are gone.

Some 600,000 square kilometers (230,000 sq. mi.) of coral reefs survive in the world's tropical seas. Unfortunately, these species-rich ecosystems are suffering widespread decline. Clive Wilkinson, a coral reef specialist working at the Australian Institute of Marine

Science, estimates that fully 10 percent of the world's reefs have already been degraded "beyond recognition." Thirty percent are in critical condition and will be lost completely in 10 to 20 years, while another 30 percent are threatened and will be lost in 20 to 40 years. Only 30 percent, located away from human development or otherwise too remote to be exploited, are in stable condition.

Throughout much of the world, coastal zones are overdeveloped, overcrowded, and overexploited. Already nearly two-thirds of the world's population—some 3.6 billion people—live along coasts or within 150 kilometers (100 mi.) of one. Within three decades, 75 percent, or 6.4 billion, will reside in coastal areas—nearly a billion more people than the current global population.

In the United States, 54 percent of all Americans live in 772 coastal counties adjacent to marine coasts or the Great Lakes. Between 1960 and 1990, coastal population density increased from 275 to nearly 400 people per square kilometer. By 2025, nearly 75 percent of all Americans will live in coastal counties, with population density doubling in areas such as southern California and Florida.

Similarly, nearly 780 million of China's 1.2 billion people—almost 67 percent—live in 14 southeast and coastal provinces and two coastal municipalities, Shanghai and Tianjin. Along much of China's coastline, population densities average more than 600 per square kilometer. In Shanghai they exceed 2,000 per square kilometer. During the past few years, as many as 100 million Chinese have moved from poorer provinces in central and western regions to coastal areas in search of better economic opportunities. More ominously, population growth is expected to accelerate in the nation's 14 newly created economic free zones and five special economic zones, all of them coastal.

Water: Distribution Woes

Nearly 75 percent of the world's freshwater is locked in glaciers and icecaps, with virtually all the rest underground. Only about 0.01 percent of the world's total water is easily available for human use. Even this tiny amount would be sufficient to meet all the world's needs if it were distributed evenly. However, the world is divided into water "haves" and "have nots." In the Middle East, north Asia, northwestern Mexico, most of Africa, much of the western United States, parts of Chile and Argentina and nearly all of Australia, people need more water than can be sustainably supplied.

As the world's human population increases, the amount of water per person decreases. The United Nations Educational, Scientific and Cultural Organization (UNESCO) estimates that the amount of freshwater available per person has shrunk from more than 33,000 cubic meters (1.2 million cu. ft.) per year in 1850 to only 8,500 cubic meters (300,000 cu. ft.) today. Of course, this is a crude, general figure. But because of population growth alone, water demand in more than half the world's countries by 2000 is likely to be twice what it was as recently as 1971.

Already some 2 billion people in 80 countries must live with water constraints for all or part of the year. By the end of the 1990s Egypt will have only two-thirds as much water for each of its inhabitants as it has today, and Kenya only half as much. By then, six of East Africa's seven nations and all five nations on the south rim of the Mediterranean will face severe shortages. In 1990, 20 nations suffered water scarcity, with less than 1,000 cubic meters (35,000 cu.ft.) of water per person, according to a study by Population Action International. Another eight experienced occasional water stress. The 28 nations represent

333 million people. By 2025, some 48 nations will suffer shortages, involving some 3 billion residents, according to the study.

China—although not listed as water short because of the heavy amount of rain that falls in its souther region—has, nevertheless, exceeded its sustainable water resources. According to Qu Geping, China's Environment Minister, the country can supply water sustainably to only 650 million people, not the current population of 1.2 billion. In other words, China is supporting twice as many people as its water resources can reasonably sustain without drawing down groundwater supplies and overusing surface waters.

Fossil Fuels: Energy Breakdown

Human society runs on energy, principally fossil fuels such as oil, gas and coal. These three account for 90 percent of global commercial energy production. Nuclear power, hydro-electricity and other sustainable resources provide the rest.

The industrialized nations, with less than a quarter of the world's people, burn about 70 percent of all fossil fuels. The United States alone consumes about a quarter of the world's commercial energy, and the former Soviet Union about a fifth. In terms of per capita consumption patterns, Canada burns more fuel than any other nation—in 1987 the equivalent of 9 metric tons of oil per person—followed by Norway at 8.9 metric tons of oil per person and the United States at 7.3. By contrast, developing nations on average use the equivalent of only about half a metric ton of oil per person yearly.

Known oil reserves should meet current levels of consumption for another 41 years, up from an estimated 31 years in 1970 thanks to better energy efficiency and conservations measures, along with new oil fields brought into production. Natural-gas reserves should meet current demand for 60 more years, up from 38 years in 1970. Coal reserves should be good for another 200 years.

But our addiction to fossil fuel has resulted in chronic, sometimes catastrophic, pollution of the atmosphere, in some cases far beyond what natural systems or man-made structures can tolerate. A noxious atmospheric cocktail of chemical pollutants is primarily responsible for the death and decline of thousands of hectares of European forests. Acid rain—caused by a combination of nitrogen and sulfur dioxides released from fossil-fuel combustion—has eaten away at priceless monuments and buildings throughout Europe and North America, causing billions of dollars in damage.

Urban air contains a hazardous mix of pollutants—everything from sulfur dioxide and reactive hydrocarbons to heavy metals and organic compounds. Smog alerts are now commonplace in many cities with heavy traffic. In Mexico City, for example, smog levels exceeded World Health Organization standards on all but 11 days in 1991. Breathing the city's air is said to be as damaging as smoking two packs of cigarettes a day, and half the city's children are born with enough lead in their blood to hinder their development.

The only way to stretch fossil fuel reserves and reduce pollution levels is to conserve energy and use it much more efficiently than we do now. Some progress has been made, but the benefits of energy conservation have been realized in only a few industrialized countries.

Recent history has shown what can happen. In the decade following the first oil shock, per capita energy consumption fell by 5 percent in the member states of the Organization for Economic Cooperation and Development (OECD)—consisting of the industrialized countries of Western Europe and North America, plus Japan, Australia and New Zealand—while their per capita gross domestic product grew by a third.

Buildings in the OECD countries use a quarter less energy now than they did before 1973, while the energy efficiency of industry has improved by a third. Worldwide, cars now get 25 percent more kilometers per gallon than they did in 1973. In all, increased efficiency since 1973 has saved the industrialized nations $250 billion in energy costs.

Even more savings could be realized through concerted efforts to conserve energy and improve efficiency. Three relatively simple, cost effective measures could be introduced immediately: 1) making compact fluorescent lamps generally available in homes and offices; 2) tightening up building codes to require better insulation against cold and heat; and 3) requiring lean-burn engines, which get up to 80 kilometers per gallon (50 mpg), in all new compact cars. These three "technical fixes" could save billions of dollars in energy costs.

Policy: Building a Future

The main population issues—urbanization, rapid growth and uneven distribution—when linked with issues of environmental decline, pose multiple sets of problems for policymakers. The very nature of these interrelated problems makes them virtually impossible to deal with in balkanized bureaucracies accustomed to managing only one aspect of any problem. Population and resource issues require integrated, strategic management, an approach few countries are in a position to implement.

Sustainable-management strategies, designed to ensure that resources are not destroyed by overexploitation, are complicated to initiate because they require the cooperation of ministries or departments often at odds over personnel, budgets and political clout. Most governments lack institutional mechanisms that ensure a close working relationship among competing ministries. Consequently, most sustainable-development initiatives never get beyond words on paper. "We talk about integrated resource management, but we don't do it," admits one Indian official in Delhi. "Our ministries are like fiefdoms, they seldom cooperate on anything."

Fragmented authority yields fragmented policies. Big development ministries—such as industry and commerce, transportation, agriculture, fisheries and forestry—rarely cooperate in solving population and resource problems. Piecemeal solutions dominate, and common resources continue to deteriorate.

The world's population and resource problems offer plenty of scope for timely and incisive policy interventions that promise big returns for a relatively small investment. As little as $17 billion a year could provide contraceptives to every woman who wants them, permitting families throughout the globe to reduce births voluntarily. This approach might produce the same or better results that would government-set population targets, according to one study. Moreover, population specialists recognize that educating girls and women provides a higher rate of return than most other investments. "In fact, it may well be the single most influential investment that can be made in the developing world," says Larry Summers, a former World Bank economist.

But time is at a premium. The decision period for responding to the crises posed by rapidly growing populations, increased consumption levels and shrinking resources will be confined, for the most part, to the next two decades. If human society does not succeed in checking population growth, the future will bring widespread social and economic dislocations as resource bases collapse. Unemployment and poverty will increase, and migrations from poorer to richer nations will bring Third World stresses to the developed world.

Don Hinrichsen

Article Questions

1. How many people are added to the human race each year? Calculate the percentage of growth annually.

2. List some of the stresses on the earth's environment as a result of unprecedented population growth.

3. What are the difficulties of lowering world population rates even if a country's annual growth rate declines?

4. How much land does a person need to survive? How does this impact wildlife, plants and land use?

5. Discuss the problem of land degradation. How much is the average amount of cropland per person projected to decline from 1990 to 2025? Discuss implications. What are possible solutions?

6. How soon will most tropical forests disappear? What are the implications?

7. What are some of the pressures on oceans? What are the ramifications?

8. How much have freshwater supplies shrunk from 1850? What are the issues here?

9. What is the effect of world reliance on fossil fuels? What are some solutions suggested in the article as well as your own?

10. Name some practical solutions to building a future policy that can sustain world population. Aside from suggestions in the article, also name your own possible solutions and approaches.

Can the Growing Human Population Feed Itself?

John Bongaarts

Demographers now project that the world's population will double during the next half century, from 5.3 billion people in 1990 to more than 10 billion by 2050. How will the environment and humanity respond to this unprecedented growth? Expert opinion divides into two camps. Environmentalists and ecologists, whose views have widely been disseminated by the electronic and print media, regard the situation as a catastrophe in the making. They argue that in order to feed the growing population farmers must intensify agricultural practices that already cause grave ecological damage. Our natural resources and the environment, now burdened by past population growth, will simply collapse under the weight of this future demand.

The optimists, on the other hand, comprising many economists as well as some agricultural scientists, assert that the earth can readily produce more than enough food for the expected population in 2050. They contend that technological innovation and the continued investment of human capital will deliver high standards of living to much of the globe, even if the population grows much larger than the projected 10 billion. Which point of view will hold sway? What shape might the future of our species and the environment actually take?

Many environmentalists fear that world food supply has reached a precarious state: "Human numbers are on a collision course with massive famines.... If humanity fails to act, nature will end the population explosion for us—in very unpleasant ways—well before 10 billion is reached," write Paul R. Ehrlich and Anne H. Ehrlich of Stanford University in their 1990 book *The Population Explosion*. In the long run, the Ehrlichs and like-minded experts consider substantial growth in food production to be absolutely impossible. "We are feeding ourselves at the expense of our children. By definition farmers can overplow and overpump only in the short run. For many farmers the short run is drawing to a close," states Lester R. Brown, president of the Worldwatch Institute, in a 1988 paper.

Over the past three decades, these authors point out, enormous efforts and resources have been pooled to amplify agricultural output. Indeed, the total quantity of harvested crops increased dramatically during this time. In the developing world, food production rose by an average of 117 percent in the quarter of a century between 1965 and 1990. Asia performed far better than other regions, which saw increases below average.

Because population has expanded rapidly as well, per capita food production has generally shown only modest change; in Africa it actually declined. As a consequence, the number of undernourished people is still rising in most parts of the developing world, although that number did fall from 844 million to 786 million during the 1980s. But this decline reflects improved nutritional conditions in Asia alone. During the same period, the number of people having energy-deficient diets in Latin America, the Near East and Africa climbed.

Many social factors can bring about conditions of hunger, but the pessimists emphasize that population pressure on fragile ecosystems plays a significant role. One specific concern Is that we seem to be running short on land suitable for cultivation. If so, current efforts to bolster per capita food production by clearing more fertile land will find fewer options. Between 1850 and 1950 the amount of arable land grew quickly to accommodate both larger populations and greater demand for better diets. This expansion then slowed and by the late 1980s ceased altogether. In the developed world, as well as in some developing countries (especially China), the amount of land under cultivation started to decline during the 1980s. This drop is largely because spreading urban centers have engulfed fertile land or, once the land is depleted, farmers have abandoned it. Farmers have also fled from irrigated land that has become unproductive because of salt accumulation.

Moreover, environmentalists insist that soil erosion is destroying much of the land that is left. The extent of the damage is the subject of controversy. A recent global assessment, sponsored by the United Nations Environment Program and reported by the World Resources Institute and others, offers some perspective. The study concludes that 17 percent of the land supporting plant life worldwide has lost value over the past 45 years. The estimate includes erosion caused by water and wind, as well as chemical and physical deterioration, and ranks the degree of soil degradation from light to severe. This degradation is least prevalent in North America (5.3 percent) and most wide spread in Central America (25 percent), Europe (23 percent), Africa (22 percent) and Asia (20 percent). In most of these regions, the average farmer could not gather the resources necessary to restore moderate and severely affected soil regions to full productivity. Therefore, prospects for reversing the effects of soil erosion are not good, and it is likely that this problem will worsen.

Despite the loss and degradation of fertile land, the "green revolution" has promoted per capita food production by increasing the yield per hectare. The new, high-yielding strains of grains such as wheat and rice have proliferated since their introduction in the 1960s, especially in Asia. To reap full advantage from these new crop varieties, however, farmers must apply abundant quantities of fertilizer and water.

Environmentalists question whether further conversion to such crops can be achieved at reasonable cost, especially in the developing world, where the gain in production is most needed. At the moment, farmers in Asia, Latin America and Africa use fertilizer sparingly, if at all, because it is too expensive or unavailable. Fertilizer use in the developed world has recently waned. The reasons for the decline are complex and may be temporary, but clearly farmers in North America and Europe have decided that increasing their already heavy application of fertilizer will not further enhance crop yields.

Unfortunately, irrigation systems, which would enable many developing countries to join in the green revolution, are often too expensive to build. In most areas, irrigation is essential for generating higher yields. It also can make arid land cultivable and protect farmers from the vulnerability inherent in natural variations in the weather. Land brought into cultivation this way could be used for growing multiple crop varieties, thereby helping food production to increase.

Such advantages have been realized since the beginning of agriculture: the earliest irrigation systems are thousands of years old. Yet only a fraction of productive land in the developing world is now irrigated, and its expansion has been slower than population growth. Consequently, the amount of irrigated land per capita has been dwindling during recent decades. The trend, pessimists argue, will be hard to stop. Irrigation systems have been built in the most affordable sites, and the hope for extending them is curtailed by rising costs. Moreover, the accretion of silt in dams and reservoirs and of salt in already irrigated soil is increasingly costly to avoid or reverse.

Environmentalists Ehrlich and Ehrlich note that modern agriculture is by nature at risk wherever it is practiced. The genetic uniformity of single, high-yielding crop strains planted over large areas makes them highly productive but also renders them particularly vulnerable to insects and disease. Current preventive tactics, such as spraying pesticides and rotating crops, are only partial solutions. Rapidly evolving pathogens pose a continuous challenge. Plant breeders must maintain a broad genetic arsenal of crops by collecting and storing natural varieties and by breeding new ones in the laboratory.

The optimists do not deny that many problems exist within the food supply system. But many of these authorities, including D. Gale Johnson, the late Herman Kahn, Walter R. Brown, L. Martel, the late Roger Revelle, Vaclav Smil and Julian L. Simon, believe the world's food supply can dramatically be expanded. Ironically, they draw their enthusiasm from extrapolation of the very trends that so alarm those experts who expect doom. In fact, statistics show that the average daily caloric intake per capita climbed by 21 percent (from 2,063 calories to 2,495 calories) between 1965 and 1990 in the developing countries. These higher calories have generally delivered greater amounts of protein. On average, the per capita consumption of protein rose from 52 grams per day to 61 grams per day between 1965 and 1990.

According to the optimists, not only has the world food situation improved significantly in recent decades, but further growth can be brought about in various ways. A detailed assessment of climate and soil conditions in 93 developing countries (excluding China) shows that nearly three times as much land as is currently farmed, or an additional 2.1 billions hectares, could be cultivated. Regional soil estimates indicate that sub-Saharan Africa and Latin America can exploit many more stretches of unused land than can Asia, the Near East and North Africa.

Even in regions where the amount of potentially arable land is limited, crops could be grown more times every year than is currently the case. This scenario is particularly true in the tropics and subtropics where conditions are such—relatively even temperature throughout the year and a consistent distribution of daylight hours—that more than one crop would thrive. Nearly twice as many crops are harvested every year in Asia than in Africa at present, but further increases are possible in all regions.

In addition to multicropping, higher yields per crop are attainable, especially in Africa and the Near East. Many more crops are currently harvested per hectare in the First World than elsewhere: cereal yields In North America and Europe averaged 4.2 tons per hectare, compared with 2.9 in the Far East (4.2 In China), 2.1 in Latin America, 1.7 in the Near East and only 1.0 in Africa.

Such yield improvements, the enthusiasts note, can be achieved by expanding the still limited use of high-yield crop varieties, fertilizer and irrigation. In *World Agriculture: Toward 2000*, Nikos Alexandratos of the Food and Organization (FAO) of the United

Nations reports that only 34 percent of all seeds planted during the mid-1980s were high-yielding varieties. Statistics from the FAO show that at present only about one in five hectares of arable land is irrigated, and very little fertilizer is used. Pesticides are sparsely applied. Food output could drastically be increased simply by more widespread implementation of such technologies.

Aside from producing more food, many economists and agriculturists point out, consumption levels in the developing world could be boosted by wasting fewer crops, as well as by cutting storage and distribution losses. How much of an increase would these measures yield? Robert W. Kates, director of the Alan Shawn Feinstein World Hunger Program at Brown University, writes in *The Hunger Report: 1988* that humans consume only 60 percent of all harvested crops, and some 25 to 30 percent is lost before reaching individual homes. The FAO, on the other hand, estimates lower distribution losses: 6 percent for cereals, 11 percent for roots and 5 percent for pulses. All the same, there is no doubt that improved storage and distribution systems would leave more food available for human nutrition, independent of future food production capabilities.

For optimists, the long-range trend in food prices constitutes the most convincing evidence for the correctness of their view. In 1992-93 the World Resources Institute reported that food prices dropped further than the price of most nonfuel commodities, all of which have declined in the past decade. Cereal prices in the international market fell by approximately one third between 1980 and 1989. Huge government subsidies for agriculture in North America and western Europe, and the resulting surpluses of agricultural products, have depressed prices. Obviously, the optimists assert, the supply already exceeds the demand of a global population that has doubled since 1950.

Taken together, this evidence leads many experts to see no significant obstacles to raising levels of nutrition for world populations exceeding 10 billion people. The potential for an enormous expansion of food production exists, but its realization depends of course on sensible governmental policies, increased domestic and international trade and large investments in infrastructure and agricultural extension. Such improvements can be achieved, the optimists believe, without incurring irreparable damage to global ecosystems.

Proponents of either of these conflicting perspectives have difficulty accepting the existence of other plausible points of view. Moreover, the polarity between the two sides of expert opinion shows that neither group can be completely correct. Finding some common ground between these seemingly irreconcilable positions is not as difficult as it at first appears if empirical issues are emphasized and important differences in value systems and political beliefs are ignored.

Both sides agree that the demand for food will swell rapidly over the next several decades. In 1990 a person living in the developing world ate on average 2,500 calories each day, taken from 4,000 gross calories of food crops made available within a household. The remaining 1,500 calories from this gross total not used to meet nutritional requirements were either lost, inedible or used as animal feed and plant seed. Most of this food was harvested from 0.7 billion hectares of land in the developing world. The remaining 5 percent of the total food supply came from imports. To sustain this 4,000-gross-calorie diet for more than twice as many residents, or 8.7 billion people, living in the developing world by 2050, agriculture must offer 112 percent more crops. To raise the average Third World diet to 6,000 gross calories per day, slightly above the 1990 world average, food production would need to increase by 218 percent. And to bring the average Third World diet to a level comparable with that currently found in the developed world, or 10,000 gross calories per day, food production would have to surge by 430 percent.

Can the Growing Human Population Feed Itself?

A more generous food supply will be achieved in the future through boosting crop yields, as it has been accomplished in the past. If the harvested area in the developing world remains at 0.7 billion hectares, then each hectare must more than double its yield to maintain an already inadequate diet for the future population of the developing world. Providing a diet equivalent to a First World diet in 1990 would require that each hectare increase its yield more than six times. Such an event in the developing world must be considered virtually impossible, barring a major breakthrough in the biotechnology of food production.

Instead farmers will no doubt plant more acres and grow more crops per year on the same land to help augment crop harvests. Extrapolation of past trends suggests that the total harvested area will increase by about 50 percent by the year 2050. Each hectare will then have to provide nearly 50 percent more tons of grain or its equivalent to keep up with current dietary levels. Improved diets could result only from much larger yields.

The technological optimists are correct in stating that overall world food production can substantially be increased over the next few decades. Current crop yields are well below their theoretical maxima, and only about 11 percent of the world's farmable land is now under cultivation. Moreover, the experience gained recently in a number of developing countries, such as China, holds important lessons on how to tap this potential elsewhere. Agricultural productivity responds to well-designed policies that assist farmers by supplying needed fertilizer and other inputs, building sound infrastructure and providing market access. Further investments in agricultural research will spawn new technologies that will fortify agriculture in the future. The vital question then is not how to grow more food but rather how to implement agricultural methods that may make possible a boost in food production.

A more troublesome problem is how to achieve this technological enhancement at acceptable environmental costs. It is here that the arguments of those experts who forecast a catastrophe carry considerable weight. There can be no doubt that the land now used for growing food crops is generally of better quality than unused, potentially cultivable land. Similarly, existing irrigation systems have been built on the most favorable sites. Consequently, each new measure applied to increase yields is becoming more expensive to implement, especially in the developed world and parts of the developing world such as China, where productivity is already high. In short, such constraints are raising the marginal cost of each additional ton of grain or its equivalent. This tax is even higher if one takes into account negative externalities—primarily environmental costs not reflected in the price of agricultural products.

The environmental price of what in the Ehrlichs' view amounts to "turning the earth into a giant human feedlot" could be severe. A large inflation of agriculture to provide growing populations with improved diets is likely to lead to widespread deforestation, loss of species, soil erosion and pollution from pesticides, and runoff of fertilizer as farming intensifies and new land is brought into production. Reducing or minimizing this environmental impact is possible but costly.

Given so many uncertainties, the course of future food prices is difficult to chart. At the very least, the rising marginal cost of food production will engender steeper prices on the international market than would be the case if there were no environmental constraints. Whether these higher costs can offset the historical decline in food prices remains to be seen. An upward trend in the price of food sometime in the near future is a distinct possibility. Such a hike will be mitigated by the continued development and application of new technology and by the likely recovery of agricultural production and exports in the former Soviet Union, eastern Europe and Latin America. Also, any future price increases could be lessened by taking advantage of the underutilized agricultural resources in North America, notes Per Pinstrup-Andersen of Cornell University in his 1992 paper "Global Perspectives for Food Production and Consumption." Rising prices will have little effect on high-income countries or on households possessing reasonable purchasing power, but the poor will suffer.

In reality, the future of global food production is neither as grim as the pessimists believe nor as rosy as the optimists claim. The most plausible outcome is that dietary intake will creep higher in most regions. Significant annual fluctuations in food availability and prices are, of course, likely; a variety of factors, including the weather, trade interruptions and the vulnerability of monocropping to pests, can alter food supply anywhere. The expansion of agriculture will be achieved by boosting crop yields and by using existing farmland more intensively, as well as by bringing arable land into cultivation where such action proves economical. Such events will transpire more slowly than in the past, however, because of environmental constraints. In addition, the demand for food in the developed world is approaching saturation levels. In the U.S., mounting concerns about health have caused the per capita consumption of calories from animal products to drop.

Still, progress will be far from uniform. Numerous countries will struggle to overcome unsatisfactory nutrition levels. These countries fall into three main categories. Some low-income countries have little or no reserves of fertile land or water. The absence of agricultural resources is in itself not an insurmountable problem, as is demonstrated by regions, such as Hong Kong and Kuwait, that can purchase their food on the international market. But many poor countries, such as Bangladesh, cannot afford to buy food from abroad and thereby compensate for insufficient natural resources. These countries will probably rely more on food aid in the future.

Low nutrition levels are also found in many countries, such as Zaire, that do possess large reserves of potentially cultivable land and water. Government neglect of agriculture and policy failures have typically caused poor diets in such countries. A recent World Bank report describes the damaging effects of direct and indirect taxation of agricultures, controls placed on prices and market access, and overvalued currencies, which discourage exports and encourage imports. Where agricultural production has suffered from misguided government intervention (as is particularly the case In Africa), the solution—policy reform—is clear.

Food aid will be needed as well in areas rife with political instability and civil strife. The most devastating famines of the past decade, known to television viewers around the world, have occurred in regions fighting prolonged civil wars, such as Ethiopia, Somalia and the Sudan. In many of these cases, drought was instrumental in stirring social and political disruption. The addition of violent conflict prevented the recuperation of agriculture and the distribution of food, thus turning bad but remediable situations into disasters. International military intervention, as in Somalia, provides only a short-term remedy. In the absence of sweeping political compromise, hunger and malnutrition will remain endemic in these war-torn regions.

Feeding a growing world population a diet that improves over time in quality and quantity is technologically feasible. But the economic and environmental costs incurred through bolstering food production may well prove too great for many poor countries. The course of events will depend crucially on their governments' ability to design and enforce effective policies that address the challenges posed by mounting human numbers, rising poverty and environmental degradation. Whatever the outcome, the task ahead will be made more difficult if population growth rates cannot be reduced.

Article Questions

1. As the population of the world will probably exceed 10 billion by 2050, name the two schools of thought and their positions in dealing with the environment and the future of humanity. What is your view before you read this article?

2. How much has food production increased in the third world between 1965 and 1990? How much has population expanded during this time period? What is the result?

3. What is the argument in the article concerning the amount of arable land in the developed world and undeveloped world?

4. What is the problem with increased food per hectare from the "green revolution" and irrigation systems?

5. Explain the issue of genetic uniformity.

6. According to the optimists, how much additional land could be cultivated?

7. How can yield improvements be achieved according to the optimists?

8. Explain the argument of the optimists concerning waste, storage and distribution losses of food.

9. How can the potential for food expansion be realized?

10. How much would food production have to rise in order to bring the Third World diet to the level found in the developed world?

11. What do you feel is the role of new technology in boosting this production?

12. Explain the author's view in accomplishing increase in food production. Explain your view.

Discussion Questions

Population Control

During the recent years, many scientists and economists have expressed a concern about the population growth and scarcity of resources. The world population has increased from 3.72 billion (1970) to 5.32 billion (1990) and is projected to be 10 billion by year 2010. Many experts believe that Earth's population is about to surpass the planet's "carrying capacity". Contrary to this, world bank figures show that food prices have declined dramatically to an historic low—reflecting improvements and a worldwide surplus of grain. The population growth rates in the developed countries are low whereas for the developing counties they are high.

To address the question of population control the United Nations (UN) held a conference in Cairo. The conference adopted a resolution for the population control. The resolution document called "Proposed Program of Action for the Cairo Conference" calls for adoption of various birth control methods including abortion for population control. The majority of the third world countries with Catholic and Muslim populations think that the UN has gone too far in making these recommendations. The UN recommendations are in direct contradiction to the religious beliefs of Catholics and Muslims all over the world. The Pope has formed a Catholic-Islamic alliance to oppose UN recommendations for population control.

1. Do you think that the UN is justified in recommending population control strategies that contradict people's religious beliefs?

2. In many third world countries the majority of people are farmers. Due to a lack of technology and resources, they believe in having large families in order to manage their farms. What population control strategy would you use to help third world farmers?

3. Many third world nations believe that Population is an asset and that the developed countries are trying to control their future potential through the United Nations. Do you agree with view? Why? Why not?

CHAPTER FIVE
WAR, POLITICS & TECHNOLOGY

Air Power Comes of Age

David Callahan

When U.S. warplanes attacked Bosnian Serb targets in April 1994, the engagement marked a turning point both in the anguished debate over U.S. military intervention in the Balkans and in the more enduring controversy over the role of air power in U.S. military strategy. Since late 1992, advocates and opponents of intervention had debated whether selective air strikes could help halt Serbian aggression in the mountainous, heavily forested terrain of Bosnia-Herzegovina, or whether such action would only lead the United States into another Vietnam-like quagmire. The Clinton administration's decision was motivated largely by the sense that Western passivity in the face of Serbian aggression had become an unacceptable option, but it also reflected a new willingness to experiment with a limited approach to the use of air power.

Ever since the invention of the airplane in the early 1900s, military analysts have disagreed about its potential to determine the outcome of modern conflicts. And after every war, there has been bitter argument about how much air power achieved and how best to use it in the future. Consensus has been elusive in large part because of the clash of powerful institutional interests. For the Air Force, claims about air power were first a ticket to bureaucratic independence and then a path to ever-larger shares of the Pentagon's budgetary pie. For the Army, such claims have long been seen as jeopardizing its central role in the nation's defense.

In recent years, following the spectacular performance of U.S. aviation forces in the Persian Gulf War, the air power debate has taken a new and important turn. Contrary to assessments made by many analysts before Operation Desert Storm, it is now clear that advances in technology and tactics mean that air power can—under the right circumstances—exact a devastating and decisive toll on armored forces in the field, even if these forces operate at night or in bad weather. While the potential of air power remains limited in many situations, especially those involving insurgency-type warfare, the outcome of the Gulf War has again raised the question of whether air power alone can win certain wars.

As the United States confronts growing pressure to intervene in conflicts around the globe, air power is increasingly seen as a way to flex U.S. military muscle without risking the lives of American ground troops. This new potential may make possible deeper cuts in military spending. Thus, the stakes of today's air power debate go far beyond a budgetary squabble between the Army and the Air Force.

New Lessons in an Old Debate

Before the Gulf War, arguments surrounding air power drew on two principal cases: World War II and the Vietnam War. To many, the lesson of both these conflicts was that air power alone could not prove decisive in defeating an enemy. During World War II, hopes that air power could smash Germany's civilian morale and defense industry proved unfounded; meanwhile, Japan continued to fight in the face of massive fire-bombings of its cities. In Southeast Asia, a military victory was elusive even as U.S. aircraft dropped three times as much bomb tonnage as was used during all of World War II. As historian Loren Baritz commented in his 1986 book on Vietnam, summing up the jaded view of many observers: "Over and over again we have to learn the lesson that air power cannot win wars, and having learned it we immediately forget it."

The wreckage of a lost techno-war stood as powerful evidence for those who preached skepticism about air power following Vietnam, yet these critics clearly misinterpreted the experiences of both this war and World War II. According to the final report by the U.S. Strategic Bombing Survey, issued in 1946, "Allied air power was decisive in the war in Western Europe." Though the long-range bombing of Germany proved disappointing, the survey found that tactical air power was vital in supporting Allied forces during and after the 1944 invasion of Normandy. The survey also claimed that even without the use of atomic weapons, the relentless pounding of Japan by U.S. bombers would eventually have guaranteed that country's unconditional surrender, without requiring a ground invasion.

In Vietnam, U.S. bombing raids repeatedly failed to sever supply lines into South Vietnam or to destroy Viet Cong forces in the field. However, the massive bombing of North Vietnam in 1972 is widely credited with helping to secure the peace agreement signed in January 1973. And though the Air Force's high-tech weapons proved disappointing through much of the war, by the early 1970s, U.S. aircraft were employing "smart" missiles and bombs in a manner that portended their later success in the Persian Gulf. U.S. pilots used these weapons with devastating effectiveness to repel the 1972 Easter invasion of South Vietnam—one of the few instances when North Vietnam employed armor in open terrain. Laser-guided bombs, a technology that became familiar even to civilians during the Persian Gulf War, were used frequently during the United States' final few years in

Vietnam to take out bridges, rail links, and other vital targets. Of the 21,000 laser-guided bombs dropped in Vietnam, some 17,000 reportedly struck their targets.

The Persian Gulf War offered incontrovertible evidence that air power can, under the right circumstances, play a decisive role in military conflict. Numerous U.S. commentators had expressed skepticism that Iraq's forces could be ousted from Kuwait without a bloody ground war, yet few later doubted that it was the awesome destruction wrought by U.S. air power that won the war. Though the Bush administration decided to launch a major ground offensive, both to end the war more quickly and to humiliate Saddam Hussein, it is clear that prolonging the air war would inevitably have led to Iraq's withdrawal from Kuwait. Rather than preparing the battlefield for ground forces, the role traditionally envisioned for tactical air power, U.S. aircraft had destroyed an enemy land army virtually alone.

At the Pentagon, officials voiced minimal disagreement about the decisive role of air power. As Secretary of Defense Dick Cheney said in 1991, the Iraqi army "was crushed, I think, by the air campaign.... [W]hen we finally did have to move our ground forces in, and we sort of kicked in the door, they collapsed fairly rapidly." In early 1992, Cheney commented that the Iraqis "didn't fight back because the air war turned out to be absolutely devastating."

The Gulf War demonstrated aviation forces' new ability, absent in World War II and Vietnam, to strike precisely at targets deep inside enemy territory. The United States crippled Saddam Hussein's command-and-control network by striking 45 key targets in Baghdad, while avoiding the kind of carpet bombing that was central to U.S. attacks against Berlin and Tokyo during World War II. Relatively small numbers of precision attacks achieved enormous success against Iraqi power supplies. In many cases, a single air strike was sufficient to disable a power plant; in World War II, by contrast, it took scores of B-17 bombers dropping hundreds of bombs to achieve the same results. The United States required roughly 500 sorties and 1,200 tons of bombs to shut down 28 of Iraq's oil refineries, disabling its oil production. In World War II, U.S. bombers dropped 185,841 tons of bombs during 50,000 sorties against 69 Nazi refineries, but cut production by only 60 percent.

In North Vietnam, U.S. forces found it nearly impossible to take out key bridges and railroads from the air until the introduction of laser-guided bombs. In the Gulf War, the United States easily destroyed 41 important bridges and 32 replacement pontoon bridges in a matter of weeks. And the performance of U.S. forces in the Gulf War showed that they could successfully confront a Third World power heavily armed with surface-to-air missiles, antiaircraft guns, and interceptor planes. While North Vietnamese air defenses had inflicted heavy losses on U.S. aircraft, U.S. forces in the Persian Gulf were able to neutralize similar defenses and minimize their losses.

Technology and Tactics

Weapons such as laser bombs and guided missiles clearly played a crucial role in the increased precision and diminished vulnerability of U.S. air forces in the Gulf War. "There is no doubt about it, precision-guided munitions validated themselves towards the end of the Vietnam War and they rewrite a whole chapter on how to conduct air operations as a result of this war," commented Lt. Gen. Charles Horner, architect of the air campaign against Iraq.

Apart from precision-guided munitions, long available but only now being used to their full potential, U.S. air forces capitalized on other advances in technology—stealth, radar imaging of ground forces, and new systems for managing communications on the battlefield—and in tactics.

Stealth technology involves the use of new designs and materials to minimize the likelihood that an aircraft will be detected by radar or infrared sensor systems. For instance, oblique angles are used to deflect radar waves away from the receiver; afterburners are eliminated to reduce heat emissions. Without stealth, U.S. bombers can still penetrate heavy air defenses, but this effort is a complicated undertaking, requiring large numbers of support aircraft to jam enemy radars and disable surface-to-air missile sites. In contrast, as Gen. John M. Loh, commander of the Tactical Air Command, explained in 1991, "Stealth gives us freedom of action, the freedom to penetrate radar defenses when and where we want at points and times of our choosing, the freedom to concentrate our mission planning on destroying targets rather than countering enemy threats, and the freedom to use the best attack option every single time." In Operation Desert Storm, says Loh, stealth "enabled us to gain surprise each and every day of the war."

The use of radar imaging has given the United States new capabilities for acquiring targets. Aircraft carrying the airborne warning and control system (AWACS), for instance, combine several types of advanced radar, sensors, and communications equipment to provide a mobile airborne command post surveying air, land, and sea. Unlike ground radar, which is fixed in position and scans overhead, AWACS aircraft enable U.S. planners to track hundreds of enemy aircraft simultaneously, even from hundreds of miles away. Though it was first deployed in the 1970s, this technology is still unavailable to most Third World countries.

During the Gulf War, the United States also deployed a system to track armored vehicles and "see" the battlefield on the ground. Called the Joint Surveillance Target Attack Radar System (JSTARS), it uses radar technology mounted on a modified Boeing 707 aircraft to link air and ground operations while flying behind friendly lines. Both wide-area and detailed radar is built into the plane's belly. Along with other technologies, JSTARS was able to pinpoint the location of heat-producing Iraqi tanks and armored personnel carriers at night and in bad weather.

The Gulf War also showed that individual aircraft using infrared sensors could locate armored forces under conditions of limited visibility. Even dug-in Iraqi tanks proved vulnerable at night because they cooled less quickly than the surrounding desert.

Advances in data processing have permitted improvements in battlefield management as well. In the past, it took military officers hours or even days to collect information about the location of enemy forces and develop battle plans based on that information. Today, faster computers and better links among different elements of the U.S. military allow commanders or even pilots to synthesize information from ground radar stations, surveillance aircraft, satellites, and listening posts almost immediately, so that they can mount attacks with minimal delay.

Complementing these technological advances are doctrinal changes implemented over the past decade that have greatly increased the effectiveness of air power. During the 1970s and 1980s, U.S. planners sought to offset a quantitative Soviet advantage in Western Europe with tactics that would take advantage of the U.S. technological edge to strike at an enemy's so-called centers of gravity. What emerged from this process was a military doctrine known as AirLand Battle. Defense analyst Michael Klare explains that the strategy places new emphasis on "identifying enemy structural weaknesses, particularly command-and-control nodes, and targeting those for early attack." AirLand Battle thus offers a means of hobbling a large force structure, quickly achieving air superiority, and paving the way for the decisive use of air power against enemy land forces. "Synchronized, violent execution is the essence of decisive combat," stated a Pentagon document describing AirLand Battle. The fruits of this doctrinal change were displayed in the first hours of the Gulf War, when U.S. aircraft struck a range of key Iraqi command targets, disabling large portions of the Iraqi air-defense system and severely damaging Saddam's ability to manage his forces.

Implications for the 1990s and Beyond

To many observers, the Gulf War proved that air power could become the primary instrument for winning future wars. "After an eighty-year maturation process, air power now dominates modern warfare," declared Air Force Col. Dennis Drew, a leading air power theorist, in a spring 1991 article in *Strategic Review*. Following Desert Storm, the Air Force stepped up lobbying for more spending on everything from the new F-22 fighter plane—a plane built to replace the F-15—to a program to convert B-1 nuclear bombers into the "workhorses" of a long-range U.S. conventional bombing force that could attack future enemies from bases in the United States.

Other analysts, however, have rightly warned against indiscriminately applying the lessons of the Gulf War to other conflicts. Iraq's dismal performance in the Gulf War is certainly cause for caution. The circumstances surrounding the Gulf War favored the United States in several respects. "What we did not learn was how to defeat a modern, well-trained, well-motivated force in a dynamic environment," commented Frank Kendall, undersecretary of defense for tactical warfare programs, in 1991.

While advances in military strategy and technology have increased air power's effectiveness against a modern nation dependent on complex command systems and fielding large armored forces, it remains a less useful instrument against decentralized insurgent forces. It is also less effective in forested or mountainous terrain. In this sense, key lessons about air power learned in Vietnam remain valid.

Air power could not decisively sway battlefield conditions in South Vietnam in part because of the jungle terrain, but also because the Viet Cong did not orchestrate their operations through a small number of centers of gravity. Nor did these operations, often executed by guerrilla forces, depend on the use of armored equipment that could be targeted with precision-guided munitions. Efforts to cut off supplies transported to South Vietnam along the Ho Chi Minh trail were doomed because the level of materiel required to sustain operations in the South was extremely low. Even with today's sophistication, air power would probably have been unable to defeat the insurgent forces operating in South Vietnam.

An appreciation of the limitations of air power underlay the Clinton administration's uncertainty about launching air strikes against Serbian artillery in Bosnia. In April 1993, former Joint Chiefs of Staff chair Colin Powell told Congress that bombing alone could not win the war. "They are locked into a conflict," he explained, "and if the killing does not take place by artillery it will probably take place by some other means."

Powell's successor, John Shalikashvili, had also expressed doubts that air power could achieve decisive results. "There is no military solution," Shalikashvili said just days before NATO issued its February 1994 ultimatum threatening air strikes in retaliation for any further Serbian aggression. "The only way the conflict will stop is if the three parties want to stop it and agree to a truce." Even Air Force analysts, many of whom supported intervention, acknowledged the many unknowns surrounding air strikes in the Balkans and questioned whether air strikes alone could persuade the Serbs to reverse their course.

The recent conflicts in the Persian Gulf and Bosnia, combined with an understanding of past wars, suggest that the truth regarding air power's potential lies somewhere between the extreme positions that have often characterized the air power debate. The specific strengths and weaknesses of air power have important implications for U.S. defense policy in the 1990s and beyond.

First, it is far from clear that Third World states heavily armed with modern weapons present the extreme danger that Pentagon officials suggest in attempting to justify annual defense expenditures of near-Cold War levels. Iraq had one of the finest integrated air defenses in the developing world, including 16,000 surface-to-air missiles and 7,000 antiaircraft guns. It also had an advanced air force that included more than 900 combat aircraft and boasted some of the best French- and Soviet-made fighters available. When war came, however, this equipment proved nearly worthless. Iraq's vaunted air defenses were quickly rendered inoperable; when aircraft did come up to intercept attackers, they proved no match for American planes.

Neither is it clear, as claimed by the Pentagon, that the United States must invest in a new generation of high-tech weapons to maintain its qualitative edge over potential new foes. In easily defeating one of the Third World's most advanced military powers, the United States was aided by the use of JSTARS, cruise missiles, and the F-117 stealth fighter, but less sophisticated weapons also played an important role. Central to U.S. operations were less glamorous military technologies like electronic warfare equipment, night-vision devices, laser-technology kits to upgrade bombs, and navigation and target pods that can be added on to planes. Many of these technologies have been in use since the 1970s and were mounted on planes that were old or not especially sophisticated. F-111 bombers built in the late 1960s, for example, were able to destroy Iraqi armor at night and in bad weather through the relatively inexpensive technique of adding on infrared systems and laser-guided bombs. Much of Iraq's armor was destroyed by the cheapest combat aircraft in the U.S. Air Force, the A-10 Thunderbolt.

The Gulf War showed that highly sophisticated air power elements can speed victory and save American lives. But it also showed that, given the weakness of Third World states, low-tech weapons are still adequate in handling many missions on the modern battlefield. In addition, the huge U.S. advantage in battlefield management proved as important as the performance of individual weapons.

Given low rates of literacy and technological competence, Third World military forces often cannot maintain and operate advanced military equipment, and lack the sophistication to exploit the full potential of these weapons. This fact was dramatically underscored nearly a decade before the Gulf War, when Israel used advanced battlefield management techniques to devastate Syrian air defenses and aircraft during warfare in 1982. "Conventional warfare depends increasingly on the skillful manipulation of electronically transmitted information," military analyst Eliot Cohen has observed. "The advantage goes overwhelmingly to combatants who can bring together information from many sources."

Toward Win-Hold-Win

In recent months, U.S. officials have focused with concern on North Korea, designating it as the leading "threat state." Yet while North Korea deploys military forces as large as Iraq's in 1990, the experience of the Gulf War indicates that this threat may be less significant than Pentagon planners suppose. "North Korea's armed forces suffer from many deficiencies," CIA director Robert Gates told Congress in 1992. "Their training and, consequently, combat readiness is questionable. They have weaknesses in air defenses and logistics.... The North Korean defense industry is based on 1960s technology and beset by quality problems."

If war came to the Korean peninsula, North Korean commanders might well find themselves, like their Iraqi counterparts in January 1991, largely blinded within the first few hours or days of hostilities as U.S. air strikes wiped out key command-and-control nodes. North Korean ground forces could find, as the Iraqis did, that turning on mobile air defenses means having them destroyed by radar-seeking HARM missiles. North Korean combat pilots might quickly learn, as the Iraqi pilots learned, that taking off is nearly suicidal in the face of U.S. systems that can track them from the moment they leave the runway and attack them with air-to-air missiles launched outside visual range. Without air defenses or close air support, North Korean forces in the field might soon conclude, as did tens of thousands of Iraqi soldiers, that flight or surrender is their best option.

None of this means that a new Korean war would be won effortlessly; on the contrary, most analysts agree that it would be far bloodier than the Gulf conflict. But it is clear that North Korea suffers from many of the same weaknesses that assured Iraq's defeat. Far from substantiating the Pentagon's argument that Third World threats can in some cases be of First World magnitude, Desert Storm undermined it, calling into question the need to spend tens of billions of dollars on expensive and sophisticated new weapons.

Pentagon officials, for example, have insisted that the expensive F-22 fighter program, conceived at the height of the Cold War, should go forward in large part to ensure air superiority over future regional adversaries. Yet the lesson of Desert Storm is that such adversaries are not even close to challenging such superiority and that the United States can indefinitely maintain its edge in the air with existing aircraft. Plans to spend billions on programs to adapt the B-1 and B-2 nuclear bombers for conventional missions should similarly be recognized as exercises in overkill. The advantage of using a larger plane is that it can drop larger quantities of bombs. However, the success of smaller tactical aircraft in precisely striking important targets deep in enemy territory during the Gulf War argues against the need for larger conventional bombers. Both the F-22 and the B-1 and B-2 conversion programs should be canceled.

The effectiveness of air power in the Gulf War also casts doubt on the Pentagon's insistence that the United States must be able to fight simultaneously two major regional wars with ground troops—the so-called win-win strategy. Last September, former Secretary of Defense Les Aspin issued the *Bottom-Up Review*, a planning document that analyzed the needs of U.S. military forces through the 1990s and reaffirmed the Bush administration's policy of preparing for a two-war scenario. Aspin and his successor, William Perry, have argued that only by preserving the capability to implement a win-win strategy can the United States avoid tempting aggressors to act in one part of the world when it is waging war in another. However, plans for fighting two wars simultaneously would require substantially larger ground forces than would be needed to fight two wars in quick succession—a strategy known as win-hold-win.

A win-hold-win strategy would use air power alone to confront and contain the attacking forces of one regional aggressor while employing a full spectrum of forces to deal with another aggressor. Once the first land war was won, U.S. ground forces would be redeployed to the theater where air power had been holding the line. Under a win-hold-win scenario, which Aspin originally favored, the Pentagon could take steps over the next few years to reduce the defense force to one large enough to handle a Desert Storm-size contingency and with enough reserves left over to conduct a large-scale humanitarian operation or other minor intervention. This would entail cutting the number of aircraft carriers planned under the *Bottom-Up Review* from 12 to 8, cutting the number of Army divisions from 10 to 8, and cutting the number of tactical air wings (analogous to Army divisions) from 13 to 10.

Several recent analyses suggest that the new effectiveness of air power makes a win-hold-win strategy viable. A 1992 study by the RAND Corp. simulated regional conflicts that might arise between 1997 and 2010. Like the Pentagon's own planning documents, its analysis focused on managing simultaneous conflicts in Iraq and North Korea, regarded as the most likely sites of future confrontations. The study hypothesized an Iraqi invasion of the Saudi peninsula that would involve a force larger than the one it deployed in 1990 and that would thrust farther south. It concluded that U.S. air power alone would be able to stop the enemy offensive in two weeks and destroy the bulk of Iraq's armor in another ten days at most. This implies that if the United States were waging a ground war in Korea, it could feel confident in its ability to contain another Iraqi invasion on the Saudi peninsula.

Less clear from the RAND study, however, is whether the reverse is also true: Could U.S. air power stop and largely obliterate a North Korean invasion force while U.S. ground troops were tied down in Southwest Asia? This scenario would place greater demands on U.S. forces. With the South Korean capital of Seoul not far from the border, a North Korean invasion force would have a greater chance of scoring significant gains before it could be stopped by air power. Moreover, as the invasion moved into densely populated areas, the United States would find it harder to employ air power, both because of the risks of killing civilians and because battlefield sensors, so effective in a barren desert environment, would be impaired in terrain filled with civilian cars and trucks.

These limitations on air power in Korea do not mean that a win-hold-win strategy is imprudent. Unlike Saudi Arabia, South Korea is hardly a sitting duck. In recent years, South Korea's annual defense budget has been twice that of North Korea's, and while its forces remain smaller than that of its communist neighbor, South Korea deploys many tanks, combat aircraft, and naval vessels that are far superior to anything fielded by the North Koreans. Its forces have also benefited from years of training by U.S. advisers and are more capable than ever of putting up a tough fight. Meanwhile, according to the CIA, North Korea's military forces are becoming increasingly obsolete. South Korean forces, backed by U.S. troops and equipment already posted in the area and limited U.S. air support, would likely deter North Korean aggression even in the far-fetched case that U.S. ground forces became tied down in Southwest Asia fending off another Iraqi invasion.

A Redistribution of Forces

The recent drawdown of U.S. forces has been carefully orchestrated to distribute new cuts evenly among the services. Shifting the balance of power within the armed forces is difficult: top Army officials bitterly contest any suggestion that ground forces have become less relevant on the modern battlefield.

"While the circumstances of warfare have changed considerably in terms of weapons system advances and capabilities . . . the essential nature of warfare has not changed," said Army Chief of Staff Gordon Sullivan in May 1993. "Units are still required to close with the enemy to get within direct fire range, engage the enemy, and either destroy him or force him to move off of contested terrain. War takes place where people live and people live on the ground. It is there that all the effects of our great military establishment are directed, to seize and control territory and make the enemy amenable to our will."

This situation underscores the need for decisive White House leadership in the area of defense policy. Since taking office, President Clinton has focused heavily on domestic matters, spending little political capital on the task of overhauling national security policy. Firmer leadership is needed to shake up a Pentagon that plans to spend nearly as much money over the next decade, in inflation-adjusted dollars, as it spent in the 1970s.

Clinton should undertake two tasks. First, he will have to take on the enduring problem of interservice rivalry, perhaps by revising the National Security Act of 1947 to broaden the powers of the secretary of defense. That legislation was aimed at breaking down divisions in the military by creating the Department of Defense. Yet it did not give the secretary of defense sufficient authority over the services. As a result, existing areas of redundancy—such as the separate air forces maintained by each service—have persisted. With the end of the Cold War and the escalation of fiscal pressures on the U.S. government, it makes sense to attempt a further consolidation of the military establishment. Along with reducing redundancy in the armed forces, this move could allow for a force structure that better reflects the new effectiveness of air power.

Second, the White House and State Department must challenge the dominance of worst-case thinking that guides U.S. defense policy and military spending. Despite a pledge to rethink U.S. defense assumptions from scratch, Aspin's *Bottom-Up Review* failed to acknowledge that the changing capabilities of air power carry profound implications for force planning: the costly and overcautious win-win regional defense strategy should be abandoned in favor of win-hold-win strategy.

Article Questions

1. List and explain the social and technological issues that you feel are important in this article.

2. What part did air power play in the Persian Gulf War? Do you think that air power alone can win wars?

3. Describe and list the differences between air power in WWII, Vietnam, and the Gulf Crises.

4. What are the implications for the 1990s in air power?

The Cold War Experiments

Stephen Budiansky, Erica E. Goode and Ted Gest

On June 1,1951, top military and intelligence officials of the United States, Canada and Great Britain, alarmed by frightening reports of communist success at "intervention in the individual mind," summoned a small group of eminent psychologists to a secret meeting at the Ritz-Carlton Hotel in Montreal. The Soviets had gotten Hungary's Joszef Cardinal Mindszenty, an outspoken anti-communist, to confess to espionage, and they also seemed to be able to indoctrinate political enemies and even control the thoughts of entire populations. The researchers were convinced that the communists' success must be the fruit of some mysterious and sinister scientific breakthroughs. By the following September, U.S. government scientists, spurred on by reports that American prisoners of war were being brainwashed in North Korea, were proposing an urgent, top-secret research program on behavior modification. Drugs, hypnosis, electroshock, lobotomy—all were to be studied as part of a vast U.S. effort to close the mind-control gap.

New revelations that government cold war experiments exposed thousands of Americans to radiation have prompted fresh congressional inquiries, including a hearing last week on tests conducted on retarded children in Massachusetts. A Department of Energy hot line set up to handle calls from possible subjects of the tests has been swamped. But the radiation experiments are only one facet of a vast cold war research program that used thousands of Americans as guinea pigs.

From the end of World War II well into the 1970s, the Atomic Energy Commission, the Defense Department, the military services, the CIA and other agencies used prisoners, drug addicts, mental patients, college students, soldiers, even bar patrons, in a vast range of government-run experiments to test the effects of everything from radiation, LSD and nerve gas to intense electric shocks and prolonged "sensory deprivation. Some of the human guinea pigs knew what they were getting into; many others did not. Still others did not even know they were being experimented on. But in the life-and-death struggle with communism, America could not afford to leave any scientific avenue unexplored.

With the cold war safely over, Energy Secretary Hazel O'Leary has ordered the declassification of millions of pages of documents on the radiation experiments, and the administration is now considering compensating the hundreds of subjects of these odd and sometimes gruesome atomic tests. But the government has long ignored thousands of other cold war victims, rebuffing their requests for compensation and refusing to admit its responsibility for injuries they suffered. And the Clinton administration shows no sign of softening that hard line. "We're not looking for drugs," says cabinet secretary Christine Varney. "At least initially, we need to keep our focus limited to human radiation."

In Clinton's Court

Now, the only hope for thousands who were injured or who were experimented on without their informed consent is that President Clinton or Congress will take action to compensate the forgotten casualties of the cold war. Continued secrecy and legal roadblocks erected by the government have made it virtually impossible for victims of these cold war human experiments to sue the government successfully, legal experts say.

Despite the administration's reluctance, Congress may be moving to seek justice for all the government's cold war victims. "It's not just radiation we're talking about," says Democratic Sen. John Glenn of Ohio, a former Marine and astronaut who is holding hearings on the subject this week. "Any place government experimenting caused a problem we should make every effort to notify the people and follow up. We ought to set up some sort of review and compensation for people who were really hurt."

Many of the stories of people whose lives were destroyed by mind-altering drugs, electroshock "treatments" and other military and CIA experiments involving toxic chemicals or behavior modification have been known for almost 20 years. But *U.S. News* has discovered that only a handful were ever compensated—or even told what was done to them. "There has essentially been no legitimate follow-up, despite the CIA's promise to track down victims and see what has happened to them," says Alan Scheflin, a professor at Santa Clara University Law School and an authority on cold war mind-control research. "It's just one of the many broken promises." A CIA spokesman last week said the agency is searching its files for radiation tests but has no plans to revisit other human experimentation.

MK ULTRA

Most victims have never been informed by the government of the nature of the experiments they were subjected to or, in some cases, even the fact that they *were* subjects. In a 1977 Senate hearing, then CIA Director Stansfield Turner said he found the experiments "abhorrent" and promised that the CIA would find and notify the people used in the tests. Turner last week insisted that "they found everyone they possibly could find." But internal memos and depositions taken from CIA officials in a lawsuit against the agency in the 1980s reveal that of the hundreds of experimental subjects used in the CIA's mind-control program, code-named MKULTRA, only 14 were ever notified and only one was compensated—for $15,000.

The 14 all had been given LSD surreptitiously by CIA agents in San Francisco in an attempt to test the drug in an "operationally realistic" setting. One of the victims, *U.S. News* discovered, was a San Francisco nightclub singer, Ruth Kelley, now deceased. In the early 1960s, according to a deposition from a CIA official who was assigned in the 1980s to track down MKULTRA victims, LSD was slipped into Kelley's drink just before her act at a club called The Black Sheep. The agents who had drugged her "felt the LSD definitely took some effect during her act," testified Frank Laubinger, the official in charge of the notification program. One agent went to the bar the next day and reported that she was fine, though another recalled that she had to be hospitalized.

Most of the MKULTRA documents were destroyed in 1973 on order of then CIA Director Richard Helms, and the records that remain do not contain the names of human subjects used in most of the tests. But they do clearly suggest that hundreds of people were subjected to experiments funded by the CIA and carried out at universities, prisons, mental hospitals and drug rehabilitation centers. Even so, according to Laubinger's 1983 deposition, "it was decided that there were no subjects that required notification other than those in the [San Francisco] project," and the CIA made no effort to search university records or conduct personal interviews to find other victims. Admiral Turner, in his 1983 deposition, conceded that "a disappointingly small number" were notified but defended the agency's continuing refusal to declassify the names of the researchers and universities involved. "I don't think that would have been necessarily the best way," Turner said. "Not in the litigious society we live in." In 1985, the agency successfully appealed to the Supreme Court to block release of that information.

One of the grisliest CIA-funded experiments—and one of only a few that have led to successful lawsuits against the government—involved the work of a Canadian psychiatrist, Dr. D. Ewen Cameron. In the 1950s, Cameron developed a method to treat psychotics using what he called "depatterning" and "psychic driving." According to a grant application he submitted in 1957 to the Society for the Investigation of Human Ecology, a CIA-funded front set up to support behavior-control research, the procedure consisted of "breaking down of ongoing patterns of the patient's behavior by means of particularly intensive electroshocks (depatterning)"—and in some cases, with repeated doses of LSD. This was followed with "intensive repetition (16 hours a day for six or seven days)" of a tape-recorded message, during which time "the patient is kept in partial sensory isolation." Cameron's application proposed trying a variety of drugs, including the paralytic curare, as part of a new technique of "inactivating the patient."

The 56-Day Sleep

The analogy to brainwashing was obvious to the CIA, which provided a $60,000 grant through the human-ecology society. Nine of Cameron's former patients, who had sought treatment for depression, alcoholism and other problems at the Allan Memorial Institute at McGill University, where Cameron was director, filed a lawsuit against the CIA in 1979. One patient, Rita Zimmerman, was "depatterned" with 30 electroshock sessions followed by 56 days of drug-induced sleep. It left her incontinent; others suffered permanent brain damage, lost their jobs or otherwise deteriorated. The case, *Orlikow v. U.S.*, was settled in 1988 for $750,000. (Cameron died in 1967.)

A more typical experience of those seeking recompense is that of Air Force officer Lloyd Gamble, who volunteered in 1957 to take part in a test at the Army Chemical Warfare Laboratories in Edgewood, Md. He told *U.S. News* that he was informed he would be testing gas masks and protective gear. Instead, he learned in 1975, he and 1,000 other soldiers were given LSD. "If they had told me of the risks, I never would have done it," he says now. "It was outrageous." He says after the test he was simply "turned loose to drive from Aberdeen to Delaware" while under the influence of LSD. "I didn't even remember having been there."

Gamble began suffering blackouts, periods of deep depression, acute anxiety and violent behavior. He attempted suicide in 1960, lost his top-secret clearance and finally took early retirement in 1968. When he belatedly learned he had been given LSD, he sought recompense. The Justice Department rejected his request because the statute of limitations had expired; the Veterans' Administration denied disability payments, saying there was no evidence of permanent injury.

The Defense Department says Gamble signed a "volunteer's participation agreement" and that he received two LSD doses. Gamble and others were told that "they would receive a chemical compound, the effects of which would be similar to those experienced from being intoxicated by alcoholic beverages." Democratic Rep. Leslie Byrne of Virginia is sponsoring a bill that seeks $253,488 for Gamble; DOD opposes the bill, saying there is "insufficient factual basis" for compensation. Such "private bills" usually are difficult to pass in the face of executive branch opposition.

Unreasonable Men?

Other cases filed by prisoners or soldiers who were given a variety of drugs have been dismissed by judges who have ruled that although the subjects did not learn until the 1970s exactly what had been done to them, the side effects and flashbacks they experienced immediately after the tests should have prompted "a reasonable man to seek legal advice" at the time.

"The failure to notify and promptly compensate the people who were victimized by these cold war excesses is inexcusable," argues James Turner, one of the lawyers in the *Orlikow* case. But he says the courts and the agencies now have made it virtually impossible for a victim to succeed in a legal claim. "Records are gone, key witnesses have died, people have moved; in the drug-testing cases, people are damaged in other ways, which undermines their credibility."

The justifications offered for these tests cover everything from cloak-and-dagger schemes to discredit foreign politicians to training military personnel. The Army exposed as many as 3,000 soldiers to BZ, a powerful hallucinogen then under development as a chemical weapon. The drug attacks the nervous system, causing dizziness, vomiting, and immobility. Thousands more also participated in the Army's Medical Volunteer Program, testing nerve gas, vaccines and antidotes.

Talkative

The earliest behavior-control experiments were part of a 1947 Navy project called Operation CHATTER, which was seeking "speech-inducing drugs" for use in interrogating "enemy or subversive personnel." The project was eventually abandoned because the drugs "had such a bitter taste it was not possible to keep the human subjects from knowing" they had been drugged.

But by 1952, undaunted by such setbacks, secret psychological research was booming. "One of the problems we had all the way along was the ingrained belief on the part of

[CIA] agents that the Soviets were 10 feet tall, that there were huge programs going on in the Soviet Union to influence behavior," John Gittinger, a CIA psychologist who oversaw the Human Ecology society's operations, told *U.S. News*.

A classified 1952 study by the U.S. government's Psychological Strategy Board laid out an entire agenda for behavior-control research. Calling communist brain-washing "a serious threat to mankind," scientists urged that drugs, electric shock and other techniques be examined in "clinical studies...done in a remote situation." The report even mused about the potential of lobotomy, arguing that "if it were possible to perform such a procedure on members of the Politburo, the U.S.S.R. would no longer be a problem to us," though it also noted that the "detectability" of the surgical operation made its use problematic.

Although there is no evidence that lobotomy experiments were ever performed, many other bizarre and intrusive procedures were. In 1955, the Army supported research at Tulane University in which mental patients had electrodes implanted in their brains to measure the LSD and other drugs. In other experiments, volunteers were kept in sensory-deprivation chambers for as long as 131 hours and bombarded with white noise and taped messages until they began hallucinating. The goal: to see if they could be "converted" to new beliefs.

As recently as 1972, *U.S. News* found, the Air Force was supporting research by Dr. Amedeo Marrazzi, who is now dead, in which psychiatric patients at the University of Missouri Institute of Psychiatry and the University of Minnesota Hospital—including an 18-year-old girl who subsequently went into a catatonic state for three days—were given LSD to study "ego strength."

Gittinger concedes that some of the research was quite naive. "We were trying to learn about subliminal perception and all the silly things people were believing in at that time," he says. One study even tried to see if extrasensory perception could be developed by "training" subjects with electric shocks when they got the wrong answer. But "most of it was exciting and interesting and stimulating, and quite necessary as it happens, during that period of time," Gittinger insists.

Another former CIA official, Sidney Gottlieb, who directed the MKULTRA behavior-control program almost from its inception, refused to discuss his work when a *U.S. News* reporter visited him last week at his home. He said the CIA was only trying to encourage basic work in behavioral science. But he added that after his retirement in 1973, he went back to school, practiced for 19 years as a speech pathologist and now works with AIDS and cancer patients at a hospice. He said he has devoted the years since he left the CIA "trying to get on the side of the angels instead of the devils."

Article Questions

1. Explain what "cold war experiments" were. Who was used for these experiments? Why?

2. List and describe the social and ethical issues that still persist today because of the "cold war experiments."

3. What is "the 56-day sleep?" Explain how it relates to Dr. D. Ewen Cameron's "depatterning" and "psychic driving."

Discussion Questions

1. How has the relationship between government and technology 'politicized' technology?

2. What impact have organizations such as the Office of Technology Assessment and the Office of Science and Technology Policy had on technological development?

3. How might regulatory agencies affect technological growth?

4. How might government prevent technological accidents?

5. Define the following: dominant sponsor, dominant regulator.

6. How should military technology be used in the post cold war world?

7. Should developed nations restrict the spread of military technologies to less developed and less stable societies? Why? How?

8. What ethical considerations, if any, are involved in the use of human beings to test the effects of new weapons technologies?

9. What is an important ethical issue regarding high-tech weapons use in the future?

10. What are global positioning systems?

11. What is thermal imaging technology?

12. Define J-Star.

13. What is stealth technology?

14. What role has technology played in changing the role of air power in military operations?

15. In your opinion, has military technology made the world safer or more dangerous?

16. How might improved military technology reduce incidents of 'friendly fire'?

CHAPTER SIX
SOCIAL RESPONSIBILITY

Whistleblowing

(Taken from "Whistleblowing" Psychology Today, August, 1986, pp. 37-43; "What It Takes to Blow the Whistle" Engineering Education, October, 1988)

As most people know, Roger Boisjoly was chief engineer at Morton Thiokol, the NASA contractor that built the Challenger shuttle booster rocket. Mr. Boisjoly is often asked whether he could have done more to prevent the disaster. Mr. Boisjoly became a whistleblower after he warned his employers of the fault with O rings which they ignored and his horror at being proved right when they caused the Challenger disaster.

Mr. Boisjoly is now a lecturer where he discusses engineering ethics and the obligation of individual engineers to disclose their reservations about safety. His moral commitments have also taken him to the courts where he has filed lawsuits against Morton Thiokol, the government and compensatory damages for a ruined career.

As early as March 1985, Mr. Boisjoly shared with his employer documented evidence about the O-ring brittleness in low temperatures. He presented data to this superiors, formed a team to address the 0-rings, wrote damning reports of the rings and finally recommended against the Challenger launch - all to no avail. Speaking up after the disaster, cost him his job. Boisjoly remains critical not only of his treatment but of Thiokol and NASA and their accountability. He states that NASA did not assess Thiokol a $10 million penalty but instead allowed the company to take $10 million less in profit (which was made up in interest saved by not paying the penalty); then Thiokol also raised the cost of the booster.

Boisjoly is equally concerned about the redesigned shuttle booster and remains unconvinced that the redesigned nozzle joint is the best or safest. He also feels the launch schedule is unrealistic and made to placate NASA.

Mr. Boisjoly feels that nothing he could have done would have changed the recommendation to launch the Challenger. Whistleblowing, he says, stems from an unsuccessful attempt to achieve change through the usual chain of command. If the response of management is unsatisfactory when issues are critical, employees have little alternative but to circumvent the chain of command and then consequently are punished by "blaming the messenger."Boisjoly states that ethical management has three main characteristics: clearly defined responsibility, authority given to enact the responsibility, and accountability.

According to interviews conducted by Myron and Peina Glazer of 55 whistleblowers and many of their spouses, most whistleblowers feel their major motivation is a strong belief in individual responsibility. Kathy Laubach, one resister's wife, says "A corrupt system can happen only if the individuals who make up that system are corrupt. You are either going to be part of the corruption or part of the forces working against it. There isn't a third choice. Someone, someday, has to take a stand; if you don't, maybe no one will. And that is wrong." Her husband, Vincent Laubach, worked for the Department of the Interior (DOI) in 1981 with the assignment of investigating the failure of strip-mining companies to pay required fines and reclamation fees for the use of public lands. He was under the impression that he had a mandate from the Reagan administration to collect millions of dollars but soon learned he didn't have the support from his superiors to do his job. He complained to the Inspector General's office that he wasn't being allowed to do his job and the allegations were reported to Laubach's superiors to DOI. They ordered Laubach to cease contacts with anyone outside his office, and a few months later fired him when he traveled to a clinic for a work related injury. He along with his wife Kathy pursued his case in the press and with members of Congress. In 1984, a House subcommittee concluded that the Interior Department had "flouted the law" and "failed miserably" in enforcing the strip-mining legislation. From a 1982 court decision in a suit from environmental groups, the Environmental Defense Fund now monitors collection efforts by DOI's Office of Surface Mining which confirms Laubach's initial charges. Finally in 1985 an agreement negotiated by the Government Accountability Project (GAP is a Washington-based organization that defends whistleblowers) and the Solicitor General's office of the DOI restored Laubach's right to his job and paid $24,000 to cover legal fees. Laubach is still not satisfied since the department has not collected the $150-200 million in assess fines and fees, and he feels that his case was settled favorable because of friends in Congress, excellent attorneys and media attention rather than the principal involved.

Article Questions

1. Define whistleblowing. How could the events presented in the cases in this chapter have been changed if someone had blown the whistle?

2. How does ethical decision-making relate to whistle-blowing? When the whistle is blown what effects does it have on the whistle-blower's life? Be specific.

3. In what situations would you blow the whistle? What if your decision saved lives but made you lose your job, family, and home? (This negative scenario is not unusual.) What do you think you would do? Why?

Aerospace Engineer
Sues Thiokol for Defamation

A Morton Thiokol Inc. engineer who told investigators about problems with rocket booster seals after last year's *Challenger* disaster yesterday accused his employer of defaming him for telling the truth.

Roger Boisjoly, in a $1 billion defamation and antitrust suit filed on the first anniversary of the space shuttle explosion, accuses the Utah defense contractor of impugning his professional reputation "to punish him for testifying truthfully before the Rogers Commission" and congressional committees that investigated the disaster.

Boisjoly, who told the panel headed by former Secretary of State William Rogers that he initially was prevented from talking to space agency investigators, alleges that Morton Thiokol threatened his job and portrayed him as "a disgruntled or malcontented employee whose views should be discounted and whose professional expertise should be doubted."

Boisjoly also accuses Morton Thiokol and the National Aeronautics and Space Administration of conspiring to give false testimony to mislead the Rogers Commission and the congressional panels that investigated the Jan. 28, 1986, shuttle disaster.

Seven crew members died in the shuttle explosion.

The lawsuit, filed here in U.S. District Court, alleges that "NASA consistently lied to the Congress and the public as to the safety record of the shuttles." NASA is not named as a defendant in the suit.

"Although Thiokol gave lip service to the idea of cooperation, in fact defendant removed plaintiff from any position where he could interact directly with NASA investigators and Thiokol publicly threatened his job, labeling him in press interviews as a 'tattletale,' " the lawsuit states.

Boisjoly alleges that since the mid-1970s, NASA and Morton Thiokol concealed from the public and company stockholders information about deficiencies in the seal joints.

Boisjoly was among the engineers who warned NASA officials the day before the *Challenger* launch of the dangers of a flight in cold weather.

The lawsuit says Boisjoly became disabled from "post-traumatic stress disorder and depression caused directly by the disaster" and "the intentional wrongdoings of NASA and Thiokol."

Article Questions

1. What was the Challenger disaster? Who was Roger Boisjoly? What did he tell NASA and Morton Thiokol about the potential dangers of launching the Challenger?

2. Why did Boisjoly sue Morton Thiokol?

3. Why do whistleblowers often get punished? Why can their testimony be threatening?

4. Why do you think that Morton Thiokol and NASA didn't stop the Challenger from being launched?

Cases

Molasses Spill
Boston, Massachusetts
1919

(Taken from "When Technology Fails" - 1994)

In the winter of 1919 in Boston, Mass. a five story-high tank of molasses fractured. Millions of gallons of molasses ran over and killed twenty-one people and injured over one hundred and fifty. Buildings, and animals were covered by 12,000 tons of molasses.

The fifty-foot high, ninety foot diameter steel tank was used by the U.S. Industrial Alcohol Company for storing up to 15,000 tons of molasses. The tank had been ordered from the Purity Distilling company. The most stressed part of the tank was the bottom ring. It and the other six rings in the tank were 5 to 10 per cent less than was shown on the original permit plans. The only way that the tank had been tested was to run six inches of water into it.

The tank held molasses for three years. It had contained varying amounts of molasees, the maximum of approximately 1.9 million gallons was held for up to twenty-five days. Several employees were aware that the seams of the tank were leaking molasses, but not one seemed to give it any thought.

Eyewitnesses said they heard sound and then saw a large river of molasses about two stories high explode and six children were immediately killed by it.

Apparently the tank had fractured, opened and a 2.5 ton part of the slower sections the tank burst into a playground 182 feet away. Another part of the molasses rive completely broke off one column of a close-by elevated railway. The river flowed at thrity-five miles per hour. At times it was fifteen feet high and one hundred and sixty feet wide. It flowed over horses, houses, men and their buggies, motor vehicles,and anything else in its path.

By the time the molasses river had stopped it had covered a two-block area. It had moved buildings off their foundations, rails from the elevated were hanging in the air. It took a week to find all of the bodies and a month to clear up the destruction.

After a trial it was found that the tank was not properly designed, built, or calculated by an engineer with experience. The failure was due to structural weakness.

Results of the Molasses Spill

1. The boston Building Department started requirements that all calculations of designers be filed with their plans.

2. That all drawings be signed by the Building Department.

3. The molasses river probably effected the adoption of engineering certification laws across the nation.

4. All plans for major structures must be checked by registered professional engineers.

5. The molasses river had resulted in many lawsuits. Over six million words of testimony filled 40,000 pages of court records. Over three thousand witnesses appeared in front of the Massachusetts Supreme court. The curt made the decision that the tank was underdesigned.

6. The total settlement for 125 damage claims was over one million dollars in 1925 dollars.

7. The molasses river heightened the attention that engineers needed to give when analyzing the impact of large stress increases at openings in metal plates or highly stressed connections.

Bibliography

Bluthardt, Robert. "Wave of Death" *Firehouse*, June 1983. pp.86-88, 136.

Brown, Burtis. "Details of the Failure of a 90-Foot Molasses Tank."

Engineering News-Record, May 1919, pp.974-76.

Frye, Ralph. "The Great Molasses Flood." *The Reader's Digest*, August 1955. pp.63-67.

Harding, Priscilla. "The Great Boston Molasses Disaster of 1919." *The American Legion Magazine*, December 1968, pp.12-15.

_____. "Bursting of Boston Molasses Tank Found Due to Overstress." *Engineering News-Record*, January 1925. pp.188-189.

Case Questions

1. If you had been working at the U.S. Industrial Alcohol company in 1919, what would have you done to prevent this accident from happening?

2. How does this case relate to social responsibility? Why do you think that the employees ignored the leaking tank seams? What is your opinion about why a tank would be approved for storing molasses when it was only tested with six inches of water? Why do you think a tank that was not properly designed, built, or calculated by an engineer with experience would be used? Why wouldn't anyone question its use when the seams began to leak?

3. How did the molasses spill change requirements, drawings, and certification laws?

Ford Pinto:
Unsafe at Any Speed

Between 1971 and 1978, the Ford Pinto was America's best selling subcompact car. Over one million units were sold. The technology applied to the Pinto made it light(less than 2,000 pounds), cheap(under $2,000) and fuel efficient. However, it appears as if the technology used to achieve those things was done at the expense of the necessary technology needed to keep Pinto owners safe. Safety flaws in Pinto's fuel tank design revealed that the tank could explode upon rear end collisions.

By the mid 1980's at least fifty nine people had been burned to death in Pinto accidents. Perhaps equally tragic was the fact that Ford executives knew about the car's safety defects and went ahead with its sale anyway.

Because Pinto was Ford's first significant entry into the small car market, it was rushed into production to keep pace with foreign competition. Development of a new car typically takes about 43 months. Pinto's was slashed to 25 months. Other corners may have been cut. Tooling for production may have occurred before the quality assurance process was completed. Ford also rejected a design plan that would place the gas tank in a less vulnerable position, claiming that to do so would eliminate valuable luggage space. The consequences of this design decision were apparently known to Ford executives, whose own testing proved that the Pinto was prone to catch fire when rear-ended.

But according to internal Ford documents the cost of correcting the problem was more than the company estimated it would have to pay out in accident related lawsuits.

Despite brisk sales, things began to unravel for Ford and its Pinto in 1977. *Mother Jones*, a San Francisco based investigative magazine published an article citing flaws in Pinto's fuel tank assembly. Specifically the article claimed that the tank sat too close to the rear bumper, that the filler tube was likely to break upon impact spilling gasoline on the ground, and that bolts on the differential housing were dangerously close to the tank and could puncture it. The magazine also charged that in the event of a crash the vehicle's front doors tended to jam shut, preventing escape. That same year Ralph Nader's Center For Auto Safety began receiving consumer complaints about the Pinto. Finally the National Highway Transportation Safety Administration took action, ordering a defects investigation of the Pinto, and hinted at a forced recall. Ford documents recovered during the investigation showed that the car's fuel tank could leak when struck by a car travelling as slow as 20 miles per hour. A safety document on fuel tank integrity said that major revision was necessary in order for the tank to withstand a 30 mph crash. Despite their own testing Ford executives defended their car as being as safe as any other of its size on the market. And they were right; Pinto did meet all established federal standards. However, in 1977 these standards did not include a requirement that cars withstand a specified rear-end collision force.

In 1978, under consumer pressure and the threat of a massive government recall, Ford voluntarily recalled 1.4 million 1971-1976 Ford Pintos. The cars were fitted with high-density polyethylene shields around the gas tank. However, the tank itself was not repositioned, which many critics argued should have been done. The recall cost Ford approximately 30-40 million dollars, and officials hoped the controversy had at last been laid to rest. But in August, three Indiana teenage girls were burned to death when their 1973 Pinto was rear-ended by a van. The suit in the wake of that accident started a flood of litigation, including over fifty civil and class action suits. Despite Ford's acquittal in the Indiana case, the negative publicity doomed future Pinto sales. The car rapidly lost market share, and in 1981 was discontinued, replaced by the Escort. However, Pinto related deaths continued through the 1980's and by mid-decade 59 people had been killed in fires caused by rear end collisions.

Case Questions

1. Describe the positive technological advances the Pinto contained.

2. What was the primary technological defect in Pinto's design?

3. What does the article say about Ford's knowledge of the problem?

4. How was the public made aware of the problems with the Pinto?

5. What was Ford's response to charges the Pinto was unsafe?

6. Consider the following scenario: you are the president of Ford; your engineers tell you about a dangerous defect in one of your automobiles and urge you to halt production. Your managers tell you that delaying production will be expensive, and your lawyers tell you that paying legal fees for accident related lawsuits would be cheaper. What would you do and why?

The Toxic Cloud Over Bhopal

Ahmed S. Khan

In the early hours of December 3, 1984 a toxic cloud of methyl isocyanate (MIC) gas from Union Carbide's plant in Bhopal,India, escaped and enveloped the hundreds of shanties and huts surrounding the plant. The deadly cloud drifted in the cool night air through streets in surrounding neighborhoods killing and badly injuring thousands of people. By dawn inhabitants of Bhopal had become victims of the worst industrial accident.

A report drawn up eight months later, by two international trade union confederations, suggested that it was a combination of management mistakes, badly designed equipment and poor maintenance that caused the accident. The gas was formed when a plant employee added water to methyl isocyanate storage tank. The water caused a reaction that built up heat and pressure in the tank, and quickly converted the chemical into lethal gas that escaped into the atmosphere. The sensors and alarms that could have detected and indicated the increase in pressure and heat in the MIC tank, were inoperative. The plant's flare tower that could have been used to burn off the escaping gas, was inoperative too. The warning sirens were used with one hour delay. There was no evacuation plan prepared beforehand for such an emergency. The civil authorities and the population of Bhopal were also not informed about the degree of toxicity and the movement of the MIC gas cloud.

Approximately twenty-seven tons of MIC vapor, and fourteen tons of reaction products, were released in the atmosphere over a period of ninety minutes and affected an area of fifteen square miles.

The MIC gas leak was not the first accident at the plant, in the preceding four years there had been six accidents, some of which involved MIC, including one fatality in 1981 which led to an official investigation. The findings of that investigation were not acted upon until after the accident in 1984.

The Union Carbide developed it's plant in 1969 at Bhopal, initially as a mixing and packaging plant for pesticides imported from the United States. Later, in 1980 it was expanded to manufacture the pesticides Sevin and Temik. One chemical used in large quantities in the production process was methyl isocyanate (MIC), a highly reactive, volatile and toxic compound. The process that reacted MIC with an other compound, was considered the leading technology for producing pesticides Sevin and Temik. The development of plant was part of Indian government effort to achieve industrial self-sufficiency. The plant was located on the outskirts of Bhopal on land leased to Union Carbide India Limited (UCIL) by the Indian state government of Madhya Pradesh, at an annual rent of about Rupees 500 ($40).

In 1984 Union Carbide reported sales of $9.5 billion, reflecting its position as one of the largest Industrial companies in the United States and the world. The International operations were responsible for approximately 30 percent of total sales that year. India was one of three dozen countries where Union Carbide had business interests. In 1984 Union Carbide India Limited (UCIL) celebrated its 50th anniversary. It operated 14 plants with an work force of 9,000 people. UCIL had sales of about $200 million annually. In 1984 the entire work force at Bhopal plant was Indian. In keeping with the government's interest in promoting self-sufficiency and local control, the last American employed at the plant had left two years before, making the plant an all Indian operation.

The legal dimensions of the Bhopal disaster began when Indian prosecutors brought charges of criminal negligence against the Indian and American management of Union Carbide in the Indian courts. In 1985 the government of India on behalf of the victims of Bhopal, filed a civil suit against Union Carbide in the Federal District Court in New York City. The U.S court decided that India was the proper site for any Bhopal action and sent the litigation there for disposition. The Indian government filed suit in India for $3.3 billion. After several years of negotiations, Union Carbide agreed to a settlement of $470 million with the government of Ragiv Ghandi. The dropping of all criminal charges against Union Carbide executives was part of the settlement.

After the elections in India, the government of new prime minister V.P Singh repudiated the Indian Supreme Court and rejected the $470 million settlement as "totally inadequate". His government announced its intention to return to the original $3.3 billion claim and to pursue criminal charges against Union Carbide executives. Following a lengthy review by the Indian Supreme court, the original settlement was upheld and the criminal proceedings were reopened. Union Carbide has paid, as ordered $190 million in interim compensation which the government of India has to distribute among survivors pending the final outcome of the settlement. Presently the Indian government is providing survivors 200 Rupees a month (approximately U.S $10). These payments are to last as long as the case remains unsettled in the Indian courts. It is expected that the litigation and debate over the criminal prosecution for negligence and financial compensation will not end soon.

No matter what kind of settlement is reached in courts, the survivors face a nightmare future of uncertainty. Thousands are now suffering from a host of ailments including acute respiratory distress, vomiting blood, conjunctivitis, damaged eyesight, pain in the abdomen and injuries to liver, brain, heart, kidneys and immune system. In addition to these problems, women are also suffering from gynecological complications such as menstrual and reproductive disorders. An epidemiological study of the yearly rate of spontaneous abortions and infant deaths in the years after the accident found rate in Bhopal to be three to four times the regional rate.

Today, at personal, local, national and international level, the Bhopal disaster, remains a reality. Like Union Carbide's plant in Bhopal, a number of chemical plants belonging to multi-national corporations, are operating in the third world countries. The lack of environmental and occupational safety regulations in the developing countries, coupled with multi-national companies desire to increase earnings per share at any cost, sets the stage for reoccurrence of Bhopal catastrophe.

The Bhopal Catastrophe	
Chemicals Leaked	Approximately twenty-seven tons of Methyl Isocyanate (MIC) vapor and fourteen tons of reaction products.
Threshold limit value (TLV) of MIC established by United States Occupational Safety and Health Act (OSHA).	0.02 parts per million over eight hour period.
Exposure area	Fifteen square miles
Deaths	2352 - 10,000
People Disabled	17,000 - 20,000
People Exposed	200,000
People Evacuated	70,000

Bibliography:

Kurzman, Dan. A killing Wind, New York, N.Y, McGraw-Hill Company, 1987.

Gottschalk a. Jack. Crisis Response, Detroit, Michigan, Visible Ink Press, 1993.

Schlager, Neil. When Technology Fails, Detroit, Michigan, Gale Research, 1994.

Goldsmith, Edward and Hildyard, Nicholas. The Earth Report-The Guide to Global Ecological Issues, Los Angeles, California, Price Stern Sloan, Inc. 1988.

Case Questions:

1. What lessons should the chemical industry have learned from the Bhopal disaster?

2. What could be done at personal, local, national and international levels to promote safety in the chemical plants?

3. In the third world more than half a million people are poisoned every year by the pesticides, but they also save millions from starvation. Should the use of pesticides be banned worldwide ?

4. What steps and measures could Union Carbide have taken to avert the disaster at Bhopal?

5. How do you feel about the $470 million settlement ? Is it an appropriate amount for 200,000 survivors for the rest of their lives?

Silicone-gel Implants—1960-1990's

(Taken from "When Technology Fails - 1994)

Since the 1960's, over one million American women have received silicone-gel implants, and until January of 1992, 120,000 to 150,000 women a year have undergone silicone-gel implant surgery.

At first, the implants were not regulated by the federal government, but in 1976, the U.S. food and Drug Administration was made responsible and new regulations were developed in 1988 which required more safety information about the products by July 1991. The implants were found to have three key problems: (1) deterioration in time where replacement is necessary; (2) the flexible sacs can leak gel; and (3) the sacs can rupture at the fate of four to six percent.

Silicone-gel implants have been linked with many health problems including arthritis, inflammations, swollen joints, rashes, autoimmune system problems and scleroderma where the skin becomes tight and leathery.

Two following case studies illustrate an apparent health risk experience attributed to the implants; however, over 90 percent of women who have had them seem satisfied, and many physicians who have studies them have concluded that the implants are safe. Negative reactions do occur but on the overall are infrequent.

Case A

In 1977, a thirty-two-year-old woman received surgery for silicone-gel implants. The next day, she came down with a 104 fever and heavy sweating. Four days after the operation, she experienced pain in her fingers and toes. Eight days after the operation, her joints began to swell. Ten days after the operation she experienced abdominal pain and her kidneys were enlarged. It became more difficult for her to breathe, her kidneys began to deteriorate and she became delirious. All the while the incision on her breasts were healing normally and tests for fluid were normal. Concerned doctors decided to remove her implants on the eleventh day after her operation where the implants looked normal. Her condition improved sharply within 24 hours. Fluid samples showed the presence of silicon compounds. Six days after the implant removal, she was released from the hospital. Three weeks after her discharge fluid samples were normal, and at the end of three months she was back to normal. After considerable testing, doctors concluded that the implants caused the incident.

Case B

In 1976 a forty-six-year-old women received silicone-gel implants for cosmetic reasons and had them replaced twice. Her second operation was in September 1987 when her doctors discovered a rupture or leak of one implant. In November, 1987, her face, hands, legs and feet became swollen at times. She went to her doctor for treatment where her symptoms improved temporarily. She continued to experience tightness of skin and firm, discolored patches of skin on her legs. In July, 1988, she was diagnosed with scleroderma which, if left untreated, could begin to affect her internal organs and cause death. The scleroderma continued to spread and worsen and her legs became so stiff that she could not continue her running exercises or aerobics classes. Because of the negative silicon-gel publicity, she had her implants removed and replaced with saline implants. After their removal, her symptoms had improved, and she returned to her running and aerobics classes.

Effects of the Controversy

Because of the safety controversy of the implants, the manufacture of the implants has slowed to almost nothing, several thousand law suits have been filed, and lastly, the FDA has undertaken a long-range study to investigate the real safety of silicone-gel implants.

- In 1988, the FDA told manufacturers of silicone-gel implants that had to present detailed safety information about their products to the FDA by July 1991. The safety information showed no clear link between silicone-gel implants and autoimmune disorders or systemic diseases, but there was a lack of long-term safety data which caused the FDA to declare a forty-five day moratorium on the sale of silicone-gel implants beginning January 6, 1992.

- The publicity of the moratorium exacerbated the legal and financial problems of silicone-gel manufacturers. In 1984 in San Francisco a jury awarded a Nevada woman $1.5 million in damages against Dow-Corning. It was later settled out of court for an undisclosed sum. In December of 1991, another San Francisco jury issued a $7.3 million verdict against Dow-Corning somewhat based on the reason that Dow-Corning had not warned doctors of a possible link of silicone implants with autoimmune disease. After the moratorium in January, 1992, lawsuits increased substantially. By February 1993, an estimated three thousand silicone-gel implant lawsuits had been filed in state and federal courts. By January 1993, a Texas court awarded $25 million to a claimant against the Bristol-Myers Squibb company. Bristol-Myers Squibb closed its silicone-gel implant business in September 1991 and Dow Corning closed its in March 1992.

- In September 1993, Dow-Corning created a $4.75 billion liability fund to compensate those injured by implants where victims could receive between $200,000 and $2 million and removal of implants. The fund would be paid into by those insurance companies, doctors, and manufacturers being sued. The plan awaits approval by a judge.

- In September 1993, a settlement was reached to end the manufacture of silicone-gel implants by US companies by 1995. One one company existed (The Mentor Corporation) by 1993.

- Silicone-gel implant surgery for women who need surgery to replace an existing device or for a mastectomy will still be allowed by the FDA.

- Because of this controversy, the FDA will conduct a long term, scientifically controlled study to determine the safety and effectiveness of silicone-gel implants.

Case Questions

1. Briefly explain the health risks associated with silicone-gel implants.

2. Why would silicone-gel implants fit into a social responsibility chapter? Whose responsibility should it have been to stop this technology from having a negative effect on women?

3. Why do you think that the implants continued to be manufactured when there was a lack of long-term safety data on them?

Discussion Questions

1. How do you define social responsibility? How does social responsibility relate to technology? Give five examples.

2. List ten technologies. What social issue relates to each technology (e.g. the correlation between the development of the birth control pill and "free love" in the sixties)?

3. Social responsibility lies with you. As an adult what are five issues that are important to you within the realm of social responsibility (e.g. responsibility for recycling to help the environment)?

4. What social and technological issues have become a concern for you at work? In educational settings? At home?

CHAPTER SEVEN
HEALTH AND TECHNOLOGY

Power Politics: Playing with Children's Lives?

Alasdair Philips

Public concern over the risk to health of electromagnetic fields is likely to become "one of the important environmental public health issues of the nineties", according to the National Regulatory Research Institute in the USA[1].

But in the UK, developers are still being allowed to build next to and underneath electrical power-lines. Some Local Authorities are now starting to introduce restrictions, but these are really as a result of the pressure of concerned individuals and so lack the consistency and backing that Central Government advice would provide.

Concern has been triggered by evidence pointing the finger at long-term chronic exposure to low-level power frequency magnetic fields as a danger to health.

Unfortunately scientific acceptance of the ELF (extremely low frequency) interaction has been hampered by lack of a credible mechanism. This has tended to mean that many scientists have dismissed the evidence out of hand, and has made the methodology and planning of experimental work difficult. Even the way that biological and physical sciences are separately taught has had a hindering effect on understanding.

But now several likely resonance mechanisms have been put forward to explain how low levels of low-frequency electric and magnetic fields could affect biological processes.

Biological Interactions

Just as a radio receiver can be used to detect and decode a specific coherent signal at an intensity below the overall background noise, there is considerable evidence that coherent time-varying fields which coincide with natural ion magnetic resonances can have biological effects at very low levels—for example effects on the pineal gland.

The pineal gland is a tiny, cone-shaped structure within the brain, whose main function is secretion of the hormones melatonin and serotonin.

Melatonin plays a major part in controlling human circadian rhythms: its production peaks at night and is suppressed by bright lights and low ELF magnetic fields. It also affects levels of other important hormones—including serotonin. Segal *et al* (1989) found considerably lowered levels of serotonin and dopamine in mercat monkeys chronically

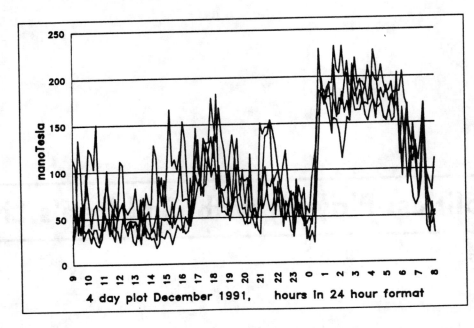

50Hz magnetic field in a domestic bedroom. RMS magnetic flux, from 415V + neutral supply at 8m distance. As most people are asleep and relatively motionless during the night, these coherent magnetic fields provide the optimum conditions for ion-resonance interaction to occur.

Prudent avoidance—the UK reaction

The term "Prudent Avoidance" was published in a report by US Office of Technology Assessment for the US Congress. It covers not only transmission lines and distribution lines, but house wiring and other electrical devices, and implies taking prudent action to minimise fields at modest cost.

Professor Ross Adey explains that prudent avoidance as a part of public policy was a "very necessary way to tackle the problem." It implied not putting power lines over people's heads, restricting the access of builders to vacant land next to high-voltage power lines, and specific avoidance of school sites as a matter of public responsibility.

"British authorities' attitudes absolutely avoid confronting the evidence as it now exists," he says, although the NRPB (National Radiological Protection Board) is doing work of the "highest merit in its scientific content, and it indicates that there is reason to be concerned."

　　　　　　　　　　　　　　　Power Politics: Playing with Children's Lives?

exposed to low levels (up to 10µT) of ELF magnetic fields. Both chemicals are known to affect mood changes and are linked with depressive illness: a study of clinically depressed people published in *The Lancet* in 1987 showed lowered levels of serotonin in every case.

Serotonin also has an important function in many bodily processes including effectiveness of the immune system.

Mechanisms for Concern

One probable mechanism, based on an ion cyclotron resonance model, is gaining considerable support.[3,4] It relates the motion of electrically charged particles to the magnitude of the steady magnetic field surrounding them.

The importance of this for humans is that blood contains ions in the critical mass range for resonance in the Earth's geomagnetic field and an alternating field between 1 and 500Hz. If a time-varying magnetic field parallel to the steady field (or an electric field orthogonal to it) is applied near the resonance frequency, then energy is transferred to the charged particle. The theory seems to be well corroborated by experimental results on calcium, lithium, sodium, and potassium ions, all of which play key roles in living systems[5].

Unfortunately use of the word "cyclotron" in the original paper has caused some problems, as what is described is not actually classical cyclotron resonance. More recently, similar models have been proposed by Lednev[21] and Dr John Male of the National Grid Research and Development Centre[22]. Both propose that a magnetic field, amplitude modulated at the cyclotron resonance frequency, can affect ion vibrational patterns, though not through actual cyclotron resonance.

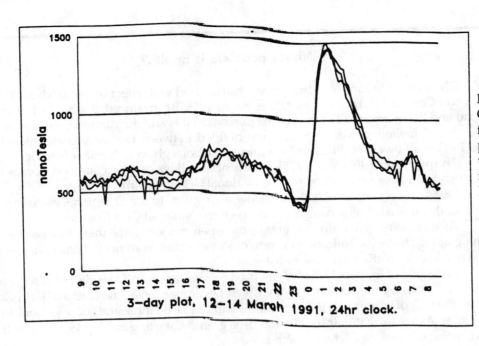

Main bedroom, Glebe Cottage, RMS magnetic flux from 33kV 50Hz power line. The field in this bedroom hardly falls below twice the level at which a three-fold increase in childhood cancer has been repeatedly demonstrated.

Drs Jafary-Asl and Smith of Salford University have a quantum magnetic resonance model which, for the Earth's geomagnetic field, relates the precession of molecules to a permanent magnetic moment[6,7].

Both mechanisms may be involved with resonances of hydroxyl (OH) and hydronium (OH3) which resonate in the 40 to 65 Hz band in the geomagnetic field[4].

Another mechanism now under investigation shows how changed spin states in haemoglobin molecules can produce a significant net magnetic moment. This attracts and traps the lymphocyte cells, greatly impairing the immune system response, and may well explain many cases of lymphatic leukaemia and other diseases[19].

Debating Point

Professor Ross Adey of the Loma Linda University in Florida, a respected researcher in this field for over 30 years, recently stated on Radio Scotland[8] that from the scientific point of view, there are four major areas about which "there can be very little doubt as to the significance of the findings".

He listed the areas as: effects on the immune system, with a reduction in the ability of the circulating white blood cells to kill tumour cells; effects on foetal development; control and regulation of cell growth—including tumour formation, and the effects on very powerful hormonal mechanisms in the central nervous system and the brain, which in turn have connections to cancer and cancer-related problems.

Professor Adey pointed out that work is being conducted in many laboratories worldwide, so that the old argument that this research describes uncorroborated experiments is no longer true. He says the most significant finding is that effects appear to be strongly synergic with chemical factors—although many of the effects could be seen from the fields alone.

Some known chemical promoters are significantly enhanced in their action by the presence of power-line frequency magnetic fields. Adey suggested that this may be a pointer to the clustering of cases where there may be a common chemical factor as well as the magnetic fields.

Looking at other possible effects, privately funded UK research work has also associated power-line magnetic fields with clinical depression and suicide[9], and headaches and depression[10] though this does not seem to have been followed up by the authorities.

Different Levels

The threshold at 60Hz above which published studies have repeatedly shown a three-fold increase in childhood cancers is 250nT. In 1990, a statement submitted to a US Congress committee by Dr Robert Becker, one of the pioneer researchers in this field, proposed that all new construction, transmission lines, sub-stations and distribution lines be required to produce "no more than 100nT" in any adjacent dwelling, school or public building. The proposal suggested the utility companies should produce a plan to bring existing installations into compliance by the year 2000.

Becker's view is probably fairly extreme, but at present there are no regulatory levels for the UK.

The current *NRPB Guidance GS11*(1989)—for electric shock and heating effects only—puts the level 20,000 times higher at 2mT, with the electric field maximum set at 12.3kV/m.

In its report R239 (July 1991) *Biological Effects of Exposure to Non-Ionising Electromagnetic Fields and Radiation*, the NRPB acknowledges that: "there are several possible areas of biological interaction which have health implications and about which our knowledge is limited."

"Aesthetics" Determine Power Line Policy

As part of their continuing studies perhaps the NRPB should investigate specific clusters already known about.

A good example is the case of the village of Dalmally in Perthshire[11]. Here at least eight people have died of cancer and three from motor-neurone disease in the last five years. All lived in houses lying near to the 275kV transmission line connecting Cruachan—the

---

Statutory limitations

Sweden's limit for ELF magnetic fields is 250nT at 0.5m in front of a VDU. New York has just set the limit for VDUs in schools to 200nT at 0.3m.

In the UK we can still sleep in 50Hz ELF fields of 10,000 times these level and Dr. Dennis (NRPB) is on record as saying that it is likely that it will be many years, if ever, that statutory limits on exposure will be applied in the UK.

In the meantime the NRPB and the Secretary of State for Health should come up with clear interim guidelines for new power-lines and building work near existing lines. The guidelines should be specified in magnetic and electric field strength levels and not just distance—though statutory rights-of-way as are used in the US would be a useful start.

Local authority planners surely have the right to be given this important information.

What price research

What is the electricity companies' approach to research? In fact both National Power and PowerGen are closing research facilities, with the loss of several hundred jobs. Since the retirement of Peter Chesters last year, nobody on the main board of National Power has full time responsibility for environmental issues. According to reports, Chesters' entire department is now being disbanded. (*Electrical Review*, Vol 224, No 23, Dec 1991).

National Grid Company's research projects associated with electrical and magnetic fields are:

Personal exposures study: 200 volunteers from the supply industry have been wearing exposure meters. Full analysis will be available by the end of 1992.

Magnetic environment research vehicles: Three vans have been fitted out to enable them to measure the magnetic environment. Initially they measured magnetic fields inside volunteers' homes. However, there seems to have been only a small output of data considering *three* vans active over *two and a half* years. Results are said to show average background levels around 50-60nT in houses.

Biological studies: Basic research is being supported in universities. Contracts were granted in 1990 for six separate studies.

Epidemiological studies: The UK Coordinating Committee for Cancer Research is planning a new large scale study of the incidence of childhood cancer in the UK. Although the UKCCR was not intending to include magnetic fields in this study, it now plans to do so.

UK's largest pumped-storage hydro-electric scheme—to the Grid, and will probably have been subject to quite high fields, especially at night when they were resting.

It should be quite easy to compare this small community with a similar one without powerlines but with all aspects of health included. Unfortunately that kind of study does not seem to get funding.

David Jeffers, National Grid's Spokesman on these matters recently put the Grid's position quite clearly, on Radio Scotland: "Our view is that there is certainly not an established link between any of the electric and magnetic fields and health effects".

National Grid was looking into the issue, said Jeffers, but that was only because it recognised that its consumers were concerned about the issue, and so it felt it should mount an effort to put their fears to rest. There may be a case on "prudent" grounds for keeping lines away from houses and National Grid had always followed that policy: "But we have done so on aesthetic grounds," he said.

As a footnote, Scottish Power says that planning is a function of local government and it sees no justification on health grounds for changing present practice with regard to the routing of power-lines.

Jeffers pointed out that the NRPB was charged with advising the Government on exposures and "there was a very clear Statement from the Secretary of State for Health last year that the NRPB has that responsibility[12]."

Replying to articles in *EW + WW* ("The Killing Fields"[17], Feb 1990), Dr John Dennis, then an Assistant Director of the NRPB said it would be "premature" to specify limits based on the possibilities for long term effects on health. Nevertheless: "there is obviously a case for avoiding unnecessary exposure and reducing exposure levels where this can be done easily" (*EW + WW*, April 1990, Letters).

Two years later the electricity companies still have not accepted even that level of concern, though they are now private companies whose combined profits last year were £1355 million. A statement by National Grid recently said that "Future research will be assessed on a commercial basis"[13].

Mistaken or Misleading?

The CEGB sponsored UK studies assume a very low background 50Hz magnetic field level of 10nT, and only take into account calculated levels due to overhead electrical lines at the birth addresses.

From my measurements I believe that a significant proportion of the UK population lives in 50Hz fields approaching or exceeding 100nT. People living near high power feeds could be subject to fields up to 25μT (25,000nT)—for example in older city areas, on the lower floors in blocks of flats, and in rural areas where power is still distributed along streets on poles.

My front bedroom is about 7m from a 415V three-phase and neutral pole supply to which only 14 houses are connected.

The figure shows the field levels experienced during one week, with the levels from four days plotted on the same graph. The resulting patterns were very similar from day to day, with noticeable peaks at 0700, 1800 and 2100hrs, and a very pronounced peak when the "Economy-7" off-peak electric storage heater demand starts just after midnight. As most people are asleep and relatively motionless during the night, these coherent magnetic fields provide the optimum conditions for ion-resonance interaction to occur. Concern about field levels caused me to get rid of my off-peak electric storage heaters a couple of years ago. Completely switching off my house supply makes negligible change in the magnetic field levels other than very close to electrical appliances.

The second figure shows the field in a bedroom of a house near to a 33kV distribution line. Again the close agreement from day to day is interesting, as is the very pronounced peak between 0100 and 0400hrs. The field in this bedroom hardly falls below twice the level at which a three-fold increase in childhood cancer has been repeatedly demonstrated, and peaks at six times that level. These graphs only show total magnitudes.

To investigate the ion-resonance theories we must know the magnetic vector details, as well as those of the local geomagnetic field. No epidemiological work published to date has used this essential extra data. (More details of the requirements are given in the section dealing with AC magnetic field measurement.)

In the introduction to its first study[15] the CEGB quotes the work by Wertheimer and Leeper, and Tomenius—both of which implicate fields above 250nT as being associated with a threefold increased risk of childhood cancer. Despite this CEGB has only chosen about 1.5% of cases and controls that were born in calculated fields of above 100nT for its own study. I have challenged the purpose and value of this study[17].

Recently[20] Dr Nancy Wertheimer, the epidemiologist working in this field since 1974, has made a number of comments about survey work. She suggests that because most studies have not checked that their control groups are actually experiencing low exposure, they are like those that compare people who smoke 2.5 packs of cigarettes a day with those who only smoke two packs. She goes on to say that evidence suggests that the critical period is between one and two years before diagnosis. Just using the birth address, as is done in the UK study, will therefore lead to invalid data.

Alasdair Philips

An extended and re-analysed[16] study allows that over 95% of cases and controls lived in calculated fields of less than 10nT, and only 0.5% in fields over 100nT and admits that the study stood "no realistic chance of detecting any raised relative risk associated with a field of more than 100nT". A more recent adult study also suffers a similar problem[18].

In January 1992, Dr David Jeffers, of National Grid, publicly stated:

We have a number of strong players in this programme. We have had what you call epidemiological studies, carried out in Yorkshire, of how childhood cancer correlates with the fields in the houses and how close the houses are to power lines, and the answer was no, we did not find a correlation in Yorkshire. A similar study on adults and leukaemia, carried out in Yorkshire and Lancashire, also did not fund an association[12].

I hope Dr Jeffers will explain to all of us his justification for describing these studies as "strong players", other than as part of "an effort to put their fears to rest".

Article Questions

1. Compare ionizing radiation with non-ionizing radiation.

2. How does ELF interact with biological tissue?

3. What is one of the important environment public health issues of the nineties?

4. What is the pineal gland? Explain melatonin. How does melatonin and the pineal gland relate to time-varying fields that coincide with natural ion magnetic resonances?

5. What happens if you change the spin state in hemoglobin molecules?

6. What effect might power lines have on the health of people living and working under them?

Withdrawal of Life-Support from Patients in a Persistent Vegetative State

We recently argued that doctors may sometimes be ethically justified in assisting the death of a patient with continued pain or distress caused by an incurable illness and who has expressed a clear and consistent wish for this outcome.[1] We believe that such a policy would be unlikely to lead to the unrequested ending of the lives of patients who are unconscious or severely demented. But could there be grounds for withdrawal of life-supporting medical treatment in such patients whose condition has been diagnosed with certainty as permanent, if they have previously expressed a similar wish? Such grounds may exist in the case of patients left in a persistent vegetative state after surviving an acute brain insult because of modern resuscitation and life-sustaining treatment.

Causes and Frequency

Patients in a persistent vegetative state have permanently lost the function of the cerebral cortex. About 40% have had severe head injury, with widespread severance of white matter fibres to and from the cerebral cortex. Another 40% have suffered massive loss of cortical cells because of hypoxia, usually after cardiorespiratory arrest due to disease, trauma, or medical accident. The others may have had various acute cerebral insults, including hypoglycaemia, poisoning, or one of several acute brain diseases. Extrapolations from surveys in Japan,[2] the Netherlands,[3] and the USA[4] indicate a likely annual incidence of over 600 newly vegetative patients from acute causes in the UK, with a prevalence of about 1500. Such estimates may be tripled if chronic diseases are taken into account: patients with chronic dementing brain disorders may eventually become vegetative, and some children with severe development abnormalities never surpass a vegetative state—but these cases are excluded from this report.

Clinical State

Such patients may have long periods of "wakefulness" with open eyes that alternate with "sleep." Jennett and Plum therefore held that it was inappropriate to regard these patients as in coma and suggested the term persistent vegetative state.[5] When awake the eyes may briefly follow a moving object by reflex, or be attracted in the direction of loud sounds. All four limbs are spastic but can withdraw from painful stimuli, and the hands show reflex groping and grasping. The face can grimace, small amounts of food or fluid put in the mouth may be swallowed, and groans and cries occur but no words are uttered. Although inexperienced observers may interpret reflex movements as voluntary responses, and vocal sounds as words, careful observation indicates no psychologically meaningful response to the environment. Breathing is spontaneous and the patient does not depend on artificial ventilation.

No available laboratory diagnostic test can indicate that a patient is permanently vegetative. Research investigation of some vegetative patients has shown a cerebral metabolic rate equivalent to that in deep anaesthesia.[4] Computed tomography and magnetic resonance imaging only show evidence of severe brain damage, not that the cortex as a whole is out of action, and electroencephalography is unhelpful. The diagnosis therefore depends on careful clinical observation over several weeks. Usually a confident diagnosis can be made 3 months after the acute insult,[6] but in young children the brain seems to be more resistant to hypoxic ischaemia and other insults, and the extent and timescale of recovery is less predictable.[7]

About 50% of patients left vegetative after an acute brain insult die within the first year. However, if they survive the first 3 months many such patients stabilise and may then live for years; there are many reports of survival for 5 years, and some for up to 30 years.[6] Prolonged survival requires continued artificial feeding, either by nasogastric tube or gastrostomy, but does not depend on an acute hospital; some patients may be looked after at home.

Survival at What Cost?

It is difficult to see how prolonged survival in this non-sentient and undignified state can be in the best interests of the patient. It is peculiarly distressing for the patient's relatives and friends to have to watch for years the unresponsive shell of a loved one. The economic and social consequences of indefinite treatment of vegetative patients may also mean that the medical and nursing care and resources that they receive, with no prospect of recovery, are denied to other patients who could benefit.

But while continued survival may not be in the best interests of patient, family, or society, the reasons commonly advanced for assisting death do not apply. Vegetative patients are not suffering, because the mechanisms for suffering have been destroyed. Nor are they terminally ill, because survival for many years is possible. Moreover, they are unable to request the withdrawal of life-supporting treatment. How can this dilemma be resolved?

Trends in the USA

There is a growing consensus in the USA that it may be appropriate to withhold life-sustaining medical treatment from vegetative patients. This attitude reflects increasing concern to respect patients' autonomy, including their right to refuse life-saving and life-sustaining treatment, and also to protect mentally incompetent patients from inappropriate medical prolongation of life.[8] In 1976, "do not resuscitate orders" emerged, and many hospitals and nursing homes now have formal arrangements to limit life-saving and life-sustaining treatments for both mentally competent and incompetent patients. Indeed, such agreements are becoming required by law, and more than 40 states have Natural Death Acts that legally recognise advance directives—in the form of living wills or durable powers of attorney—which enable people to anticipate the need for decisions to be made about their medical care when they can no longer express their wishes. Declarations on withdrawal of life-support, including reference to vegetative patients, have been made by a President's Commission,[9] the American Medical Association,[4,10] the Office of Technology Assessment,[11] and an international consensus.[12] Many US courts have approved requests to withdraw life-support from vegetative patients—usually when hospitals have insisted on a court order before agreeing to the requests of families—but several have recently commented that doctors and families ought now to decide and act without reference to the courts, except when there is serious disagreement. The US Supreme Court recently agreed with the principle of withholding life support from vegetative patients, but by 5 votes to 4 decided that a State could require convincing evidence that the patient had previously expressed a wish not to be kept alive in a vegetative state.[13,15]

What Treatments May Be Withdrawn?

Doctors who look after vegetative patients frequently agree with families and nursing staff to withhold antibiotics and cardiopulmonary resuscitation. But cardiorespiratory arrest seldom occurs and, even without antibiotics, repeated infections are often survived. May there be ethical grounds for artificial feeding to be withheld?

The first question to be addressed is whether artificial feeding is a form of medical treatment. The consensus in the USA, supported by professional and legal authority, is that feeding by nasogastric or gastrostomy tube is medical treatment; we agree with this view.

Secondly, will withdrawal of food and water cause the patient to suffer the unpleasant physical sensations usually associated with starvation and dehydration? We agree with the American view that there is no remaining neurological mechanism to make pain or suffering possible,4 and that good oral hygiene can be maintained by appropriate nursing care after food and fluids have been withdrawn.

Finally, giving food and water to the sick has symbolic significance as a mark of continuing care and an expression of humanity. But the symbolic significance of an act cannot be divorced from its purpose and context. In vegetative patients the normal purpose of sustaining life and easing the ravages of hunger and thirst do not apply, and feeding does not benefit the patient.

Conclusion

The majority view of the IME working party is that it can be morally justified to withdraw artificial nutrition and hydration from patients in a persistent vegetative state. The diagnosis and prognosis must be beyond doubt, and should be agreed by more than one experienced doctor. In such circumstances withdrawal of life-sustaining treatment could be agreed by them, by other carers, and by the relatives or friends of the patient. Some relatives may be reluctant, because they believe that life must be preserved in all circumstances, or because of unfounded optimism derived from certain manifestations of the vegetative state—a view which may be encouraged by some carers. Whilst the wishes of relatives should be respected, the working party believes it is unfair and unkind to allow unrealistic optimism to be sustained. In such circumstances many relatives may wish the patient to die at home, and occasionally a decision may be made to withdraw life-sustaining treatment from a patient who is already at home. However, relatives should not make such a decision on their own, without medical advice and support, because of possible legal repercussions.

The working party recognises that the legal position of such decisions, even with full medical support, is unclear in the UK—where there has been much less public discussion of these issues than in the USA,[16] and where living wills are not formally recognised.[17,18] For this reason it urges professional bodies to recognise publicly that withdrawal of artificial nutrition and hydration may be an appropriate way to manage vegetative patients. The availability of such declarations by professional bodies would enable individual doctors to raise this possibility sensitively with relatives, and would promote discussion of this difficult subject between professional carers and with the public.

References

1. Institute of Medical Ethics Working Party. Assisted death. *Lancet* 1990, 336: 610-13.

2. Higashi K, Sakata Y, Hatano M, et al. Epidemiological studies on patients with a persistent vegetative state. *J Neurol Neurosurg Psychiatry* 1977; 40: 876-85.

3. Minderhoud JM, Braakman R. Het vegeterende bestaan. *Ned Tijdschr Geneeskd* 1985; 129: 2385-88.

4. AMA Council on Scientific Affairs. Persistent vegetative state and the decision to withdraw or withhold life support. *JAMA* 1990; 263: 426-30.

5. Jennett B, Plum F. Persistent vegetative state after brain damage. A syndrome in search of a name. *Lancet* 1972; i: 734-37.

6. Jennett B. Vegetative state: causes, management, ethical dilemmas. *Curr Anaesth* 1990 (in press).

7. Campbell AGM. Children in a persistent vegetative state. *Br Med J* 1984; 289: 1022-23.

8. Mackay RD. Terminating life-sustaining treatment—recent US developments. *J Med Ethics* 1988; 14: 135-39.

9. President's Commission for the Study of Ethical Problems in Medicine and Biomedical and Behavioral Research. Deciding to forego life-sustaining treatment: ethical, medical and legal issues in treatment decisions. Washington, DC: US Government Printing Office, 1983.

10. AMA Council on Ethical and Judicial Affairs. Withholding or withdrawing life-prolonging medical treatment. *JAMA* 1986; 236: 471.

11. US Congress Office of Technology Assessment. Institutional protocols for decisions about life-sustaining treatments. Washington, DC: US Government Printing Office, 1988 (OTA-BA-389).

12. Stanley JM. The Appleton consensus: suggested international guidelines for decisions to forego medical treatment. *J Med Ethics* 1989; 15:129-36.

13. Angell M. Prisoners of technology: the case of Nancy Cruzan. *N Engl J Med* 1990; 322: 1226-28.

14. Lo B, Rouse F, Dornbrand L. Family decision making on trial: who decides for incompetent patients? *N Engl J Med* 1990; 322: 1228-32.

15. Annas GJ, Arnold B, Aroskar M, et al. Bioethicists' statement on the US Supreme Court's *Cruzan* decision. *N Engl J Med* 1990; 323: 686-87.

16. Williams BT. Life-sustaining technology: making the decisions in learning from America. *Br Med J* 1989; 298: 978.

17. Higgs R. Living wills and treatment refusal. *Br Med J* 1987; 295: 1121-22.

18. Gillon R. Living wills, powers of attorney and medical practice. *J Med Ethics* 1988; 14: 59-60.

Article Questions

1. Should there be grounds for withdrawal of life-supporting medical treatments? When? Who should decide? Do you believe in "living wills"?

2. At what cost (emotional, physical, and economic) should a patient stay alive? Should cost be eliminated as a factor in this difficult decision?

3. What is the current trend in America towards this issue?

4. At what point should patients be allowed to die?

Asking the Courts to Set the Standard of Emergency Care—the Case of Baby K

George J . Annas, J.D., M.P.H.

Almost two decades ago, Dr. Franz J. Ingelfinger predicted that if physicians kept turning to the courts "to resolve essentially medical matters," the medical profession's unfortunate "dependence on the lawyer in reaching essentially medical decisions will continue."[1] One can argue about what decisions are "essentially medical," but the trend that worried Dr. Ingelfinger has continued, and now physicians and a hospital have sought legal and judicial guidance about how—and whether—to treat an anencephalic infant known as Baby K.

Treating Baby K

Baby K was born by cesarean section on October 13, 1992, at Fairfax Hospital in Falls Church, Virginia. Anencephaly was diagnosed prenatally, and her mother decided to continue the pregnancy despite recommendations for termination from both the obstetrician and a neonatologist. The newborn had difficulty breathing at birth, and mechanical ventilation was begun. Within days the physicians began urging the mother (the father was only distantly involved) to agree to discontinue ventilation, since it served no therapeutic or palliative purpose and was therefore medically inappropriate. The mother refused. The physicians turned to the hospital's ethics committee and met with a subcommittee composed of a family practitioner, a psychiatrist, and a minister. On October 22 the subcommittee concluded that if the impasse between the physicians and the mother continued, a legal resolution should be sought.

Baby K was transferred to a nursing home on November 30, a time when she was not dependent on mechanical ventilation. Her mother agreed to the transfer on condition that the hospital would take the baby back if her respiratory difficulties recurred. On January 15, 1993, Baby K returned to the hospital for ventilatory support and stayed there until February 12. She has returned at least twice since. At this time she continues to reside at the nursing home. Assuming her diagnosis is correct, she may be the longest-lived anencephalic infant in medical history.[2]

Fairfax Hospital went to federal court seeking a ruling that it was not obligated to render "inappropriate" medical treatment to Baby K under existing federal and state law should Baby K again come to the emergency department in respiratory distress. The mother's position was that "all human life has value, including her anencephalic daughter's life."[3] She has "a firm Christian faith . . . [and] believes that God will work a miracle if that is his will.... God, and not other humans, should decide the moment of her daughter's death."[3] The hospital, the guardian ad litem appointed by the court, and Baby K's father all believed that further ventilatory assistance to Baby K was medically and ethically inappropriate.

The Opinion of the Trial Court

The trial judge, District Court Judge Claude Hilton, focused almost exclusively on antidiscrimination legislation in his opinion. Under the Examination and Treatment for Emergency Medical Condition and Women in Active Labor Act (Emergency Treatment Act), enacted by Congress to prevent the arbitrary refusal of treatment to uninsured people ("patient dumping"), all hospitals with emergency departments that receive Medicare funds must treat any person who arrives with an emergency medical condition and must continue treatment until the person's condition is stabilized and the person can be safely transferred.[4] Fairfax Hospital conceded that respiratory distress was an emergency condition but argued that the statute should be interpreted to include an exception for treatment deemed "futile" or "inhumane" by the hospital physicians. The judge disagreed for two reasons: first, the statute did not contain this exception, and second, even if it did, the exception would not apply to Baby K because her breathing could be restored; therefore, mechanical ventilation could not be considered either futile or inhumane. The judge added:

> To hold otherwise would allow hospitals to deny emergency treatment to numerous classes of patients, such as accident victims who have terminal cancer or AIDS, on the grounds that they eventually will die anyway from those diseases and that emergency care for them would therefore be "futile."[3]

Judge Hilton also ruled that section 504 of the Rehabilitation Act[5] and the Americans with Disabilities Act[6] both prohibited discrimination against Baby K based on her anencephaly. Finally, the judge ruled that as a general matter of law, "absent a finding of neglect or abuse," parents have the right to make decisions about medical treatment for their children.[3] When parents disagree with each other, the judge concluded that the courts should support the parent who decides "in favor of life."[3]

The Court of Appeals

On February 10, 1994, the U.S. Court of Appeals, in a two-to-one opinion, affirmed the July 1993 judgment of the trial court.[7] The appeals court, however, examined only one question in reaching its decision: Did Congress, in passing the Emergency Treatment Act, provide an exception for anencephalic infants (or anyone else) in respiratory distress? The court found the language of the statute clear and unambiguous: hospitals are required to stabilize the medical condition creating the emergency. In the court's words, "a straight-forward application of the statute obligates the hospital to provide respiratory support to Baby K when she arrives at the emergency department of the hospital in respiratory distress and treatment is requested on her behalf."[7]

In making its ease, the hospital suggested four reasons why the rule should not apply to Baby K, all of which were rejected. Two of the reasons merit discussion. The first was that Baby K's emergency condition was not respiratory distress, but anencephaly. The court disagreed, noting that it was her respiratory distress, not her anencephaly, that brought her to the emergency department. Second, the hospital argued that Congress did not "intend to require physicians to provide medical treatment outside the prevailing standard of medical care" in passing the Emergency Treatment Act. The appeals court seemed to agree with the hospital that the "prevailing standard of medical care for infants with anencephaly is to provide only warmth, nutrition, and hydration."[7] Nonetheless, the court held that the statutory language was "unambiguous" and included no such limitation on the hospital's responsibility to stabilize emergency conditions:

> We recognize the dilemma facing physicians who are requested to provide treatment they consider morally and ethically inappropriate, but we cannot ignore the plain language of the statute because "to do so would transcend our judicial function.... The appropriate branch to redress the policy concerns of the Hospital is Congress."[7]

Later in its decision the appeals court reiterated the point: "It is beyond the limits of the court's judicial function to address the moral or ethical propriety of providing emergency stabilizing medical treatment to anencephalic infants."[7] The court concluded that the Emergency Treatment Act makes no exception either for such infants or for

> comatose patients, those with lung cancer, or those with muscular dystrophy—all of whom may repeatedly seek emergency stabilizing treatment for respiratory distress and also possess an underlying medical condition that severely affects their quality of life and ultimately may result in their death.[7]

The dissenting judge argued that the Emergency Treatment Act was enacted to prevent patients from being dumped for economic reasons and that since dumping was not an issue with Baby K, the statute was irrelevant. He also argued that it was wrong to consider Baby K's treatment as involving a series of discrete emergency conditions; rather, her care should be "regarded as a continuum," since there is "no medical treatment that can improve her condition [of permanent unconsciousness]."[7]

Mixed Messages and Confused Roles

Many misjudgments were made in this case, but all relate to the failure to distinguish among medical standards, ethical precepts, and legal requirements. After birth Baby K was given mechanical ventilation. This was a medical misjudgment (assuming the physicians really believed it was medically inappropriate) that may have given the mother the impression that the doctors would provide medically inappropriate treatment to her child if she so desired. Since the physicians had known for months that she would be delivering an anencephalic baby, the issue or mechanical ventilation should have been resolved with the mother before the birth. If the physicians believed (on the basis of medical standards) that mechanical ventilation was contraindicated, the mother should have been informed that it would not be used and given an opportunity to find alternative care givers. If ventilation was to be used, the goal of this intervention (e.g., to confirm the diagnosis) should have been clearly specified, and support should have continued only until the goal was reached or was found to be unattainable.[8]

The ethics subcommittee at the hospital also misconstrued its role. It seems to have discussed nothing ethical at all. Composed of two physicians and a minister, it gave advice on medical practice and legal strategy, concluding that if the physicians could not reach agreement with the mother, the hospital should seek judicial relief. The subcommittee should have insisted that discussion with the mother continue until a resolution was reached, and it should have tried to facilitate this communication.

The hospital's administration and attorney seem also to have overreacted, though much more predictably. Instead or supporting their physicians in their application of existing medical standards or encouraging further discussion with the mother, they decided to go to court, because they saw Baby K's ventilatory support as a legal issue that might affect the institution, rather than an issue of medical practice or medical ethics.

The chief misjudgment by the trial judge was to try to act like a physician. His opinion can best he understood as that of a medical consultant who believes he has been asked one technical question: Can ventilatory support help an anencephalic infant in respiratory distress breathe more easily? His answer was yes.

The judge viewed this as a case of arbitrary discrimination by physicians against a mentally handicapped patient. He was correct that hospitals with emergency departments must provide medically appropriate treatment to stabilize the condition of all emergency patients. The physicians' desire not to give Baby K ventilatory support was, however, explained not by prejudice or financial concern, but instead by adherence to reasonable medical standards. Thus, the judge was chillingly wrong to equate Baby K (and anencephalic infants as a class) with patients with cancer or AIDS who are injured in automobile accidents. It is because of her anencephaly itself that Baby K cannot benefit from any medical intervention.[2] Patients with AIDS or cancer can, of course, benefit from emergency treatment.

To treat Baby K is not, however, inhumane (as the physicians argued), since she can neither feel pain nor suffer. But it is degrading to treat her for either our own symbolic purposes or those of her mother, because to do so is to treat her as an object—as a means to someone else's ends.[9] If the mere maintenance of biologic functioning in the absence of cortical function (vitalism) were a reasonable medical goal, physicians would be prohibited from ever discontinuing cardiopulmonary resuscitation in any patient, since it maintains circulation and ventilation. Nor has the judgment about treating anencephalic infants been made only by physicians. Congress and the executive branch have also been involved—the "Baby Doe regulations," for example, specifically recognized limits on care and the role of reasonable medical judgment in setting those limits.[9-11] The regulations themselves specified, and Surgeon General C. Everett Koop agreed, that a decision not to treat an anencephalic newborn is not discriminatory if based on a "legitimate medical judgment" that treatment would be "futile," because such treatment would "do no more than temporarily prolong the act of dying."[12,13] A parental request for treatment does not alter the physician's obligation to exercise reasonable medical judgment. The Child Abuse Amendments of 1984 are also consistent with this view.

By the time the case reached the more rarefied atmosphere of the Court of Appeals, the outcome was predictable. In answering its narrow question about the reach of the Emergency Treatment Act, the appeals court was correct: Congress provided no exceptions for anencephalic infants. On the other hand, I think the hospital was also correct in asserting that Congress did not intend to require physicians to provide emergency care "outside the prevailing standard of medical care." Certainly, neither side could point to any statute by which Congress has ever required physicians to violate existing standards of medical care. Nor is there any evidence that Congress intended to amend or in any way change the Baby Doe rules when it enacted the Emergency Treatment Act. It seems that the appeals court simply believed that the trial court had not acted unreasonably in favoring a mother who wanted her child treated over a hospital that wanted the child to die sooner rather than later.

The Role of Medical Standards

The logic of the Emergency Treatment Act as interpreted by these courts, although understandable in context, is incorrect because the technological imperative is limitless. To avoid cases like this one, Congress should have included the phrase "consistent with reasonable medical standards" in its requirement for stabilization. If the legal rule really were that hospitals and physicians had to provide any and all life-saving treatments to anencephalic infants that were wanted by the parents, they could be required to provide not only ventilatory support, but also other types of support, such as kidney dialysis for renal failure, and ultimately a heart-assist device when the child's heart begins deteriorating. As the dissenting judge properly argued, the focus must be on the patient as a person, not on the patient as reduced to a group of separate organ systems.

It is true that parents have (and should have) wide discretion in choosing among treatment options for their children. In the absence of evidence that a particular decision constitutes child abuse or neglect, we should presume that families can make the best decisions for their children. But it does not follow that physicians must do whatever parents (or adult patients themselves) order them to do regardless of standards of medical practice. Parents can choose among medically reasonable treatment alternatives, but they cannot prescribe treatment or demand that they or their children be mistreated.[14]

In the leading Supreme Court case cited by the trial judge, the Court upheld a state statute that permitted parents to commit a minor child to a mental institution without first providing the child with a court hearing.[15] But it did so only because the Court believed that the psychiatrist at the institution would act in the best interests of the child and not admit him or her unless the psychiatrist made an independent medical assessment that institutional care was in the child's best interests.[9,15] In another case, the Court ruled that retarded persons in state custody have a constitutional right to habilitation but that the content of that right should be left to the judgment of medical professionals.[16]

Thus, it is not the law that physicians must do whatever parents want. Rather, the law that parents should usually consent to treatment decisions made for their children is based on the premise that physicians will exercise independent medical judgment and not follow parental orders if the physician believes they are not in the best interest of the child or patient. In passing the Emergency Treatment Act, Congress was responding to situations in which physicians were refusing to treat patients in emergencies for economic reasons— not because of an exercise of medical judgment or standards of medical practice.

George J. Annas, J.D., M.P.H.

Because medicine has become a consumer good in many respects, and because many physicians and hospitals treat medicine as a business in which medical services are provided on the basis of the patient's desires rather than medical indications, it is becoming more and more difficult for physicians to refuse whatever patients and their families demand. Thus, for example, it is impossible for physicians to argue credibly that treating patients in persistent vegetative states is contrary to standards of medical practice, because most physicians actually provide continuing treatment if the family insists.[17,18] Treating medical care as a consumer good is a central reason why medical costs are out of control and why a national health plan that gives physicians financial incentives not to treat seems attractive to many policy makers.

What Should Be Done?

Before the case of Baby K, the medical standard of practice was to provide no artificial ventilation to anencephalic infants. Now, physicians in emergency departments are legally obligated to provide assistance, ventilatory and otherwise, to anencephalic infants who need it to survive. Emergency physicians can live with this rule, because the case is not likely to arise again.

There are three possible scenarios for the future. In the first, physicians will do whatever patients want (as long as they can pay for it), because medicine will be seen as a consumer commodity like breakfast cereal and toothpaste. This will make medicine even more unbearably expensive than it is. Therefore, the second scenario, a variation on Dr. Ingelfinger's vision, is more likely. The task defining "appropriate medical care" will be removed from physicians altogether and put in the hands of payers and government regulators, who will decide the content of medicine.

To avoid either of these scenarios, physicians must work toward a third, in which they not only set standards for medical practice, but also follow them. Physicians cannot expect parents, trial-court judges, insurance companies, or government regulators to take practice standards more seriously than they do themselves. If physicians cannot set standards for the treatment of anencephalic infants and adhere to them, standard-setting by physicians is a dead issue.

References

1. Ingelfinger FJ. Legal hegemony in medicine. N Engl J Med 1975;293:825-6.

2. The Medical Task Force on Anencephaly. The infant with anencephaly. N Engl J Med 1990;322:669-74.

3. In the Matter of Baby K, 832 F. Supp. 1022 (E.D. Va. 1993).

4. Emergency Medical Treatment and Active Labor Act, P.L. 99-272, 42 U.S.C. sec. 1395dd (1985) (renamed in 1989).

5. Rehabilitation Act of 1973, P.L. 93-112, 29 U.S.C. sec. 701-796i (1973).

6. Americans with Disabilities Act, P.L. 101-336, 42 U.S.C. sec. 12101-12213 (1990).

7. In the Matter of Baby K, 16 F. 3d 590 (4th Cir. 1994).

8. Paris JJ, Schreiber MD, Statter M, Arensman R, Siegler M. Beyond autonomy—physicians' refusal to use life-prolonging extracorporeal membrane oxgenation. N Engl J Med 1993;329:354-7.

9. Elias S, Annas GJ. Reproductive genetics and the law. Chicago: Year Book, 1987.

10. United States v. University Hospital, State University of New York at Stony Brook, 729 F.2d 144 (2d Cir. 1984).

11. Office of Human Development Services, Dept. Health & Human Services. Child abuse and neglect prevention and treatment program; final rule. Fed Regist 1985;50(72):14878-901.

12. Krushe H, Singer P. Should the baby live? New York: Oxford University Press, 1985.

13. Office of the Secretary, Department of Health and Human Services. Nondiscrimination on the basis of handicap relating to health care for handicapped infants; proposed rules. Fed Regist 1984;49(8): 1621-54.

14. Annas GJ. Judging medicine. Clifton, N.J.: Humana Press, 1988.

15. Parham v. J.L. and J.R., 442 U.S. 584 (1979).

16. Youngberg v. Romeo, 457 U.S. 307 (1982).

17. Miles SH. Informed demand for "non-beneficial" medical treatment. N Engl J Med 1991; 325:512-5.

18. In re Wanglie, No. PX91-288 (Prob. Ct., Hennepin Co., Minn., June 28. 1991).

Article Questions

1. Who was Baby K? What are the legal, technological, and social issues that relate to her case?

2. Do you agree with the decision of the Court of Appeals? Why? Why not? Do you believe that she should have been revived at the hospital? Should medical technology stay out of this decision? Explain.

3. Was mechanical ventilation a medical judgment? What are the ethical considerations that would need to be made by doctors and parents in this decision?

4. If you were the parents what would your decision have been? If you were the lawyers what would your decision have been?

5. How have the laws changed due to this case?

George J. Annas, J.D., M.P.H.

Making Artificial Organs Work

Stella Jones Fitzgibbons

Researchers took an important first step toward the creation of artificial organs when they developed kidney dialysis in the 1950s. The idea was to use a machine to perform the kidney's main filtering function, pumping the patient's blood past a semipermeable membrane that allows higher-concentration elements in the bloodstream, such as toxins and waste products, to diffuse out of the body. With the machine's success, loss of kidney function immediately ceased to be a death sentence, and kidney dialysis has since extended the lives of at least a million people worldwide.

But kidney dialysis hardly meets anyone's criteria for an ideal organ substitute. Patients must spend at least 12 hours a week hooked up to an external machine by means of surgically implanted connectors, and they must follow special diets and limit their intake of fluids. Equally important, the dialysis machine adapts to changes in a patient's bodily functions only with the aid of an extensive infrastructure. Nurses must monitor blood pressure and a laboratory is needed to scrutinize substances carried in the blood; a medical specialist must be on hand to adjust the dialysis machine and the patient's dose of synthetic hormones to compensate for functions lost by the native kidneys.

An ideal kidney substitute would perform all these functions itself. It would be small enough to be implanted inside the body, with no external connections that might foster infection. It would adapt to changes in the body's activity or workload, not only removing toxins, metabolic wastes, and excess water but also modifying its function in response to nerve impulses and hormone signals from other organs.

Decades of experience with dialysis machines have also taught us that the kidney is much more than a filter. Many early dialysis patients developed unexpected problems, including painful bone disease, severe anemia, even mental deterioration.

Bone disease occurred because the organ substitute was not completing all the kidney's tasks. Besides filtering waste products, the kidney converts vitamin D to an active compound that regulates the absorption of calcium from the intestines. Calcium levels in blood drop without this essential compound, forcing the body to compensate by absorbing it from the bones. The result can be weakness, pain, and even fractures. Doctors began fulfilling this overlooked function in the 1970s by administering synthetic vitamin D compounds.

The anemia suffered by patients on dialysis remained a mystery that could be treated only by frequent blood transfusions. Researchers finally discovered that the kidney regulates oxygen levels in the blood by producing a hormone called erythropoietin, which stimulates bone marrow to make oxygen-carrying red blood cells when oxygen levels in blood become low. In 1987, teams of researchers at the University of Washington and at London's Royal Postgraduate Medical School first used erythropoietin—synthesized using recombinant DNA techniques—to alleviate the anemia in these patients with far fewer blood transfusions.

Organ substitutes also run the risk of introducing new problems into the body. For years kidney specialists diagnosed "dialysis dementia," a disabling loss of mental capacity that arose months or years after treatment began. Its cause was found in 1976: aluminum, present in the water used to make dialysis fluids and in the antacids commonly consumed by many dialysis patients. Aluminum deposition in the bones also appears to account for another type of bone disease that occurs in many patients with kidney failure, leading to pain and loss of mobility. An iron compound can be used to remove aluminum accumulations, but the process is slow and the treatment causes side effects like nausea. Fortunately, different antacids and aluminum-free dialysis fluids now prevent the problem from occurring.

Creating successful artificial organ substitutes clearly requires an extraordinarily detailed understanding of the body's interwoven systems. Designers must know not just what organs do but how they interact. This multipurpose approach is quite different from the single-function concept that governs most machines. Designers must always be mindful that each organ works in conjunction with all others: liver failure damages the brain and kidneys; the lungs and heart function in an intimate relationship. Lack of attention to the whole can be as lethal as any individual failure.

Thus, formidable challenges remain in making organs that can duplicate all the functions of their natural counterparts, although technology is making partial and at least temporary replacements possible.

Complementing the Heart

The most famous efforts to create artificial organs stem from the quest to develop an implantable artificial heart. Today artificial heart research is led by scientists at Pennsylvania State University, the Texas Heart Institute in Houston, the University of Utah, and the Cleveland Clinic Foundation, all of which receive support from the National Institutes of Health; the Milwaukee Heart Institute is developing its own device with private funding. Dozens of patients at these centers have now lived with an implantable artificial heart for up to several months. Unfortunately, optimism is tempered by numerous complications with the device; a seemingly simple pump has been hard to duplicate.

Barney Clark, the first patient to receive the Jarvik-7 implantable heart, died of strokes caused by blood clots formed when the platelets in his blood—the components that promote coagulation—contacted the synthetic material, clumping together and releasing chemical substances that stimulate the clot-forming process. Newer plastics used as pump materials interact less with cell membranes and so do not stimulate the platelets, but infections have been more difficult to prevent.

The most common site of infection, not surprisingly, is the chest, as Penn State researchers Bartley Griffith and Robert Kormos have discovered in patients who receive heart transplants after days or weeks with a substitute. Pockets of dead space around the artificial pump allow bacteria to breed. With no native blood vessels supplying these areas, infection-fighting white cells and antibiotics are unable to attack the bacteria.

The challenge, therefore, is to find materials that will neither stimulate the formation of blood clots nor allow bacteria to adhere to their surface. In-depth research efforts are under way in the United States and abroad to find the ideal materials for both the lining of the artificial heart's pump, which is in contact with blood, and the outer layer, which must seal to body tissues. Some research indicates that mere contact with many artificial materials damages surface membranes of immune cells. Researchers at both DuPont and 3M are designing polymers that do less damage to blood cells, and artificial hearts being developed at the Cleveland Clinic, the University of Utah, and Houston-based Baylor College use a gelatin (natural protein) coating on the parts that contact blood. Donald Schmidt and his coworkers at the Milwaukee Heart Institute are working on an even more "natural" approach, encasing the pump with cells cultured from the patient's own tissues.

Even when the artificial heart fits tightly in the chest, its rhythmic movement creates stress on surrounding tissues, particularly sorter connective tissue caught between the artificial heart and relatively unyielding bone and cartilage. The trauma not only damages enough tissue to serve as a breeding site for bacteria, it also prevents the body from forming a bond of scar tissue around the device that would seal off the open areas.

Some researchers have tried to overcome these problems by enclosing the pump in a "compliance chamber," which fills with air or fluid in synchrony with the pump to maintain a constant volume for the entire apparatus. The Jarvik-7, developed in Utah, uses this method. Researchers at the Texas Heart Institute have developed an even simpler solution: the left and right sides of their device pump alternately, so that a constant volume is maintained.

Leonard Golding and William Smith at the Cleveland Clinic use a pump that doesn't pulsate, carefully sized for a tight fit in the chest. Pulsating flow does not appear to be necessary, since by the time blood passes from large arteries to small ones and finally to the tiny ones that supply the body's cells, the blood's flow rate is no longer cyclic. The filling-and-emptying cycle in the native heart acts primarily to allow the heart muscle to rest during the filling phase. Models of the non-pulsating device tested in animals perform well; infection rates for the non-pulsating device are much lower than for the University of Utah's pump.

All of these efforts employ fixed-rate pumps. Patients with completely artificial hearts must therefore lead fairly sedentary lives because the pump cannot respond, as the natural heart does, to the need to run for a bus or the stress of an exercise program. Developing an artificial heart that could respond to internal signals such as those from the central nervous system, which increase flow rates when we get excited, is beyond the present state of the art. In the meantime, some researchers, like O. Howard Frazier at Houston's Texas Heart Institute, favor the approach of the world's first heart-assist devices, which are attached to the left ventricle of the native heart. Newer models of the so-called left ventricular assist device (LVAD) aid the pumping of the lower portion of the heart. The original heart remains in place, responding to signals from the rest of the body and changes in workload by increasing or decreasing the number of beats per minute, and also giving feedback to the rest of the body by means of hormones.

Thermo Cardiosystems, based in Woburn, Mass., has designed an LVAD pump called the Heartmate that can be implanted in the abdomen, where softer tissues accommodate its motion better than the rigid ones of the chest. The Heartmate returns blood flowing into the patient's left ventricle to the aorta, the body's largest artery. Two openings admit tubes connected to the outside (for air and electricity); the power source is small enough to be carried in a shoulder bag by the patient. Patients awaiting heart transplants have lived over a year with this device, which lets them not only leave the intensive care unit but walk around the hospital.

The Heartmate or one of its competitors, teaming a synthetic device with the patient's original heart, may come closest to the ideal of an implantable artificial organ: the only part outside the body is a lightweight power pack. The Heartmate device is already close to offering a permanent solution for some patients, but concern remains over these patients' propensity toward irregular heart beats—or arrhythmias—that could send them into heart failure. The prospect requires them to be monitored closely. Presumably, more clinical experience with the device and some modifications will allow these patients even greater latitude. Most researchers in the field believe that it will not be long before patients with artificial hearts will be able to function independently outside of a hospital setting.

Liver Assists

Some researchers foresee the development of a liver-assist device that could likewise be used as an intermittent treatment for people with failing livers, especially those who lose function gradually due to diseases like hepatitis B. Much like kidney dialysis, patients in such a scenario would spend some 10 to 20 hours per week attached to the artificial liver. But many difficult questions remain before such a device can become a reality.

If the kidney's main job is to serve as a filter, the liver is best described as an organic chemical plant fed on substances carried in the blood, such as nutrients and the toxic waste products of normal metabolism (including the ammonia produced when the body digests amino acids in proteins). The liver produces other compounds from these substances, such as the proteins needed for normal blood clotting. The liver also helps regulate blood sugar, storing it in the form of starch and releasing it when serum sugar levels drop. And the liver produces the bile acids that begin the intestinal process of digesting the fats in food.

The interwoven nature of the functions of the body's organs is clearly revealed in people whose livers fail suddenly from infection or poisoning. These patients develop nausea, jaundice, and internal bleeding followed days later by mental confusion, coma, and death as the nervous system is poisoned by toxins the liver can no longer clear. The stress on the body as it faces these multiple threats often leads to breathing problems as well, as substances released from dying cells break down blood vessels in the lungs and allow fluid to fill the air spaces. The toxins that build up in the blood also decrease blood flow to the kidneys, causing them to fail, too. And every support device used by doctors, from simple intravenous lines to machines that assist patients' breathing, leaves an opening through which bacteria can enter and cause life-threatening infection.

Until recently, liver transplantation—often on extremely short notice—has been the only hope for patients with liver failure. But transplants, requiring major surgery, are not only expensive and dangerous: there are simply not enough donor organs to go around. Unlike other organs, however, the liver does have the ability to regenerate, producing new cells from older ones to replace those damaged by toxins, surgery, or disease. A temporary liver substitute can therefore make some transplants unnecessary if the patient can be kept alive until enough cells accumulate to restore the liver's normal functions.

The first attempts to use artificial means to help patients with liver failure relied on an external bank of activated charcoal columns to absorb toxins from blood. The procedure is still standard treatment for some types of drug overdoses and other poisonings. But John G. O'Grady and Alexander Gimson, of King's College in London, found in 1988 that this "charcoal perfusion" treatment, while successfully eliminating toxins, made no difference in patients' death rate since it did not replace other liver functions. The charcoal even caused additional problems by removing calcium (essential for muscle contraction) and platelets (endangering the blood clotting process) from the blood. Newer filter columns made of synthetic absorption agents, such as those in use by Peter Konstantin and coworkers at the Medical College of Hanover, Germany, avoid calcium-absorption problems but still remove only some of the toxins and don't replace other functions.

More recent work has used actual liver cells, grown in special cultures suspended in a column behind a semipermeable membrane. As the patient's blood filters through the column, the liver cells absorb substances like toxins and nutrients and return beneficial chemical products to the blood. Dan F. Neuzil and Jacek Rozza, of Vanderbilt University, have improved the condition of liver-failure patients by using porcine liver cells, but the approach is cumbersome: red blood cells must be removed from the blood before it passes through the column to prevent them from clumping together or being damaged by the fiber material. The process can also inadvertently provoke the human immune system to attack foreign proteins in the animal liver cells.

Recently, James Kelly, a biochemist at Baylor, has solved the latter problem by using a culture of self-replicating human liver cells. Hepatix, a firm begun by Kelly, has developed a device in which membranes that are less damaging to cell surfaces are used in a modified dialysis unit. Whole blood passes through hollow fibers to which the laboratory-grown liver cells adhere. The machine provides about 20 percent of normal liver function—enough to keep a patient alive while his or her own liver is recovering.

Like kidney substitutes, the Hepatix machine requires a sophisticated external technology and monitoring infrastructure. For example, the liver-assist device necessitates the use of anticoagulant drugs to prevent blood from clotting, and these drugs can worsen patients' already severe bleeding problems. Patients must now stay in intensive-care units where their condition can be monitored continuously for problems from infection to bleeding ulcers.

But Kelly, along with Norman Sussman, Milton Finegold, and James Barish, obtained the first clinical success with this device at Texas Children's Hospital in 1992, working with a 12-year-old girl whose hepatitis made her lung and kidney problems so serious she could not qualify for a liver transplant. The girl's own liver recovered enough after 58 hours to allow treatment to be stopped, and her other problems slowly resolved. She left the hospital a few weeks later.

Sussman and Kelly have now treated 11 patients with liver failure, four of them in a "bridge-to-transplant" situation, buying them hours or days until a liver donor could be found. The work offers much cause for optimism but the mortality rate is still over 50 percent: the liver is often not the only organ that is failing, so treatment must sometimes be interrupted or discontinued before it is fully effective. New clinical tests recently begun in the United States as well as in Britain, France, and Germany should help to yield data that can improve the survival rate with the device.

Toward an Artificial Lung

The lungs perform the apparently simple process of "oxygen in, carbon dioxide out" by transferring those gases between blood and air across ultrathin membranes. Thousands of microscopic air pockets called alveoli are lined with these membranes, providing a surface area of about 700 square feet that allows hemoglobin in the blood to suck up oxygen and the blood's liquid to release carbon dioxide. The blood leaving the alveoli—full of oxygen—returns to the heart, which then pumps it to the rest of the body.

But no artificial lung today deals with the lung's subtle, subsidiary functions. Angiotensin II, a hormone produced in the cells lining the alveoli, interacts with the kidney and adrenal gland to keep blood pressure from falling too low. Pressure receptors in the lung's blood vessels regulate the flow rate of blood to and from the heart. And lungs respond to signals from the brain and muscles that adjust breathing rates and oxygen exchange according to the body's needs—which may change drastically from one minute to the next, such as when a person sits at a bus stop, climbs onto the bus and hurries to find a good seat, then sits down again.

Unlike proposed liver and kidney substitutes, an artificial lung must be used constantly. And it must respond within seconds or minutes to changes in demands on its capacity. There is little margin for error: failure to meet oxygen requirements or remove carbon dioxide rapidly enough can cause cardiac arrest far more quickly than stopping dialysis or liver treatments.

Before patients with any of the artificial lungs now in use can leave the intensive care unit, a complex and sensitive control system must be in place that enables the lung to adjust to changes in heart rate, oxygen consumption and even body position. So far, no one has met this challenge; developing such a system, then integrating it with the rest of the body's control mechanisms, will be far more difficult than simply exchanging one gas for another.

In the meantime, mechanical ventilators are used to support lungs that cannot fill and empty fast enough to remove carbon dioxide or supply enough oxygen to the blood. These devices, available for decades, can provide precisely calculated volumes of air to the patient's lungs through a tube in the windpipe, with technicians regulating the level of oxygen according to the patient's needs. Ventilators often provide assistance long enough for a patient's lungs to recover.

But mechanical ventilation can cause problems. Too high a percentage of oxygen in the air mixture can damage the delicate cells of the alveoli by causing a buildup of unattached atoms called free radicals. Lungs that have lost their elasticity because of illness or scar tissue may also require such high pressures to inflate that they "blow out," leaking air into the chest, compressing the rest of the lung, and preventing inflation. And sometimes the lung disease or injury is so severe that not enough functioning alveoli remain for gas exchange to occur.

One solution to the problem has been available since the advent of open-heart surgery in the 1950s: heart-lung bypass machines that keep patients alive while their hearts are being repaired, taking oxygen-poor blood from large veins and passing it through an oxygenator before it is returned to the body. Unfortunately, these machines can be used for only a few hours at a time; contact with the pump's artificial polymer, as well as a long circuit of synthetic materials through which the delicate blood cells must pass, damages blood cell surfaces, not only the white cells of the immune system (allowing infections to develop) but also the red cells that deliver oxygen to the rest of the body.

Because the oxygenator component causes less damage to blood cells than other parts of the system, the device—the extracorporeal membrane oxygenator (ECMO)—has been used since the 1970s for days at a time to help newborn infants with pneumonia or other lung problems. Infants' high levels of hemoglobin and the more favorable surface-to-volume ratio of their immature lungs make them comparatively strong candidates for the treatment. But U.S. progress was slowed when a multicenter study, conducted by the National Heart, Lung and Blood Institute (NHLBI), found that ECMO did not reduce the death rate in older children and adults with failing lungs.

Recent ECMO work in Europe has led to a resurgence of interest. One team at the University of Milan, Italy, headed by anesthesiologist Luciano Gattinoni, has used new materials that improve the device's gas-transfer membranes. The team has also developed a technique that returns blood directly to the lungs rather than to the heart's left ventricle so the high oxygen content can help them recover from injury or disease.

With these developments, work has revived in the United States—at the Extracorporeal Life Support Organization in Ann Arbor, Mich., and participating medical centers. This recent work has established that ECMO must be used before lung damage becomes irreversible, and before so many organs are failing that the patient's chances of survival are already dismal; if damage is due to scar tissue or toxic gases, or accompanied by other problems such as heart failure, ECMO may do no more than delay the inevitable. Many of the patients in the earlier NHLBI study were such "desperation cases." Today, ECMO combined with antibiotic treatment can often enable lungs affected by pneumonia to recover, and it has been used successfully on patients for spans of one month or more.

P. Pearl O'Rourke, Charles Stolar, Robert Bartlett, and their coworkers in Ann Arbor recently found that ECMO kept nearly half of 285 critically ill children alive, compared with 15 percent of similar samples using older ECMO techniques. Another Ann Arbor study reports a survival rate of 45 percent among adults. The researchers caution, however, that more work needs to be done to improve the ECMO materials' compatibility with blood, and in deciding which lung problems are most likely to improve.

Extracorporeal, of course, means outside the body. The apparatus offers many points of entry for bacteria. Anticoagulants must also be given to the patient to prevent clots that would not only block the tubing but could travel to blood vessels in the brain (causing stroke) or other organs (cutting off their blood and oxygen supply, resulting in organ failure).

To address this problem, J.D. Mortensen at Cardiopulmonics in Salt Lake City has recently developed a gas-exchange device that brings us a step closer to an implantable artificial lung. The intravenous oxygenator (IVOX) system, inserted into the patient's largest vein in the chest, consists of hundreds of tiny, thread-like plastic tubes that resemble the lungs' own gas-transfer membrane. As blood flows through the patient's veins, oxygen-carbon dioxide transfer takes place across the walls of each of the IVOX's hollow fibers. Patients still need to be connected to an extracorporeal oxygen source and a vacuum pump, but the IVOX device provides enough oxygen to make patients far less dependent on mechanical ventilators. And the lower pressures and higher oxygen concentrations make it easier for a patient's recovering lungs to heal. IVOX's designers also coat the device's fibers with anticoagulants to avoid the need to administer drugs in such high doses that they prevent clotting in other parts of the body.

IVOX, so far used on 150 patients, has kept them alive for only a month or less. Still, some have been able to leave the hospital who would have been considered virtually hopeless a few years ago. The system's biggest drawback is its small gas-exchange capacity, usually less than half that of normal lungs: the large femoral vein in the groin, where IVOX is normally inserted, can admit a device only 5 to 10 millimeters in diameter.

To allow more space for gas exchange, Mortensen's group has now tested six models of a larger version of the device—truly an implanted artificial lung—for use in patients whose single remaining lung is ailing. After the patient's nonfunctional lung is removed, the oxygen entry port of the exchanger is connected to the patient's windpipe. The larger device employs precisely the same gas-exchange system but, instead of being inserted into a vein, it is contained within the chest cavity. Blood from the pulmonary artery flows through the IVOX-like device in its own polymer container to allow gas exchange to occur. Early results have been encouraging; the device permits more oxygen exchange than the IVOX, and removes more carbon dioxide.

It is still unclear how long the current device can be successfully implanted; tissue reactions to the synthetic material may cause problems for the long-term user or interfere with gas exchange. And dividing the workload between natural and artificial lungs to optimize the patient's condition while supplying the healing natural lung with oxygenated blood may require monitoring and control systems as complicated as those already used in intensive care units.

Longer Range Thinking

In addition to the technological problems that present significant barriers to the further development and use of artificial organs, there are also economic pressures and regulatory restrictions. The fact is, the type of treatment a patient receives is often influenced as much by institutional factors as by medical ones. Conventional kidney dialysis centers, for instance, represent a considerable investment by both government and industry. An alternative treatment uses a patient's own membrane around the intestines to diffuse the body's fluids. In this technique, called peritoneal dialysis, an implanted catheter infuses and withdraws fluid from the abdomen. Although such dialysis can be done at home and requires far less equipment, it is not for everyone, since it requires a well-motivated patient capable of following sterile technique. Still, the approach could free many patients from dependence on a dialysis center and costs considerably less.

Unfortunately, peritoneal dialysis has not been widely used. The large investment in hemodialysis centers encourages their continued use. Third-party insurers are often reluctant to pay for "unconventional" therapies despite their merits. Even patients eligible for kidney transplants sometimes choose to continue dialysis because Medicare pays for only the first year of the expensive drugs required to prevent rejection of a transplanted organ. Similarly, hospitals with a big investment in existing lung ventilators (and the technicians who maintain them) may be reluctant to adopt a new device like the IVOX lung substitute even if the Food and Drug Administration gives its developers their long-awaited license to market it.

A limiting factor is how much society is willing to spend to prolong a single human life—sometimes for only several weeks and with an admittedly poor quality of life at that. Dramatic medical procedures of any kind are expensive—a liver transplant or bone marrow transplant, for example, can cost $150,000. And untried new techniques almost always cost more, at least initially. But the value of a new technique transcends the individual case. It is essential that third-party insurers consider not just the additional few weeks of a particular patient's life, but the changes a new technique can bring over the next few years as it develops, This longer view suggests that support for new approaches can often save many more lives—and dollars—in the long run. Those patients who use prototypes in the early stages expand the possibilities for others later on. Such long-range thinking is as necessary now as it was in the 1950s when high-priced research was conducted on the first kidney machines.

Article Questions

1. What are the ethical considerations in this article?

2. Give three examples of the problems that medical technology causes for the patient.

3. Do you believe that patients with artificial hearts will be able to experience a "quality" lifestyle.

4. Explain how using actual liver cells will help patients with liver dysfunction.

5. What are some of the complications faced by patients who have artificial lungs transplanted in their body?

The Organ Factory of the Future?

David Concar

At a secret location in Cambridgeshire, researchers inject human DNA into a pig embryo. Six months later Astrid, the world's first transgenic pig, is born—of a virgin, in a sterile stable, on Christmas eve. The hope is that the implanted gene will make pig organs compatible with the human immune system, thus helping to solve one of medicine's fastest growing problems: the shortage of organs for transplant surgery. Astrid produces offspring, the research gathers pace. But there are problems, too: antivivisectionists launch firebomb attacks and medical ethicists get jumpy.

It could be the plot of a TV drama about the future of genetic engineering, but it isn't. Astrid, the "pig with a human heart" as she is dubbed in headlines, is as real as the surgical aspirations of the British scientists who created her two years ago. Now the transgenic clan has grown to some 200 pigs. And Imutran, the company behind the project, is taking the next step—testing what happens when human blood is pumped through hearts taken from some of Astrid's descendants.

This week, Imutran's research director, David White reports the first findings to delegates at an international conference on "xenotransplantation" in Washington DC. "It's absolutely clear that hearts from transgenic pigs work better than those from normal pigs and show fewer signs of immune rejection," he told *New Scientist* beforehand. "But what isn't clear is whether that result will correspond to better survival rates of xenografts in primates or humans."

If it does, the rewards—financial as well as medical—could be considerable. Last year in the US alone some 2800 people died waiting for human organs to become available, and in Britain at present about 25 per cent of heart patients die waiting. Such figures are set to climb next century as conventional transplantation techniques improve and patients who are now considered too old or sick to benefit from new organs are put on waiting lists.

All being well, Imutran expects trials in humans to begin in 1996. But hard on its heels are two American biotechnology companies replete with glossy brochures featuring transgenic pigs, some designed to function as organ donors. Moreover, the American companies have already started transplanting genetically-altered pig tissue into primates—

experiments whose outcome will be vital to persuading ethics committees that there is a case for proceeding to trials in humans.

Surgeon's dream

A bountiful supply of designer organs sounds like a transplant surgeon's dream. But before it can be turned into reality, Imutran and its rivals must clear some towering obstacles. First, nobody has yet begun to draw up guidelines on the ethics of using genetically-engineered animal organs in surgery, and especially how to preempt any needless experimentation on humans. Falter here, and the pig engineers could find the public set against them. Secondly, the law on patenting transgenic animals is still desperately unclear, raising the prospect of a legal dispute over commercial rights. But the biggest question of all rests with biology: can genetic engineering really deliver animal organs that look like "friend" rather than "foe" to the human immune system?

At the moment, everyone is focusing on making pigs with genes designed to disarm a powerful immune response known as hyperacute rejection. After conventional transplants, organ rejection can, in most cases, be prevented with drugs— such as cyclosporin— that act to "handcuff" aggressive white blood cells known as T cells. But when organs are transplanted from species to species, rejection is too fast and violent to be pacified with drugs alone. The immune system treats the graft much as it would a solid clump of bacteria, unleashing agents that destroy the epithelial cells at the surface of the grafted organ while triggering a massive clogging of the arteries supplying it with blood. Within hours, the graft is reduced to a blackened mess.

Much of the damage is caused by a team of hostile blood proteins called the complement cascade. If antibodies and white blood cells are the ground troops of the immune system, the complement cascade is its air force. Normally reserved for attacking microorganisms, its proteins can punch lethal holes in cell membranes, producing an effect which, in White's words, is "like a bomb going off."

It was a desire to defuse this bomb that led the Cambridge researchers to inject human DNA into pig embryos in August 1992. Human cells are spared from attack because they carry markers—molecular "white flags"—that can pacify complement proteins. The researchers reasoned that if they could transfer genes for these white flags into pigs, the complement cascade might be fooled into holding its fire. One candidate for the job was a gene encoding a protein called Decay Accelerating Factor. In human tissue, it was clear that DAF molecules stuck out of the surfaces of cells, warding off complement proteins. Could they do the same in pig tissue?

The latest results on perfusing transgenic hearts with human blood, reported this week in Washington DC, suggest the answer is a qualified "yes". "We see little or no signs of any hyperacute rejection of pig hearts expressing DAF," says White, who nonetheless stresses the limitations of perfusion tests as a measure of immune compatibility.

Mouse hearts

A similar picture is emerging from Imutran's rivals in the US. About 18 months ago, Boston-based DNX Corporation began producing mice and pigs carrying not only DAF but human genes encoding two other "white flag" proteins, CD46 and CD59. Experiments involving perfusion with human blood show that transgenic mouse hearts are not attacked by the complement cascade, says John Logan, DNX's vice-president of research.

The latest company to join the race, a Yale firm called Alexion Pharmaceuticals, is hoping to gain ground with a genetically-engineered protein designed to combine the talents of both DAF and CD59. Having just filed for a patent on the protein, Alexion is cagey about details but decidedly upbeat about clinical potential. "We've taken engineered pig epithelial cells that produce high levels of protein and transplanted them into primates," says Stephen Squinto, the company's programme director. "Normal pig cells are destroyed by hyperacute rejection within minutes. The engineered cells survived for hours."

Alexion expects to be transplanting designer pig organs into primates this autumn. "If we can get decent survival, we'll move on to humans," says Squinto. "We'll probably start with high risk patients and will most likely transplant hearts. The heart is a priority because there's little you can do with dying patients. You can't put them on dialysis.

If the Cambridge researchers are anxious about this competition, they are certainly not showing it. "Everything is beginning to hot up," says White, "but we like to think we're still in the lead."

Even those who normally preach caution on xenotransplants seem to be caught up in the excitement. Mindful of past failures to transplant baboon organs into humans, Roy Calne, a pioneer of kidney transplantation and a surgeon at Addenbrooke's Hospital in Cambridge, warned researchers at a conference in Cambridge last autumn against rushing into more xenotransplants on humans without getting a firmer grip on the biology that causes such transplants to be violently rejected. However, in the next breath, and only half in jest, Calne conjured up a new era in transplant surgery based on the "self-pig".

One day, the vision goes, transgenic technology may be so cheap and easy that we may all take the precaution of paying for the creation and upkeep of a custom-made transgenic pig, an immunological twin in porcine clothing that would come to the rescue in the event of an accident or disease. Contract hepatitis, and self-pig would provide a new liver; develop Alzheimer's disease, and a supply of personalised pig neurons would be at hand. Heart failure? No problem.

It sounds far fetched, and for the time being it is. Yet a decade from now, self-pigs may fall within the reach of genetic engineers. But whether such animals will ever see the light of a sanitised sty is another matter.

The genes that enable our immune systems to distinguish "self" tissue from foreign tissue, and which make each of us immunologically unique, are encoded by a vast tract of DNA known as the "major histocompatibility complex". To make self-pigs, you would have to disable each animal's MHC genes and replace them with copies of those belonging to each human "twin". But until recently that would have been unthinkable on technical grounds. Gene "knock out" techniques were too laborious and imprecise, and it was possible to transfer only relatively short pieces of DNA from animal to animal.

Now things are quietly changing. Researchers bent on reprogramming animal genomes are discovering the benefits of "yeast artificial chromosomes", which can be used

David Concar

to transfer stretches of DNA as long as 500,000 base pairs or more. And that could revolutionise the whole business of making transgenic pigs.

Take the case of Astrid and her siblings. White and his colleagues created them by injecting an embryo with an artificially "edited down" version of the natural DAF gene. Partly because of its size the gene is expressed somewhat erratically: not all organs in all pigs bear the DAF white flag. If nothing else, say the researchers, YACs could help to solve that problem by allowing the insertion of a much fuller version of the gene.

But scientific feasibility is only part of the equation. Just as important is commercial viability. And this is where the idea of self-pig could fall into the trough. To prospective backers, donor animals that must be genetically tailored for each and every patient years in advance of any medical problem would surely seem more like a legal and financial nightmare than a life-saving innovation. Or as Squinto puts it: "I don't see how you could market such animals."

Nor, sadly for fans of self-pig, does there seem to be any middle ground between creating "generic" organ donors—animals that could be used by everyone—and creating animals with genes specific to individual patients.

Yet commercial promise alone will not be enough to speed generic pig donors from the laboratory to the clinic. For a start, militant antivivisectionists in Britain are unlikely to call off their campaign of threats. Even moderate animal rights groups will continue to lobby for a European moratorium on the genetic manipulation of animals, or at least for restrictions on the patenting of such animals. In the case of transgenic pigs, they fear that tampering with immune genes could harm the animal, perhaps by causing immune disorders or a loss of resistance to infections that could be inherited.

Others also see this kind of genetic engineering as something of a slippery slope. "You're not treating the animal as an end in itself but as a means to an end," says Richard Nicholson, editor of the *Bulletin of Medical Ethics*. And has anyone bothered to consider the psychological impact on patients of using animal organs in transplant surgery?

Xenograft researchers react to such concerns with the air of an elephant staring down the barrel of a peashooter. There is no evidence of ill-effects in any of the transgenic pigs and mice produced so far, insist all three companies. And, as if to outface the worriers, conferences on xenografting seldom run seminars on ethics. Instead, one view on animal rights is invariably chanted like a mantra from the podium: the idea of using pigs as organ donors is on a moral par with eating bacon. Speakers concede that primate donors, with their social hierarchies and seemingly richer emotional lives, might never be acceptable to the public. But who could question using an animal that is bred by the million for food and whose heart valves are already being inserted into humans?

Playing God

This line on ethics (by strange coincidence) harmonises perfectly with the practicalities. Baboons are slow breeders and are difficult to keep free from viral infections, some of them potentially lethal to humans. Pigs, by contrast, are about the same size as humans and can more easily be bred in sterile conditions. And surely the prospect of saving thousands of human lives justifies slotting the odd human gene into a porcine chromosome?

Perhaps. Yet even if proponents of xenografting triumph over animal rights (as seems likely), that won't be the last of the social obstacles. Just as worrying for the public is the surgeon-playing-God scenario, the fear that transplant teams armed with genetically-engineered animal organs will indulge in reckless experiments on human patients.

In the past decade in the US, there have been three attempts to transplant baboon organs into human patients, all failing, and all generating storms of controversy. Despite that, international guidelines on xenotransplants are still nowhere in sight, and decisions about operations remain in the hands of individual hospital or regional ethics committees. National medical guidelines, it is true, stress the need for "reasonably informed consent" in all medical experiments. But what this would amount to in the case of a xenograft experiment is far from clear.

At last year's conference in Cambridge, delegates were shocked to hear that surgeons at Cedar-Sinai Hospital in Los Angeles had already attempted to transplant a pig's liver into a 26-year-old woman. Within a day the organ had been rejected. "What you saw in this experiment was what you would predict from 30 years of literature—blockage of arteries and a mass of hyperacute rejection," says Squinto. "Without agents to block the hyperacute response, the experiment was premature." The condemnation seems unanimous. "Before doing this kind of trial on humans you have to show that the grafts can survive in animals," says Logan. "But that wasn't the case."

Will it be the case when surgeons want to experiment with transgenic pig organs? Might not the intense commercial competition encourage recklessness? Imutran and its rivals insist that a premature transplant with a negative outcome is the last thing they want. "We wouldn't want to go into clinical trials until we can be sure of getting survival rates similar to those for human-to-human transplants—a 70 to 75 per cent chance of surviving for more than a year," says White. Any trade in, and clinical use of, transgenic organs could be adequately policed by government watchdogs such as the Food and Drug Administration in the US, argues Logan.

A plentiful supply of transgenic animal organs might even help to reduce some long-running ethical concerns about transplantation surgery, say some researchers. The current shortage of human organs requires surgeons to make tough decisions about who should be put on waiting lists. Should organs go to the sickest patients, or those who can most benefit from them? And what about age? In Britain, there are no official age limits, but the vast majority of heart recipients are under 60.

Animal organs could change that. And in the long run, say their proponents, they could also lead to patients being spared some of the unpleasant and debilitating side-effects of immune suppression. "Xenotransplantation swings the focus away from interfering with the host immune system to interfering with the organ," says Squinto. "Why use drugs to produce broad suppression of the host's immune system when you can modify the graft?"

Even so, reassuring the public may require an openness about data that conflicts with commercial ambitions. Eager to protect the interests of their shareholders and backers, all three companies breeding transgenic pigs have filed for patents. As night follows day, an unseemly courtroom battle is now on the cards and a veil of secrecy hangs over many experimental details. For example, DNX declined to explain its gene constructs and experiments on primates two weeks ago citing "commercial sensitivity."

To purse their commercial rights, the American companies may have to challenge a patent filed by the Cambridge researchers in 1989 which embraces the whole concept of using genes and proteins to protect animal tissue from attack by human complement. There are broader problems looming, too. For lawyers, the awkward thing about pigs is that they procreate. If company A makes a transgenic animal using techniques owned by company B, then it is certainly infringing the patent. But is that still the case if company A breeds offspring from this animal and sells them? And what happens if company A tries to sell a kidney from these offspring? "The issue is at best cloudy," says White.

Big though these social and commercial obstacles may be, they might ultimately be dwarfed by a more fundamental question: can animal organs ever be refashioned sufficiently to be fully compatible with the human body? Certainly, say die-hard optimists such as Stephen Grundy, a surgeon at the Medical Center of Loma Linda University, where the first baboon-to-human transplant was carried out a decade ago: "There are no biological barriers to xenotransplantation, just a series of small steps."

Others are more measured in their analysis. It is not just a question of immunology, says Calne. In addition to looking like a "friend" to the immune system, a transplanted organ must function properly too. "Even proteins produced by close species such as the baboon are different from their human counterparts," he notes despondently.

Even when it comes to immunology, the science of xenografting is still desperately young. "Five years ago it had the status of alchemy," quips one surgeon. It could take researchers years to hit on exactly the right combination of drugs, antibodies and transgenic donors to reach their final goal of producing complete tolerance.

A key worry is whether blocking the complement cascade will be enough to prevent hyperacute rejection of pig organs in humans. The complement cascade is certainly important: animals born with genetic defects in complement genes are unusually tolerant to xenografts. But it might prove to be just the first of many hurdles. There is increasing evidence, for instance, that antibodies also contribute to hyperacute rejection. Everyone seems to carry antibodies in their blood that can attack pig tissue, and over the past two years it has become clear that a main target of these antibodies is a sugar molecule called gal(alpha-1,3)gal which is found on the surfaces of pig epithelial cells.

Cells of wrath

Removing this sugary target could be vital to eliminating the hyperacute response, says Squinto. One approach would be to disable, or "knock out", the pig gene that encodes one of the enzymes needed to tether the sugar to the surfaces of cells. Making transgenic pigs of this kind is no easy task as it requires special manipulations of embryonic stem cells. But with Alexion and others now poised to try, there seems little doubt that "knock-out" pigs will be among the donor animals of choice next century.

And if they are, genetic engineers won't necessarily stop at removing the pig's troublesome sugar molecule. For even if the threat of hyperacute rejection can be completely silenced that way, xenografts will still be subjected to the gentler wrath of T cells—just as human-to-human transplants are. In conventional surgery, hostile responses of T cells are suppressed with drugs. But with pig organs, those responses could turn out to be much stronger. In which case, say researchers, it may be necessary to identify exactly which pig molecules trigger responses in human T cells, and eliminate them with genetic engineering. Commenting on the work still to be done, White says: "At the moment we're making a Model T Ford. But everyone would like to make a Ferrari."

But in the end, even a Ferrari-style donor may not be quite enough. To produce tolerance to animal organs, it may still be necessary to manipulate the patient's immune system; to administer "friendly" monoclonal antibodies that bind to antibodies that would otherwise attack pig tissue; even to transplant bone marrow tissue from a pig to the patient.

Bone marrow cells being the progenitors of all the body's immune cells, a pig-to-human transplant of this kind could —in theory—produce a host immune system with a conveniently split personality: enough donor immune cells to induce specific tolerance to donor tissue; and enough host immune cells to sustain normal human immunity. Some see this as a recipe for chaos in the immune system. But this week in Washington DC Elliot Lebowitz and his colleagues at BioTransplant in Charlestown, Massachusetts, report what they claim are promising results on rodents and primates.

In one experiment, the researchers used the bone marrow approach to transplant kidneys between primates of different blood groups, an operation that can be as risky as xenografting. The animals have survived for over a year, says Lebowitz—and without needing to have their immune system suppressed with drugs. The key to success he says, is to kill off "mature" T cells in the recipient and remove troublesome antibodies before injecting the bone marrow cells and transplanting the donor tissue. That way, he adds, "a new immune system can be generated that accepts both the donor tissue and self tissue".

Lebowtitz is convinced the dream of producing tolerance to xenografts can become a reality. He is not alone. "It's time again for xenotransplantation in the clinic," said Grundy uncompromisingly in Cambridge last autumn. An evangelist for the cause, Grundy likes to confront sceptics with a slide show of transplant heroes: a group of "xeno-goats", alive and well despite their sheep hearts, and a grinning baboon called Max who survived 502 days with a heart from a rhesus monkey and a little help from immunosuppressive drugs. How long before this gallery includes the face of a human being, alive and well and living with a pig's heart?

Article Questions

1. What is a transgenic pig?

2. What ethical considerations come into play in using genetically-engineered animal organs for transplants into humans?

3. What part does animal rights play in this decision?

4. What are "cells of wrath?"

Engineering the Future of Antibiotics

Lori Valigra

Sitting on a metal bed in a bleak hospital ward in central London is Jim. Jim is sick. He has pneumonia, and when he breathes he wheezes like a steam train. For the first time in many years, Jim's prognosis is not certain. In April a woman patient at Guy's Hospital in London died from pneumonia caused by an antibiotic-resistant strain of *Streptococcus pneumoniae* that defeated every one of the doctors' antibiotic weapons.

Increasingly, the medical columns of newspapers and magazines have been busy documenting the rise of strains of bacteria that no longer succumb to antibiotics. First there was drug-resistant *Mycobacterium tuberculosis*. TB now accounts for one in seven new cases in the US and five per cent of these patients are expected to die. In Britain, the number of hospitals that sent the Central Public Health Laboratory's Antibiotic Reference Unit samples of penicillin-resistant *S. pneumoniae* rose from around 25 in 1987 to over 130 in 1993. And in 1992, 13,300 hospital patients in the US died from bacterial infections that refused to respond to antibiotic treatment.

Fading Magic

The message seems clear: antibiotics are losing their magic touch after decades of incautious prescription, improper use and the inevitable spread of bacterial genes that confer drug resistance. "We have always assumed we will have another antibiotic saviour up our sleeves," said Alexander Tomasz, professor of microbiology at Rockefeller University in New York, when speaking at the American Association for the Advancement of Science meeting in February. "We can't make that assumption any more."

In the 1980s, many drug companies and researchers gave up trying to develop new approaches to antibiotics, believing that existing drugs (or modified versions of them) could keep pace with infectious bacteria. "It seemed that we had everything we needed, and there was a greater medical need for drugs to treat ailments such as high blood pressure," says Mike Marriott, head of chemotherapy for Glaxo Group Research. Now the quest for antibacterial drugs and therapies has become hot science as laboratories move away from research based solely on penicillin-style compounds.

In the old days scientists looked for antibiotic substances mainly in organisms from soil. But today researchers are broadening their search to include creatures as diverse as frogs and sharks. In some laboratories, the break with tradition is even greater. Instead of focusing on drugs that block bacterial growth, researchers are trying to develop carbohydrate or protein molecules that can boost people's natural defences against bacteria. In the end, say advocates of this immunological approach, it might be the only way to deal with the small pockets of resistant bacteria that survive antibiotic treatments.

New Wave Agents

Most of these "new wave" antibacterial agents have yet to make it into clinical trials, and the researchers behind them are keeping the molecular structures close to their chests. Leading the way are small American companies with names like Alpha-Beta Technology (Worcester, Massachusetts), Microcide Pharmaceuticals (Silicon Valley) and Magainin Pharmaceuticals (Plymouth Meeting in Pennsylvania). But competition from mainstream companies, such as Glaxo, is gradually building up. It is hard for anyone to be indifferent when people are once again dying from TB, pneumonia and meningitis, and the traditional antibiotics such as the penicillins, cephalosporins and quinolones are beginning to fail.

These drugs work by blocking bacterial cell division. Some species of bacterium can produce between ten and twenty million offspring in a day. Penicillins, the oldest class of antibiotics, stop bacteria making the peptidoglycans needed to build the polysaccharide wall that surrounds all bacteria. Cephalosporins work in a similar way, while quinolones act by blocking DNA synthesis.

Once antibiotics have halted the growth of a bacterial colony, any survivors must be dealt with by the immune system. But bacteria are no slouches. If the immune system fails to eradicate all drug-resistant survivors, these bacteria will begin to pass their genes to other bacteria in the host. And that can spell disaster, for a single gene can make all the difference between a bacteria being vulnerable or resistant to a drug. Some strains of M. tuberculosis, for example, owe their resistance to the drug isoniazid to the lack of a gene encoding an enzyme, catalase, which plays a part in activating the drug.

Alternatively, resistant bacteria can be transferred from person to person, or animal to animal simply by direct contact or non-sterile instruments. In hospitals, the threat of resistant bacteria running amok has never been greater, with more and more patients suffering from impaired immunity—not just people with HIV, but transplant patients, the elderly and people undergoing chemotherapy.

This is why there is such interest in developing antibacterial therapies that work by boosting immunity. One such compound is Betafectin, a carbohydrate polymer based on glucan, a substance found in yeast cell walls. Alpha-Beta Technology is developing Betafectin as a way of stimulating the body's natural defences against infection by enhancing the efficiency of white blood cells called macrophages and neutrophils, explains Spiros Jamas, chief executive officer of Alpha-Beta.

These cells are the body's first defence against invading bacteria and other pathogens. Their job is to destroy the invading organisms before the body produces antibodies against the foreign proteins. Betafectin is thought to work by mimicking a bacterial attack. When a bacterium comes into contact with a white blood cell, it stimulates an antenna-like molecule found on the cell's surface known as the B glucan receptor. This in turn triggers a series of biochemical messages which increase the antibacterial activity of the white cells, at the site of infection as well as attracting more macrophages and neutrophils to the area and in some instances increasing the number of white cells in the blood. The result is an improved immune response.

Betafectin seems able to act as a sentinel for the immune system, locking on to the B glucan receptor to raise the alarm. This type of stimulation could offer great benefits to people with impaired immune systems, says Jamas. He points out that healthy people have few problems "mopping-up" the bacteria left over after antibiotic treatment. But people with damaged immunity may never eradicate all the pathogenic bacteria, so providing a breeding ground for antibiotic-resistant bacteria In these circumstances Betafectin may give the immune system the boost it needs to destroy the residual bacteria.

Immune Response

Alpha-Beta did its first clinical trials on healthy volunteers in 1992. The trials showed that a single intravenous dose of Betafectin increased the number of macrophages and neutrophils in the volunteers' blood and improved their killing capacity. The increased immune response could be related to the amount of the drug given. A trial of Betafectin began in late 1992 when the drug was given to 17 patients undergoing major surgery. These patients are often given a cocktail of antibiotics as a prophylactic. This has several unwelcome side effects. The first is that the antibiotics will kill off harmless as well as harmful bacteria. It also gives drug-resistant bacteria a chance to swap genetic material, so encouraging the growth of bacteria which are resistant to many drugs.

In the Betafectin trial, the patients given the drug spent on average five days less in the hospital, and three days less in intensive care than the 13 control patients who were given a placebo. If Betafectin proves effective enough to win approval from the US Food and Drug Administration, it is most likely to be used alongside traditional antibiotics, rather than as a replacement. But Alpha-Beta hopes that the drug will enable doctors to reduce the number of antibiotics used before major surgery. The company believes Betafectin may be useful for patients suffering from severe burns who are prone to bacterial infections and it could help patients with AIDS fend off opportunistic bacterial and fungal invasions . Betafectin is unlikely to face the problems of resistance seen with antibiotics, says Jamas, because the drug is stimulating a natural immune response.

Other companies have looked at boosting the immune systems, but Alpha-Beta is the first to use a genetically engineered carbohydrate. Jamas began his research into Betafectin in the early 1980s at the Massachusetts Institute of Technology. At that time it was becoming clear that the vast numbers of complex carbohydrate molecules found on the surfaces of cells act like distinctive chemical signatures, allowing cells to recognise each other and deliver biochemical signals. In 1985 Joyce Czop, associate professor of medicine at Harvard Medical School discovered the B glucan receptor.

Czop worked with Alpha-Beta on the structure of this receptor and on screening glucans to find the carbohydrate that elicited the best immune response. Once the glucan structure had been identified, Alpha-Beta engineered a strain of yeast that could produce this optimised carbohydrate in usable quantities. As part of this process, the company identified the genes involved in the synthesis of the optimised B glucan, and it is now in the process of cloning these genes.

Another start-up company in the US is also investigating the therapeutic potential of carbohydrates. In Pennsylvania, Neose is considering using a carbohydrate as an antibacterial agent. But its aim is to make the carbohydrate compete with bacteria for the protein receptor sites on epithelial cells. It is known, for example, that a carbohydrate on the surface of *Helicobacter pylori*—which his associated with ulcers—attaches to protein receptor sites on epithelial cells. Neose believes it can reduce the impact of infection by giving a patient a large amount of carbohydrate structurally similar to the one on the bacteria.

There are, however, limitations with carbohydrate drugs. One of the main criticisms levelled against Betafectin, for example, is that acids in a patient's stomach break down the carbohydrate so that the drug can only be injected or given by an intravenous drip.

Small is Practical

That is why other companies are more interested in making antibacterial drugs based on smaller molecules. Abingdon-based Oxford Glycosystems, for example, have identified carbohydrates that play a part in the immune response, and these are being used as lead compounds. They hope to use their knowledge of the carbohydrates to produce molecules that look like these carbohydrates. Glaxo Group Research is also interested in small molecule drugs. And it is in the process of developing a new range of penicillin-related drugs using this technique. The company also hopes to make small molecule drugs that are specific for a particular strain of bacteria such as *M. tuberculosis*.

Interest in developing these specialised killers is high. Microcide Pharmaceuticals (MPI) was founded in 1992 with the aim of developing novel antibacterial agents to treat infections, including antibiotic resistant infections acquired in hospitals and nursing homes. Michael Sterns, director of operations and business development for MPI says that the company's approach is to understand the genetic regulation of bacterial infections. From this work MPI hopes to identify new target processes for antibacterial agents to attack. The next stage is to identify small molecule lead compounds that can be screened for their ability to attack these targets using a variety of chemical and computer-based molecular modelling techniques. The most successful will be refined for clinical use.

But not all the research into future antibiotics is so specific. There are still some companies who are looking beyond the laboratory for their inspiration. One example is Magainin Pharmaceuticals. Michael Zasloff, Magainin's executive vice president, shot to fame in the late 1980s when he publicised his discovery that African clawed frogs (*Xenopus laevis*) contained a chemical in their skin that helped them fight infection. He called this chemical "magainin", the Hebrew word for shield.

Magainin was found to be a small peptide (around 20 amino acids long) that was stored in the frogs' nerve endings, called granular glands. The chemical not only killed bacteria, it also appeared to be effective against fungi, parasites and even some tumour cells. Since the initial discovery in 1986, Zasloff has found another magainin in frogs, as well as similar substances in humans and insects. He also recently found a new antibiotic substance in dog fish sharks. This chemical (squalamine) is a steroid found in the blood and tissue of the fish.

Zasloff believes all these natural antibiotics work in a similar way: by attaching themselves to the foreign cell's membrane, and then creating holes so that the unwanted organism becomes leaky and dies. In the case of magainin, the peptide is thought to identify bacteria and fungi by their negatively charged surface.

Magainin Pharmaceuticals has synthesised antibiotics based on the magainins. The first US clinical trials of a drug based on frog magainin did not produce a significant result, but Zasloff is still confident that the chemical has useful antibacterial activity. He is also excited by the potential of squalamine: "We've produced its structure. It's an extremely potent, broad-spectrum agent that could be used in many types of diseases. It acts against many types of fungi, protozoa and bateria," says Zasloff.

Excitement over discoveries such as magainin and squalamine has prompted other researchers to go back and look at other naturally occurring substances that have antibacterial function. Researchers have known for over ten years that a lipid produced by the fat glands in human skin has antibiotic potential. And last year Raza Aly, adjunct professor of dermatology, microbiology and immunology at the University of California at San Francisco, showed that this lipid called sphingosine could kill common bacteria such as staphyloccus and streptococcus.

Further discoveries of this type are likely, says Zasloff. "We've only begun to touch on the diversity of antibiotics from animals and marine creatures. Most traditional drugs come from sifting soil. The real future has to do with antibiotics animals make in their gut and wet epithelial surfaces."

But regardless of whether the next antibiotic is going to come from the natural world or the artificial world of computer modelling, one thing that all researchers agree on is that something must be done soon. The laissez faire days of the 1980s are over, and without new antibacterial treatments the doors of the TB wards and isolation units may need to be reopened.

Article Questions

1. Why is it that antibiotics may not be able to cure diseases like streptococcus pneumoniae?

2. How has the human body changes in its reactions to antibiotics? Why are people resistant to them?

3. Where are companies looking for new antibiotics?

4. Do you think that it is true that if new antibiotics are not found soon, the doors of the TB wards and isolation units may need to be reopened? Why?

Lori Valigra

If You Can't Beat 'em, Modem

James Coates

Say goodbye to your computer—it's about to disappear. That is, it will be so much a part of your life that you won't even know it's there.

That may or may not be good news, but it's going to happen, perhaps faster than you can say "voice-recognition" software. And in some ways, it already has. It's in your coffeemaker, your CD player and under the hood of your late-model car. That you haven't noticed it is more by design than by accident. People, it seems, accept technology better when they're not confronted with it.

But total acceptance isn't here yet. The optimists among us foresee immense growth in human productivity, thanks to technology. Life will get easier, more pleasant and meaningful as computers become our constant allies. So say the digital evangelists.

Pessimists, conversely, fret that the worrisome things we already know about computers will just get worse. As computers become all-pervasive, they argue, their ability to invade our privacy, run our lives and make us less self-reliant simply will multiply.

Gurus such as Weiser, head of computer research at the Xerox Palo Alto Research Center, the think tank that counts photocopiers, the computer mouse and software with windows among its discoveries, call the phenomenon "ubiquitous computing." Actually, ubiquitous computing already is a reality, even as more microprocessed miracles—and, perhaps, some accompanying nanosecond nightmares—seem a future certainty.

Everything from telephones to toothbrushes and coffeemakers to cab meters now perform their tasks at the command of microprocessors, those wonder chips that can hold on a small wafer the sort of computing power it once took a whole room to hold.

"[Computer technology] is amazingly powerful already," says Bertrand Cambou, chief chip scientist for Schaumburg-based Motorola Corp. Soon, he says, all-pervasive computers will be doing things that are "indistinguishable from magic."

In reality, human voice-recognition software and hardware already in use on some desktops already seem like magic by allowing you to write by merely speaking. Just say the words and watch them pop up on the compute's word-processing screen.

If that's not magical enough, this same software, sold under names such as Voice Blaster, can switch appliances and furnaces on and off by speech.

This Brave New World isn't as far away as you think: You can buy needed appliance-controlling hardware at Radio Shack right now, and voice-recognition software is on the shelves at Egghead Software.

Perhaps most magical of all is a $1,295 hardware-software device now on the market by Psychic Lab Inc. of New York City that allows users to send commands to Macintosh desktop computers by brain waves. The device was a star attraction in mid-January at Macworld, the annual computer show that focuses on the Apple Computer Inc. line of machines.

Anyone who is so inclined can put on a Psychic Lab headband and think about something—the color purple, for example—and watch how the computer displays your brain waves as you think "purple." You then repeat the process a few times until every time you think about the color purple the same display comes on screen.

What purpose might this serve? you ask. The Psychic Lab software will let you link a computer command you want executed anytime the unique pattern of your thinking about the color purple are detected. Thus, a computer can detect an operator's brain thinking about purple and start playing a programmed song. Prince's "Purple Rain," perhaps?

With such wonders already on the shelves, Cambou notes, future models seem certain.

"Welcome to the world of 2006," begins a recent press release he issued shortly before bing interviewed for this article. "Miniature computers implanted into the human body are saving lives by automatically monitoring and controlling blood pressure, temperature, heart rate and cholesterol levels. Glasses and contact lenses are obsolete because implanted semiconductors reshape signals received from defective eye tissue....

"Pocket-sized devices combine audio, video, graphics and text, allowing you to compute, video-conference, create, access, store and transmit data and interact with other such devices anywhere on earth.

"Your kitchen appliances understand the spoken word....

"Your car, with its hybrid gas/electric engine, drives itself and uses a positioning indicator to tell you where you are and how best to arrive at your destination. Complete, under-the-hood electronic systems control everything from the fuel/air ratio of your engine to the tilt of your steering wheel."

In many ways, what Cambou described already exists. It's called the Cadill Northstar system and is available in several models.

There are other manifestations of the hidden-computer phenomenon. According to Tom Beaman, Chicago-based marketing executive for General Motors Corp., the only way carmakers have been able to achieve such things as EPA-required emissions controls and federal fuel-consumption guidelines is through heavy duty chip technology.

As a result, automobiles now are designed around two computers, the "engine computer," which does things like control fuel mix to improve mileage and limit emissions, and the "body computer," which controls heating, cooling, defrosting, seat adjustments, outside-temperature sensing, interior lighting, door locks, etc.

Each auto computer rivals the processing power of today's office desktop machines and, although the experience of driving a car today is virtually indistinguishable from that of a decade ago, a stinning transformation has happened under the hood and beneath the dashboard.

The engine computers on various models and in the Northstar system alike use sensors embedded in each cylinder to monitor temperature, fuel mix, etc. and to operate the machine optimally.

For example, when the cruise-control chip tells the engine chip that the car is on an upgrade and thus needs more power to maintain speed, the engine computer orders up more fuel and shifts the transmission downward.

As part of that process the engine computer "knows" the exact temperature in each cylinder, a fact that makes it possible to drive a Northstar-equipped vehicle even if its V-8 engine loses all of its coolant.

These V-8s work with two banks of four pistons running side by side. Each piston moves up and down in its own cylinder in response to controlled explosions of gasoline. The piston is connected to a shaft that turns with each firing and thus makes the wheels go around.

But heat in excess of 268 degrees permanently damages cylinder walls, so water is pumped through the engine to keep the cylinders cooler as the gasoline explosions take place.

When the Northstar sensors show a temperature greater than 268 degrees in any cylinder, the computer shuts off fuel to all four cylinders in the bank containing that cylinder.

The four unpowered pistons then move up and down without creating heat, thus pumping air into them to cool the metal surfaces. When those four are cooled, the computer switches the power and spark back to them and shuts it off on the other bank, thus cooling those cylinders.

The computer keeps switching and cooling each bank as needed, allowing the car to limp in to a service center. A Car and Driver magazine test of the Northstar system first drained the radiator and then found that with the computer switching between banks roughly every three seconds, the car had a range "dry" of at least 50 miles.

Chipmakers such as Cambou call this phenomenon "embedded technologies," ordinary devices that now are operated by the extraordinary "brains" on a board of silicon known as microprocessors.

How pervasive is the computer? If you get your music via compact discs, your home music system is a computer. So is your digital wristwatch, your microwave oven and just about every other gadget in your life.

The box on the wall that you use to turn the heat up and down at home now may be a computer, as is the device you use to open the garage door.

Consider that a modern television set produces pictures on the screen by first storing on a computer chip the data for every colored dot (pixel) required for every frame and then ordering the chip to display the picture.

Most new sets thus offer "PIP" (picture in picture) where it is possible to simply add one more memory chip and display a smaller version of another channel in a second on-screen window. But PIP is just another gadgetry wrinkle in a life besotted with electronic bells and whistles, and chances are even the most technology-resistant consumer doesn't know computer wizardry is at work.

If you've bought a camera lately, it, too, is most likely as much a computer as it is a camera. Canon's phenomenally successful EOS camera, for example, is completely controlled by Motorola-built chips that operate the lenses, aperture settings and the motor drive for advancing film after each shot.

If you have a modern sewing machine, it almost certainly uses internal computers to produce stitches, repair button holes and perform other tasks.

Xerox's Weiser compares the computer chips of today to the electrical motors of yore.

Shortly after the turn of the century, a typical factory owned one very large electric motor that supplied power to drive dozens of machines and tools through complex arrays of shafts, pulleys and belts.

Today, cheap, powerful electric motors are everywhere, and no one gives them a thought. A typical automobile contains 22 motors that do everything from start the engine to lock the doors and play the music. Motorized screwdrivers, knives, toothbrushes, blenders, food processors and all the other denizens of the micromotor pantheon are undeniably legion.

Even 20 or 30 years ago many of these tiny motor-driven gadgets would have been considered miracles. In the 1950s, futurists churned out articles predicting a miraculous future of "servomechanisms" (automatic control systems) that would transform human life.

As Weiser notes, that servo magic arrived just as predicted. But it came on the scene gradually and was deeply embedded in everyday life almost before it became noticed. Servomotors are "profound" additions to human life as a result.

In the same way, computers are now becoming profound. And, like servomotors, they often become major components of human existence even before society takes up questions such as whether the new powers they grant are profoundly good or profoundly bad.

"Embedded microprocessors simply do what we already can do in other ways, but they do them much, much more efficiently," explains Cambou, who works at Motorola's Phoenix-based semiconductor product group.

Examples familiar to most of us include the cable converter box on top of your TV that replaced the rabbit ears; it is a computer run by Motorola and Intel chips. Likewise, the remote-control box that replaced the channel-selection knob is a computer.

Converters already have memory chips capable of switching among upward of 100 channels and of remembering the last 15 or 20 that were selected, making it possible to "program" the computer for favorite channels from the armchair.

Soon the devices will handle 500 channels. That will happen when the cable companies start moving video in digitized, computer-friendly form—the information highway that is as prominent in today's headlines as Watergate was a couple decades ago.

But there is a downside to all this magic.

Coping with 500 channels will make the editing of which ones to scan in any one viewing session essential. And, of course, there is an electronic log of what you have been watching recently in the box's memory banks that allows the cable companies to "poll" their boxes and track who is watching what. Cable operators can monitor not only what you watch regularly but what makes you pause when using the little plus arrow to "channel surf."

With the cable box, TV becomes a two-way street. That's how the cable folks now know where to send those pay-per-view movies and other special events. While you're viewing, Big Brother already is watching.

This is an important new wrinkle to the spread of the computer, and it prompts fierce debate at places like the WELL, an "online" gathering of computer-savvy, socially conscious folks whose roots harken back to the 1960s Whole Earth Catalog movement.

WELL stands for Whole Earth 'Lectronic Link. Participants exchange messages by linking their personal computers to the Well's bigger computer via telephone modem hookups, another aspect of computing that is as much a part of modern life as the modem sold with virtually every home computer.

Howard Rheingold, author of the newly published Addison-Wesley book "Virtual Community: Homesteading on the Electronic Frontier," sounded a note of the alarm voiced by his WELL comrades:

"I am absolutely enamored of computer technology. I adore the fact that our lives just seem to get better and better as technologies take over and make things work better and produces them cheaper.

"But I really worry that people don't think enough about the hidden implications of technological revolution."

As computers proliferate—even before their full impact is debated—great dangers loom, the critics warn.

Imagine, for example, the implications of Election Night 2000 in an America on line:

If your choice is the Republican, tune to channel 100. If you prefer the Democrat, tune to channel 200. Ross Perot? Try channel 300. The cable company will tally the votes and announce the results on the Larry King show, where most of the Presidential debates had been held anyway.

Obviously there are weighty social and political issues to be resolved over such Huxleyesque spectres as voting via interactive television, of having your television watch you while you watch it.

It's worth keeping in mind, of course, that 98 per cent of all Americans today are linked together by the interactive electronic device known as the telephone. There has never been a panic, though, over dial-up voting.

But the technology required to conduct elections—elections that could be monitored far more accurately for cheating via cable converter boxes—is not science fiction. Television sets already are sending household data to cable companies, as well as receiving it.

In addition, the new face of computing impacts social policy in other ways beyond the democratic process by fiber-optic cable. As Rheingold says, there are particularly compelling questions of human privacy that sometimes don't even get noticed.

With the knowledge that virtually everything there is to know about virtually every person in the country already is stored in some sort of database somewhere, the future of ubiquitous computers can summon some Orwellian nightmares.

Many of the reservations arise simple because embedded computing lets computer operators put everything together far easier and faster than ever before.

The implications, though, are not always as innocuous as the miracle engine of a Cadillac. Consider this scenario:

A customer at a Jewel grocery store in Chicago gives the clerk one of its "Preferred Customer" cards, which is scanned in along with the customer's purchases. Jewel's computers thus know the name, address and phone number of this person who bought a bottle of vodka, a carton of cigarettes and a copy of Rolling Stone.

There is nothing to prevent the store from using that data to produce a mailing list of people with similar purchases and offer them deals on products that seem to match the lifestyle demonstrated by the purchasing history in question.

Dianne Maffia, a spokeswoman for Jewel, confirms that the chain developed the card program to help it with future marketing initiatives such as targeting customers on the basis of their past buying habits, as disclosed by the card. She emphasizes, however, that the Jewel computer experts consider any such efforts something for the long-term future rather than the present.

Mindful of the privacy issues involved, Maffia adds that Jewel will issue the cards, which also are used for check-cashing approval and discount coupons, without recording the user's address on its computers each time a purchase is made.

But, as critics like Rheingold note, the grocery checkout scanner, another example of chip-driven technology, not only can count your change and call out the name of each product you buy in a human-sounding voice, it also can store a record of what you bought and where you live.

And, as the case with Jewel illustrates, users sometimes must count on the good will of the people who gather the data not to use it in ways the consumer does not desire.

Consider what happens as new technologies make vast amounts of computer data widely accessible—all the way down to the desktop level—through the easy availability of powerful computing devices.

Using data called "the TIGER set" and made public by the U.S. Census Bureau after the 1990 census, it now is possible, for example, to use home computers to find the racial, ethnic, sexual and economic characteristics of the people living on any street in America.

This data now is distributed to most major public libraries on CD-ROMs (Compact Disc-Read Only Memory) that can be read on any home computer equipped with a device costing about $500. Millions of homes already use these "readers" for "interactive multi-media" encyclopedias, computer games and other applications.

Using another set of CD-ROMs called PhoneDisc USA, which costs $300 and includes nearly every listed phone in the country, it is possible to get the name and phone number of most of the people who live on the street where the TIGER data has described the population's makeup.

Together, these two CD-ROM sets can put awesome research powers into the hands of just about anybody from cat burglars to politicians and mom-and-pop grocery-store managers who want to use it for their unique purposes. Combined with data like that compiled by a company such as Jewel, the implications for mischief become greater still.

The CD-ROM readers that bring such powers to the smallest of personal computers now are in an estimated 2 million American homes and are expected to become universal components of personal computers in coming years.

In this case, no one entity set out to lay bare the soul of just about every individual in America by collecting data and storing it. But the combination of technologies that have blossomed for other purposes can be combined to turn the microprocessor into a very good semblance of long-feared Big Brother, according to many observers of the WELL and elsewhere in cyberspace.

Meanwhile, even as we struggle to cope with the social-policy implications of the current state of the art, the machines that so vex us become orders of magnitude more complex and sophisticated approximately every two years.

Even as some critics warn that we're not coping with the technologies already at hand, we're hit with still more wonders to cope with.

Consider the cable box. Last April, Chicago-based General Instrument Corp. joined forces with chip-making giant Intel Corp. and software behemoth Microsoft Corp. to build a new generation of cable boxes that include an Intel 386 microprocessor and a version of the Microsoft Windows software, similar to today's more powerful desktop computers.

With these cable boxes, users will operate their televisions using a remote controller called an "air mouse," which is all but identical to the mouse used on many computers. The gadget will let TV viewers move a little arrow about the screen just as people use a mouse to move a cursor-arrow on a personal computer.

The home television screen thus will become almost indistinguishable from the home computer screen, which already is a landscape of small pictures called "icons" that represent actions the machine will take if you move the cursor over them and "click" the proper button on the mouse.

Just days after the General Instrument plan was announced, that company's archrival, Scientific-Atlanta, said that it would team with Motorola Corp. and Apple Computer Inc. to produce a competing version.

Apple's Macintosh, which now accounts for about 14 per cent of the personal-computing market compared to the 80 per cent owned by PCs, is based on Motorola chips.

The result is that you soon will have either a Macintosh or a PC sitting on top of your TV and you won't even know it. In fact, designers almost universally acknowledge that they go out of their way to make computers look like anything but computers.

Matt Miller, vice president for technology at General Instrument, and his company went to substantial lengths to avoid adding a keyboard to the cable box converter-computers, even though doing so would have been easier than not doing so.

When General Instrument announced the Intel-Microsoft box in April, Miller described the future of ubiquitous computing via home television in an interview the day the Apple deal was announced:

"Say you point and click, and up comes a button that says 'topics.' You click on 'topics,' and up comes 'sports' and 'movies' and 'comedy.' So you click on 'sports,' and it will tell all the sports that are on....

"Or suppose you're watching MTV and you wonder what the lyrics are to a song that's playing, so you click a button, and the lyrics start to scroll along the bottom of the screen.... Or you click a button that says 'cover,' and up comes a picture of the cover for the CD that's playing. Maybe another box says, 'Do you want to buy this CD?'"

All these computerlike things will be done without a single stroke on a keyboard, Miller emphasizes. Computing will remain computing, but the traditional keyboards that warn today's generation they are using a computer will disappear.

"People are afraid of keyboards," says Paul Saffo of the Institute for the Future in Menlo Park, Cal.

In November, IBM began marketing a computer that can recognize several hundred words, thus sparing users the indignity of having to type them in via keyboard. Thus looms the disappearance of the personal computer as computing evolves into other forms. Even such devices as word processors and spreadsheets, now the traditional stuff of personal computing, likely will be much different when people input data by voice and view it in a window on their television screens. Just as millions upon millions of people start buying them and just as they start debating their possible dangers.

When you're using your voice to input words into your computer, and when you're reading those words on your television screen, your personal computer, with its keyboard, monitor and hard drives, becomes extraneous. It disappears into your home entertainment system and thus becomes ubiquitous.

And, as with coffee pots and cable boxes and cars and cameras, such change comes gradually and in unexpected ways. Thus, as Weiser of Xerox points out, the most profound of human revolutions pass virtually unnoticed, and, usually, undebated.

The gap between what we were and what we become can be enormous.

As futurist Saffo puts it: "A 1920s time traveler would be lost in the touch-tone complexities of our 1990s phone system. Yet if we traded places, we would be equally confused and infuriated by endless and time-consuming transactions with human operators."

Among the questions that should have occurred to the people in the 1920s, long before telephones became commonplace and thus accepted, were such issues as the advisability of publishing entire books listing where everybody lives. Not to mention the question of whether unsolicited calls from telemarketers should be allowed.

The immediate future likewise offers the opportunity for substantial debate about today's far more chilling issues—issues that explore whether embedding computers into the fabric of life will be extremely beneficial or extremely dangerous.

"And, still," said Motorola's Cambou in the press release that inspired this article, "we'll just be beginning."

Article Questions

1. What is computer heaven? What is computer hell?

2. What is the main theme in this article?

3. What are the social implications relating to technologies mentioned?

4. How has technology changed in the last twenty or thirty years?

Technology Combats Disabilities

John A. Adam

Most people, if they live long enough, will become disabled. Millions already—whether by birth, or through illness or an accident—have physical limitations that affect their mobility or their ability to see, hear, or speak.

Fortunately, helping to overcome such difficulties are advances in technology that now allow computers to supply information for impaired senses and for controlling limbs and other bodily functions. As a result, people who are deaf, blind, or confined to a wheelchair are integrating into society as never before.

"Technology is increasing their independence—in some cases, making them totally independent—and opening up job opportunities," observed speech and language pathologist Gail Pickering, who works for the Office of Disabled Student Services at the California State University, Northridge.

That boost to self-reliance has largely resulted from two trends. One is the eagerness with which people have accepted the Information Age. The text and graphics basis of computer networks disregards disabilities like deafness or lack of speech. With the emergence of electronic mail as a conversation equivalent, access to many kinds of interaction and even employment is possible from anyone's home.

The second trend is the development of more powerful tools for people who are disabled. Much has changed since the early 19th century invention of Braille. In the last few has taken off. Engineers, with disabled people in mind, are designing products ranging from robotic devices to virtual reality interfaces. Examples include an apparatus that helps those suffering from strokes to lift objects, large vocabularies of accessible synthetic voice that aid people with speech impediments, and more capable wheelchairs.

The multidisciplinary field is known as rehabilitation engineering. In any previous age, the attainment of its loftiest goals would have been called a miracle—to give sight to the blind, hearing to the deaf, speech to those who cannot talk, and mobility to the paralyzed. Nonetheless, despite the enormous strides made in the last 20 years, "the present level of available functional restoration still pales in comparison to the capabilities of nondisabled individuals," said Charles J. Robinson, chairman of the department of rehabilitation, science, and technology at the University of Pittsburgh. He is also editor of the *IEEE Transactions on Rehabilitation Engineering*.

A more modest goal in rehabilitation engineering is to develop products and aids from which individuals can select. Some items substitute for biological systems, such as cochlear implants for hearing; but more often today, they are assistive technologies with which people can work around biological impediments.

Users like variety, commented Lawrence Scadden, senior program director of the National Science Foundation's Persons with Disabilities Program. For one application, a blind person might prefer to use a speech-generating computer, and for another, refreshable Braille output, which can be read at over 250 words a minute.

Growing Market

Definitions of disability vary. The U.S. Census Bureau states that 49 million people—nearly one-fifth of the U.S. population—are in some way disabled; nearly half—24.1 million—have a severe disability, in which a physical shortfall is coupled with a mental illness like Alzheimer's disease. About 37 million persons in the United States over the age of 15 are affected by functional limitations (the focus of this series), according to an analysis by Irving K. Zola in the *Journal of Disability Policy Studies* (Vol. 4, no. 2, 1993).

Changing demographics will add to the latter group. In the United States alone, the 1990 census counted more than 31 million people aged 65 or older, comprising 13 percent of the adult population. In 1980, this age group was 11 percent of a smaller total. In another decade and a half, the percentage is likely to start rising steeply as the post-World War II Baby Boomers reach retirement age.

With suitable technological assistance, these elderly men and women may prolong their independence and reduce or postpone their need for specialized care. Their quality of life may be improved and the costs of their health care reduced.

Products originally designed for persons with disabilities have sometimes proved useful to the able-bodied as well. The typewriter was intended for blind users, and the telephone resulted from Alexander Graham Bell's work for the deaf. More recently, disabled persons have helped develop speech-recognition technology, although the initial research was targeted for fighter pilots, according to Susan Brummel, director of the Clearinghouse on Computer Accommodation of the U.S. General Services Administration, Washington, D.C.

Attacking barriers in multiple ways opens up new possibilities for everyone, said Brummel, who believes information should not be limited to a single means of output.

For individuals with disabilities, an extra choice of output may be vital. For society in general, an array of choices offers convenience and flexibility. Citing electronic mail, Brummel asked rhetorically, "Who would have thought typing words would be preferred to the telephone?" Similarly, the augmentation of visual information by speech systems can be handy for car drivers as well as for blind persons.

Closed captioning on television was developed for the hard of hearing, but is also being used to teach English as a second language and better speech to the semiliterate, observed Dinah Cohen, director of the Computer Electronic Accommodations Program at the Defense Medical Systems Support Center, Alexandria, Va. Voice-recognition systems may do as much for persons whose hands are occupied as for those with paralyzed limbs.

They can also be used in data entry to reduce the number of keystrokes needed and hence the incidence of repetitive strain injuries, noted Brummel.

Multiple Access

Multiple modes of access are stirring interest as a possible feature of more consumer products. This news could cheer not only the disabled but anyone who has encountered trouble in programming a videocassette recorder.

"We've been pretty passive in taking what's been pushed our way," Brummel said. "People have been accommodating the technology rather than vice versa."

Ease of access to consumer products is not covered by the 1990 Americans with Disabilities Act, which prohibits discrimination against the disabled in almost everything else—employment, public services, accommodations, transportation, and telecommunications. But some companies, under the aegis of the Electronic Industries Association (EIA), Washington, D.C., are looking at designing accessibility into general products right from the start. The effort is driven by market demographics (notably the aging Baby Boomers) and the desire to anticipate Government mandates.

Products that give accessibility to the disabled and elderly may also make life easier for the general population, according to acting director Timothy Farr of the technology applications program of the Electronic Industries Foundation (EIF), an EIA offshoot. Participating companies in the nascent EIF project include AT&T, Thomson, and Matsushita.

"You can't design a product that every single person in the world can use," Farr conceded. "But the intent is to maximize the potential." The goal is to make products simpler and easy to use. Farr envisions computers with voice output commonly being purchased in the general market. Stereos will have larger readouts as well as voice output. The incremental costs of many functional redundancies of this nature, if planned during the design stage, would be marginal, Farr believes. Computing advances will continue to expand functionality at lower costs.

The EIF effort, which Farr expects to be in full swing within a few years, would confer a sort of EIA label of accessibility on consumer products. Optional cassettes might be available at stores for those who cannot read the manual. Various icons would indicate accessibility in any combination of seven categories: blindness, poor vision, mobility and dexterity, deafness, and impairment of hearing, cognition, or speech.

Independence at Home

Equipping people who are disabled and elderly with the means to be more independent also could help control health care costs. A recent study by the World Institute on Disability, a think tank in Oakland, Calif., showed that when state agencies cared for individuals with disabilities, the cost was nearly double that of independent contractors. The use of technology might further that reduction.

The possibilities are evident in a 135-year-old historic home outside Baltimore, Md. The house was recently gutted and fitted with high-tech gear by the Volunteers for Medical

Engineering (VME), a group founded in 1982 by John Staehlin, an electrical engineer at Westinghouse Electric Corp.

Opened in June, the Future Home Institute demonstrates how current technology can make houses more accommodating to inhabitants, no matter what their functional limitations—and can lighten the load on their families and caretakers, said Jeffrey Jerome, director of Future Home.

Briefing a *Spectrum* visitor on a tour of the showcase house in August, Jerome showed how monitoring gear installed in all the rooms made residents feel confident that any developing emergency would be detected quickly.

In many cases, Future Home has conveniences that any upscale technophile would pounce upon, underscoring the universal design element. "There are five or six ways to control everything in this house," boasted Jerome. Among the choices are track balls, push buttons, remote controls with large buttons or touch screens, and voice-recognition units.

Also conducting the tour was Charles ("Dave") Ward, whose concept it was—along with VME—to build the house. Ward, who will be living there with his wife and a caretaker, has been active in designs of this kind since a fall from a tower in 1977 paralyzed him from the neck down at the age of 31.

Ward said that he plans soon to graduate to a powered wheelchair. Then, for the first time since his injury, he will be able to leave home on his own, thanks to the house's automated doors and the chin controller on the chair.

Occupants of the house control its workings through menus on TV sets in various rooms. The TV set won out over a computer as the central control unit "because it is less intimidating" and can be accessed from a distance, said Jerome. Without interrupting normal television programming, a viewer can touch a remote device to pull down the screen menus. By choosing options on the menu, the user can open power windows for ventilation, check images from infrared video cameras in bedrooms or entryways, or activate the closed captions for, say, the "Oprah" show.

Users can also call up a CD ROM from a Tandy player to read in large print what is shown on the television screen. The basic hardware and operating system for the TV interface were produced by Interior Systems Designs, Sun Valley, Calif., which does building automation work. Software was custom-written by VME.

When someone enters a room, infrared and wheelchair sensors signal doors to slide open and lights to turn on. At just the push of a button, kitchen cabinets and counters descend electrically, and temperature and water flow from the faucets are adjusted. The need to move around is minimized because many of the house's features, including the powered windows and the front door lock, can be manipulated from a chair, wheelchair, or bed.

Ward's 30,000-word Dragon Dictate system now enables him to enter about 30 words per minute. Previously, he had to hold a mouse stick between his teeth to input data to a 486 computer, and managed perhaps six to eight words a minute. "My teeth would ache at the end of the day," he said. The new unit, from Dragon Systems Inc., Newton, Mass., lists for $695 (or $995 for a Windows version).

The fact that the household functions are programmable means they can be matched to any combination of disabilities (mobility, visual, auditory, or cognitive). Telephone calls may be placed by voice anywhere in the house, providing residents with a sense of security, even without a full-time caregiver. Reminders for cognitively or memory-impaired individuals—that they take a pill, for instance, or make a check-in call—can be announced over the house's intercom system.

At Future Home, demonstrations are also given of easy-to-use interfaces for a home office that will incorporate such features as home banking, shopping, and so on, as the services develop. Ward said he looked forward to the Baltimore County Library coming on-line.

For the project, low-voltage wiring—5000 meters of it—was installed, as well as US $65,000 worth of technological equipment, including three computers, three voice-recognition units, and another 10 products containing computers. The most expensive item had a retail price of $5000; most items were less than $1000. The costs are relatively small compared to the $40,000-$50,000 yearly cost of institutional care, according to the VME.

Cautionary Notes

Even although technology has greatly improved the quality of life for the disabled. experts like Brummel warn that such developments as the rich sensory environments of multimedia communications threaten to bypass them. The protection of disabled people's right to access information is prominent in the Clinton administration's concept of the emerging National Information Infrastructure.

At its demonstration center in Washington, D.C., the U.S. General Services Administration's Clearinghouse on Computer Accommodation shows visitors model developments in information technology that assist disabled people, like appropriate multimedia kiosks. The clearinghouse's Brummel said the Government in this instance appears to be leading industry.

Other notable efforts are under way at the Trace Center at the University of Wisconsin, Madison, which is working with computer and software makers to improve accessibility to their products, as well as at Stanford University's Center for the Study of Language and Information, where researchers are working on next-generation technologies with the disabled in mind.

According to Lynn Bryant, director of Abledata, a clearinghouse of information for the disabled located in Silver Spring, Md., some 19,000 products of assistive technology are being produced by 2500 manufacturers. "In the past, assistive devices have been enormously expensive," she said, in part because they followed the health care model (where costs are dissipated among large bureaucracies). But now consumers, who are more economy minded, are comparison shopping with the help of clearinghouses like Bryant's.

In many instances, "each one of the products is the lifeblood of the person," noted Lucy Trivelli, project director at Resna, an Arlington, Va.-based interdisciplinary association for the advancement of rehabilitation and assistive technologies.

Because of the essential nature of many of these devices, concern over product liability can scare small companies away, noted Steve Reeger, director of rehabilitation technology at the Cleveland Clinic Foundation in Ohio. And the fact that many are niche markets deters large companies. For instance, 1.2 million people use wheel chairs in the United States, and perhaps only a few hundred thousand will buy a new one each year.

To woo small companies, the National Technology Transfer Center, in Wheeling, W. Va., is designing a strategy to help them develop assistive technologies. "Most producers are small and the failure rate is very high," said Jerry Duskin, a consultant at the center who believes greater cooperation with Federal laboratories may be an answer.

As disabled persons gain influence and a greater acceptance into everyday society, technology is helping them to grow more independent. How to ensure—and enhance—that participation seems a goal well worth pursuing.

To Probe Further

Upcoming conferences on technology and disabilities are scheduled. The IEEE Engineering in Medicine and Biology Society's annual conference in Baltimore, Md., will be held Nov. 3-6 (contact Steve Martin, Meeting Management Inc., Irvine, Calif.; 714-752-8205). On March 14-18, the 10th annual "Technology and Persons with Disabilities Conference" is to take place in Los Angeles (contact Harry Murphy, California State University, Northridge; 818-885-2578).

The American Association for the Advancement of Science, Washington, D.C., offers publications to encourage children with disabilities to pursue careers in science and engineering. Call 202-326-6440.

The Future Home Institute, which runs the new showcase home outside Baltimore, is open to the public by appointment and also provides consulting. Call 410-243-7495 or 410-455-6397.

The Abledata information clearinghouse on product information can be reached at 800 227-0216 or 301-588-9284. (Both lines provide voice and text telephone access.)

Technical journals include the Department of Veteran Affairs' quarterly *Journal of Rehabilitation Research and Development*, published in Baltimore, Md. The IEEE publishes the quarterly *Transactions on Rehabilitation Engineering*. Resna publishes the quarterly *Assistive Technology* (Arlington, Va.; 703-524-6686).

Information on the American with Disabilities Act (ADA) is available electronically from the U.S. Department of Justice's ADA bulletin board. It is accessible from the National Technical Information Service's online FedWorld system, reachable from the Internet (telnet fedworld.gov) or directly by modem at 703-321-8020. Also on FedWorld is a report titled *Information Infrastructure: Reaching Society's Goals*, which offers a disabilities paper by the General Services Administration for comment.

Article Questions

1. Give examples of ways that technology combats disabilities.

2. What concerns might you have about the technologies mentioned in this article?

3. How do you think technology will combat disabilities in the future?

Discussion Questions

1. Many of the medical technology issues presented in this chapter have ethical issues attached to them. For example, when medical technology keeps an individual alive, at what point do you allow the person to die or survive on his own? What issues would play a part in this decision?

2. What part does the quality of life play in current medical technology? If a medication saves your life, yet causes blindness, is that okay? If you can save a premature baby, but it has permanent brain damage, is that okay? If you survive a heart transplant, but you have to take medicine forever and your lifestyle is restricted by 60%, is that okay?

3. Give five examples of ways that medical technology help people survive. What are the possible negative ramifications of those technologies?

4. If you were going to die and your only chance for survival is accepting a baboon heart in your body, would you do it? Explain your answer in detail.

5. How do you define death?

6. What is the difference between euthanasia and suicide?

7. What ethical limits should be defined for genetic research and how should they be imposed? Discuss recent advances in cloning and genetic engineering.

8. A classified advertisement reads "Womb for hire at right price" Call 1-800-xxx-xxxx. Comment.

CHAPTER EIGHT
TECHNOLOGY &
THE THIRD WORLD

The "Third" World

William J. Grimm

The French demographer Alfred Sauvy coined the phrase "third world" in 1952. He felt that the aspirations of the nations moving toward independence from the European colonial powers were not unlike those of the Third Estate in France at the time of the French Revolution. Like the French commoners who in 1789 faced off against the clergy and aristocracy, these nations wanted freedom, dignity and control over their own destinies. Calling them the "third world" was a forward-looking, hopeful way of describing what was happening in Africa and Asia. It described nations from their own perspective. Today, however, the phrase has shifted its sense to a point that it obscures reality. It is time to excise the phrase from our vocabulary.

Talk of a "third world" inevitably gave rise to the coinages "first world" and "second world." The "first world," meaning the (mainly Western) industrialized and technologized economic powers, has had a hardy history. The "second world" was supposed to mean the Communist nations of Eastern Europe with their government-controlled economies, but that second designation never really caught on.

With the growing hegemony of the term "first world," the meaning of "third world" shifted. It no longer referred to the aspirations of nations hoping to develop independent governments and economies. It became a term of comparison. The third world was now defined in terms of the first. The third world was the agglomeration of nations that were struggling to feed, house, clothe and educate their people while hampered by poverty, climate, oppression, war and the aftereffects of colonialism. The phrase became a label to be applied by the West on the basis of norms arising outside of the regions that it was meant to explain.

Today the popular definition of "third world" would likely be some variation of "any non-white country whose economy is as bad as or worse than Poland's." No matter how desperate the economic situation may be in Eastern Europe or on parts of the Iberian Peninsula, those places are never spoken of as being in the third world, which is a world of brown-, black- or yellow-skinned people. No white, Western nation is described with the term even though that country may be economically worse off than, for example, Thailand. When whites ruled Rhodesia, it was not in the third world. Now that it is black-ruled Zimbabwe, it is. The South African Government's decision to regard Japanese as honorary whites for purposes of enforcing the apartheid laws is instructive. Japan (soon to be joined by Korea and Taiwan) is allowed into the "first world" designation because the Japanese, by becoming one of the world's wealthiest and most powerful nations and by allying themselves with American and European interests, have succeeded at playing the Western economic game. It is a game that non-whites can sometimes win, but no white can lose.

The idea of "losing" is a natural outgrowth of phrases primarily used in giving evaluations and rank. The first-world/third-world dichotomy can give a sense of moral superiority to those told they are in the first world. After all, first prize goes to the best player. This ranking fosters a chauvinistic nationalism that allows Americans and others to look down upon the suffering peoples of the world as somehow or other deserving of their problems.

By placing such people in the category of losers in some sort of contest, the West is able to ignore the fact that much of the suffering in the world's poor nations is the result of Western history, economic structures, greed and plain unwillingness to sacrifice in order to help others. Of course, the history, policies, economic structures and greed of people in those nations are also important factors, but we should not allow them to blind us to our own responsibility.

Placing ourselves in the "first" world, we become unable to see the rest of the world on its own terms. The concept gives us a feeling of being somehow or other in control, either as the leaders and saviors of the poor, or as the chief oppressors and villains of the world. We are neither, but the phrase gives us an exaggerated sense of our centrality in the world. It can also allow those who govern in suffering areas to shirk their duties by placing the blame or cure for their problems outside their responsibility, outside their own societies.

Our self-designation as "first world" vis-à-vis a "third world" is inaccurate. The United States owes the world's biggest international debt. We have inadequate medical care, a high infant mortality rate, illiteracy, homelessness and a myriad of other problems that should, in all fairness, cause this nation to be relegated to the third world. But, having proclaimed ourselves the winners, we can ignore the evidence of defeat and failure in our decaying inner cities and bankrupt family farms.

The West has set the membership standards for the first and third worlds. Basically, these standards are economic. This is a form of intellectual imperialism. The difficulty lies in the fact that the nations characterized as "third world" may have values and orientations that they consider more important than economics, such as history, culture or religion.

This may be that phrase's biggest drawback. It so determines the way we view other nations that we no longer actually see them. The phrase prejudices not only how we see the rest of the world, but what we see there. The rich variety of customs and cultures in the world is homogenized out of existence when any designation allows us to lump together Bedouins and Bengalis, Peruvians and Pygmies.

Our values have become skewed because of our socioeconomic definition of the third world. The hunger of a child in a Somali refugee camp is a sin that calls for repentance and action by those who made him hungry or keep her hungry. But is that hunger the only thing we can say about the child? What about the rich African traditions of family, of hospitality? What about the gifts of that particular child? By having a handy catch phrase to describe one element of reality, we can, in effect, ignore the child's more particular existence as our brother or sister and child of God. He or she no longer has anything to offer us, to teach us. We see one problem, and then respond to that problem on our terms.

This tendency to see socioeconomic problems to the exclusion of other elements has even infected the church. In reaction, perhaps, to an angelism that put too great an emphasis upon "spiritual" goods and allowed the church and its members to be oppressors, we have become like the drunk in Martin Luther's story. Having once fallen off our donkey on the side of "the spiritual," we now fall off on the side of "the material." As a result, many foreign and domestic projects are one-sided, emphasizing social and economic problems without at the same time giving due emphasis to nonmaterial religious, interpersonal and aesthetic needs.

The peoples whom we characterize as "third world" have riches we need. Many of them have cultures and histories that were already ancient when America had not yet been discovered. The origins of Indian culture and religion, for example, predate the Old Testament and enshrine thousands of years of human experience. Community, hospitality, family, reverence, tradition, play, respect for nature—all of these are lessons the so-called first world desperately needs to learn. They would be taught us by other peoples if we could go to them without the condescension our vocabulary makes nearly inevitable.

Not only have we become blinded to the reality of other peoples and cultures, we have lost sight of our own. We measure someone's worth in dollars. Seeing the world in "first/third" terms reinforces this bias, further isolating us from our own historical, cultural and religious riches.

This loss limits our ability to share with others some of the very things they would be most interested in sharing, things in which they would be most able to meet us as equals or superiors. We have more to offer traditional societies, for instance, than food, flashlights and Western economic systems. We have human traditions as well, a history that can be shared with the rest of the world to our mutual advantage. The Western reverence for the uniqueness of the individual and our tradition of law based upon principles, though often betrayed, have both been important gifts to the rest of humankind. We have more to offer the poor nations of the world than philanthropy or guilt feelings.

There can be no effective response to the life-and-death problems confronting so many of our brothers and sisters until we are willing to see them on their own terms, in their cultural and individual uniqueness. If we continue to use jargon in speaking of them, they will become less and less real to us and turn into objects for our projects. A phrase that once recognized the dignity of other peoples will only reinforce isolationist condescension. There is no "third" world. There is only one world, and only one family living in it.

Article Questions

1. Define the following terms:

    a. First world

    b. Second world

    c. Third world

    d. developing economy

2. Do you agree with the author that our self-designation as"first world" visa-vis a "third world" is inaccurate?

3. Many people in the "third world" believe that they are the victims of "technology imperialism" imposed by the "First world". The developed countries do not allow economic growth and transfer of technology to developing countries because it may lead to "elimination of jobs" and affect the standard of living in the developed countries. Do you agree with their view?

4. What can the people in the "first world" learn from the people in the "third world"?

Appropriate Technologies

Gadi Kaplan

The ending of the Cold War has released more energy for tackling the concerns of underprivileged populations. "One billion people in the developing world still lack access to clean water...nearly 2 billion lack adequate sanitation...Electric power has yet to reach 2 billion people," the World Bank noted in its June *World development report 1994: infrastructure for development.*

A country's infrastructure includes services based on electrotechnology, such as electric power, telecommunications, and road, sea, and air transport. Developing countries in round figures pour US $200,000 million every year into new infrastructure, amounting to 4 percent of their national output and a fifth of their total investment, according to the World Bank report.

In purely human terms, the situation of these people is unacceptable. Technologically, it dares electrical and electronics engineers to devise remedies by applying proven technology at an affordable cost.

One challenge may well be to upgrade the infrastructure in developing countries. At present, for example, about 40 percent of their power-generating capacity is on average unavailable when needed, as a result of malfunction or scheduled maintenance; elsewhere, in the best-performing power sectors in the world, the percentage is half that figure, according to the 1994 World Bank report.

To cut back on waste and improve efficiency, the bank is embarking on a thorough reform. Among its goals are to see the infrastructure managed as a business, and not as a bureaucracy; to see competition introduced; and to give those who use the services a stronger voice in and responsibility for their operation than has been the custom.

But what exactly is a developing country? The World Bank often refers to "developing economies" as those with low or middle per-capita income, derived by dividing the gross national product (GNP) by the population count.

Low-income countries, with US $675 or less per capita, include Burundi and Benin in sub-Saharan Africa, Egypt in North Africa, Cambodia in East Asia, Tadjikistan in Central Asia, and Haiti in the Americas. Senegal, though, and Thailand, Turkey, Iran, Algeria, and

Chile are representative of middle-income economies, with $675-$8356 per capita income (in 1992). (All dollar figures are for U.S. currency.)

In this issue, *IEEE Spectrum* is launching a series of articles on technology appropriate for developing countries. Topics will include applications, telecommunications, computers and networks, and electrotechnology applications in such areas as transportation and agriculture. Intuitive, qualitative criteria for appropriateness have been adopted for the series. An appropriate technology is one that:

- Fits in the country's infrastructure.

- Is affordable.

- Can be properly maintained.

- Is not destructive to the environment.

The requirements need not imply technological inferiority. Indeed, a developing country quite often seeks to leapfrog straight into the 21st century, particularly if the leap makes sound economic sense. Indonesia is doing just that. Looking to a rapid expansion of its urban telephone network, it is installing a radio-based, cellular telephone system in Jakarta and West Java for a total of 280,000 subscribers.

The first topic covered in the appropriate technology series is photovoltaics, which has the potential of bringing electric energy to millions of remote rural households, greatly enhancing their quality of life.

So rosy, in fact, is its promise that the 12th European Photovoltaics Solar Energy Conference and Exhibition devoted a parallel symposium to photovoltaics in developing countries. Inspired in part by that symposium, which was held in April in Amsterdam, the Netherlands, the following report includes an overview of the technology's applications and two regional studies, one on a large project in West Africa, and the other about India.

Photovoltaics is attractive because it can help countries avoid the huge expense of expanding electric grids into rural areas, at an estimated cost of $20,000-$30,000 per kilometer, reports Erik H. Lysen, the head of a department at Novem, the Netherlands agency for energy and the environment located in Utrecht. But if affordable power is to be supplied by this means to millions of rural households, the worldwide manufacturing capacity for photovoltaic modules and systems will have to be substantially enlarged, he noted. Furthermore, funding for photovoltaics applications by national and international organizations would have to be increased by orders of magnitude, he said.

International cooperation counts heavily toward the success of photovoltaics applications. Evidence of that comes from projects in Vietnam and the republic of Kiribati in the mid-Pacific.

In West Africa, high grades are scored by a program for installing photovoltaic systems with 1200 peak kilowatt capacity for water pumping, refrigeration, and lighting. And in India, about 62,000 rural photovoltaic systems have already been installed under a government-assisted program, and the installation of 60,000 units that power VHF remote radio links is under way.

From these and other reports it is clear that designing "appropriate" technology may sound easier than it is. In the West Africa project, for instance, inverters for water pumps had to be flexible enough to accommodate various pump capacities, pipe sizes, and water heads, but this flexibility could not be bought by sacrificing efficiency. Protection of the photovoltaic system against lightning and the safety of maintenance personnel also came into the picture in a big way.

Even so, the obstacles that photovoltaics must overcome are more institutional in nature than technological, as became very clear at the Amsterdam meeting. More than 30 years in the making, photovoltaics is mature enough in itself, but will require innovative breakthroughs in financing as well as changes in energy policy, the experts believe.

Photovolts for Villages

Erik H. Lysen

Two billion people are without an electrical connection, but the cost of hooking up their homes to a conventional grid system will be too high for most developing countries. Photovoltaic solar systems are a cheaper alternative and can reach virtually any site on earth. Granted, new and bold initiatives are necessary to realize the required 20,000-MW peak power of photovoltaic capacity. But the breakthroughs needed are less technical and more in the areas of financing and energy policy.

Energy is not the most pressing problem of the developing countries, partly because oil prices are at present so low. Instead, they have to worry about the poverty of most of the inhabitants, their food supply, the creation of sufficient and meaningful jobs, competition in the international markets for their products, and, sadly enough in some cases, the presence of war. The main energy problem in rural areas still is to find enough wood for cooking meals. In some developing countries, biomass for cooking accounts for over half of the national energy consumption.

For some decades now, photovoltaics (PV) has been on the energy scene in the developing world, particularly in established niche markets such as telecommunications, marine beacons, railway signaling, and cathodic protection of pipelines. The challenge will be to apply PV to the provision of energy to rural homes for lighting, refrigeration, and TV.

The most successful to date is the individually owned solar home system: typically a 50-W solar panel that charges a battery by day and powers loads after dark. Owners are proud of having their own power system and are not susceptible to grid failure or inconsiderate neighbors, while the equipment itself can be expanded when required. Of course, the systems must be well designed, properly maintained, and paid for by the owner, because giveaways seldom last long.

On the face of it, it looks strange that people in rural areas and nonindustrialized countries are satisfied with a fraction of a kilowatthour a day, whereas residents of industrialized countries "need" 10 kWh or more per day. The explanation is that people are not interested in kilowatthours as such, but in light, a working TV set, or a refrigerator. In other words, they want the services of the energy regardless of whether it amounts to 0.1 kWh or 10 kWh per day. And as only a limited number of solar kilowatthours are available, people cannot afford to waste them and must use efficient lighting, low-power TV sets (a golden market for future flat-screen TV sets with liquid-crystal displays), and efficient refrigerators.

The only thing that matters to the owner is: how much do I have to pay for these services every week or month? As a first estimate, a reasonable part of the rural population can raise $5 to $8 per month. This is what they are paying now for kerosene lighting and for battery charging at grid-connected centers. (All dollar figures in this article refer to U.S. currency.)

As is well known, nearly all utilities in developing countries are losing money on rural electrification. Investment capital is not the problem, being available at comparatively low rates from large multilateral banks like the World Bank and Asian Development Bank. High costs are the issue, stemming from long transmission lines to remote customers, low consumption, the need to charge only low tariffs, and high technical and nontechnical losses (transmission and distribution losses and illegal connections)—20-40 percent in some countries. And these high costs are usually cross-subsidized by urban consumers.

Line costs are the heaviest burden, usually accounting for 80-90 percent of the budget of a rural electrification project They typically run $20,000-$30,000 per kilometer. Another factor is the widely variable number of users per kilometer of line, which may be as low as two but in Bangladesh must be at least 75. As a result, the average cost per rural connection also varies wildly: Mohan Munasighe, an energy expert with the World Bank quotes a range from $200 to $3650 (in 1983 prices). The monthly power consumption of rural consumers is usually low: 20-40 kWh, leading to high per-kilowatthour costs of 10-20 cents to $1.

Power to the People

A recent report from the World Bank on its role in the power sector notes that the number of power connections in developing countries in the period 1969-89 grew by 9 percent per year, or 2.5 times the average population growth. In spite of this rapid growth, rather few members of the population are yet connected to an electricity supply. Average real power tariffs declined from 5.2 to 3.8 cents per kilowatthour in the period 1979-88 (in 1986 dollars).

Nevertheless, governments and utilities in developing countries have impressive plans for expanding their power sectors. The idea is to increase the total power supply capacity from the 471 GW of 1989 to 855 GW in 1999. It is estimated that no less than $1 trillion will be needed to achieve the desired 384-GW increase. Approximately 40 percent of this sum is in foreign exchange, and it is clear that the $40 billion needed annually cannot be mobilized, even by the large multilateral banks (the present level of World Bank lending for the power sector is around $7 billion per year).

The conclusion seems inescapable. Governments in the developing world will face great difficulties in expanding their power sectors as planned. Obviously, too, priority will be given to industry and the urban sector. This prospect underlines the need to consider other alternatives for rural electrification, such as pre-electrification through PV or other renewable sources.

The Story Till Now

One of the earliest references to photovoltaics in a rural setting is to a system installed in Chile in 1960. In the '60s, PV cell development was dominated by research for space applications (the first satellite was launched in 1957).

Rural energy developments in the '70s were typically the so-called "integrated energy systems" promoted by the United Nations. These projects characteristically exploited various sources of renewable energy (such as the sun and wind, biomass, and organic waste), and they distributed the electricity thus obtained through a regular grid system in the village. In practice these systems never came up to expectation; they demanded too much maintenance, were poorly designed, gave unreliable service and, most importantly, were more or less forced upon the village inhabitants.

Individual solar home systems were introduced more or less independently in the Philippines, the Dominican Republic, and Indonesia in the early 1980s.

The Philippine-German Solar Energy project (1982-88) started with a 13-kW plant for a small village. The plant was found to be not economical for wide dissemination. The second phase emphasized small PV systems for use in rural areas, namely, solar home systems and communal battery-charging stations. The first 100 of these home systems were installed at Burias Island. A would-be owner had to make a down payment of $140 and 36 monthly payments of $13.

An important lesson was learned. Solar home systems have become a status symbol because they are one of the few high-tech systems available outside urban areas and they open the door to radio, TV, and video. At present, about 105 kW of solar systems are installed in the Philippines, of which 70 kW is in residential systems and 35 kW is in systems intended for telecommunications, pumping, and other purposes.

In the Dominican Republic, a true catalyst for the development of photovoltaics was the presence of Richard Hansen, founder of Enersol Associates (USA). In April 1984 the first PV system was installed in Bella Vista. Right from the beginning, owners had to pay for the system (48 monthly installments of $10). Soon a solar credit fund was created (Adesol) with seed money from the U.S. Agency for International Development, and from the installments paid by its clients new systems could soon be bought. Local entrepreneurs were trained for servicing and sales of new systems.

By mid-1987 more than a hundred systems were up and running. That year, the Solar-Based Rural Electrification Concept was introduced, as a model for intervention by a nongovernmental organization, and gradually spread. By 1992 the number of PV systems grew to 4000. More than 10 installation businesses are active in the Dominican Republic.

The development of solar home systems in Indonesia was the fruit of cooperation between individuals and the Dutch PV company R&S (Renewable Energy Systems), the Indonesian Ministry of Research and Technology, and the Indonesian Ministry for Cooperatives. A start was made in 1987 and in 1988 the systems were demonstrated in Sukatani, a village 110 km from Jakarta. The seed money was provided by the three organizations listed above plus the Netherlands Ministry of Foreign Affairs.

Sukatani has a lower than average amount of sunshine. The idea was that if the system worked there (which it did), it would work throughout Indonesia. The local cooperative took responsibility for fee collection and simple maintenance.

The President of Indonesia became so enthusiastic about the Sukatani project that he started the Banpres project, with interest-free credit for 3000 solar home systems, which have since been successfully installed. Additional credit schemes through revolving funds have been started, one example being the $50,000 revolving fund grant from the North Holland utility PEN, for solar home systems in the village of Lebak.

By 1993 more than 10,000 home systems had been installed throughout Indonesia. The average investment has dropped below $400, and with a down payment of 35 percent the solar home system owner pays the equivalent of $8 per month.

Five Types of Problems

As with every new technology, all was not smooth sailing. Problems that arose during the systems' introduction fall into the following five categories: financial, institutional, infrastructural, and technical.

Financing the purchase is still the most forbidding hurdle. The average price of a solar home system is about $500. But in many countries, only 10-20 percent of rural families earn more than $100 per month. Assuming that 10 percent can be spent on a solar home system, this means they can afford a maximum of $10 per month, and preferably less. The problem therefore is how to reduce the monthly installments to, say, $5 per month.

Institutional conflicts are the next concern. Electric utilities are traditionally either hostile or at best indifferent to small autonomous systems such as solar systems for the home. It can happen that a nongovernmental organization pushes hard to install solar home systems in a village, only for the utility to show up with a grid extension a few months later. Confusion is created and part of the investment in home systems suffers. Rural electrification policies seldom include pre-electrification options such as solar home systems, or wind or microhydro supply systems.

Experience has shown that interpersonal relations were often mishandled. People were not properly involved in a timely fashion in the decision to introduce PV systems. They were not informed about the performance of the solar home system and its pluses and minuses compared to a grid connection. Training of the owners was sometimes inadequate, so that batteries were discharged too deeply if poor (or no) controllers were present. Simple but essential repairs took much too long, so that people lost confidence in the system. The key factor here is proper communication with the users.

This situation is closely linked to infrastructural weakness. Often after-sales service was either nonexistent or poorly organized. Publicity was insufficient, wrongly targeted, or even negative. Stories about failures tend to stick in people's minds for a long time, and 10 times as many successes are needed to eradicate them.

Then of course there were the technical problems associated with a new technology. Interestingly, there were hardly any problems with the PV modules. The trouble came from conventional parts of the system—batteries, controllers, and lights and switches. Controllers worked poorly or were omitted to save money, so batteries had a short life. Cheap fluorescent light tubes were used, which blackened quickly; electronic ballasts failed and switches malfunctioned.

In essence, the financing problem can be solved by lowering the investment cost of the PV system and by enabling the customers to pay smaller amounts over longer periods. The first part of the solution is largely for the manufacturers to implement and is influenced by Western development programs. The developing countries' governments can help by lowering or waiving import duties.

Several options for lowering the monthly costs for consumers have been proposed and are being practiced: revolving funds (started with grants); presidential loans (as in Indonesia); local bank loans; the Finesse approach (financing of energy services for small-scale energy consumers); and supplier's credit.

Energy experts made a good point during the Finesse workshop held in October 1991 in Kuala Lumpur with the support of the World Bank, the U.S. Department of Energy (DOE), and the Netherlands Ministry of Foreign Affairs. Given that large power companies have access to very cheap capital for new power plants and rural electrification projects, they argued, smaller-scale power options that complement the grid supply should also be allowed to tap just a fraction of those funds, and on the same conditions. Solar home systems were seen as a case in point.

This is in essence the aim of the Asia Technical Alternative Energy unit of the World Bank, which is supported by (among others) the DOE and the Netherlands Ministry of Foreign Affairs. The unit at present is active in Indonesia, India, Sri Lanka, and China.

On the institutional level, clashes with the electricity companies can be avoided if the initiatives in solar home systems are coordinated or even channeled through them. The utilities should permit, spur on, or even contract with the private sector and nongovernment organizations to start offering solar home systems in certain areas. They should make it clear to the customers that this is a pre-electrification option, and that if in the future the utilities have the means to reach the village by the grid, the PV panels can be resold to the private sector (or kept as an emergency option).

Events in the Philippines, Dominican Republic, and Indonesia prove that the early involvement of potential customers is crucial to the success of any PV project. People should be properly taught about system operation and properly informed about comparative performance and costs. A warning system for larger breakdowns should be set up, to ensure quick repairs and maintain confidence in the system. Local cooperatives should be used to collect fees and carry out basic maintenance. Local youths should be trained as PV technicians and paid for their work.

Improvements in product quality have occurred over the last few years, thanks to lessons learned from simple technical problems. Controllers and lamp ballasts have improved, some of them locally produced; battery indicators have now become available so people can "see" how much is left in their battery (as was their custom with bottles of kerosene).

The wattage needed for rural electrification of the 2 billion people as yet without electricity can be estimated. The average bad load of a rural connection is around 350-500 W, so with an average family size of five and 400 million as yet unwired households, an additional capacity of 140-200 GW is needed. At a conservative value of $2500/kW, this capacity would cost $350 billion to $500 billion. In addition, the annual fuel bills of the developing countries will be increased by $5000 to $10,000 million.

Governments in developing countries are already hard pressed to expand their industrial and urban capacity as fast as necessary. They will find it impossible to invest also in rural electrification. If, however, the latter task could be achieved through individual solar home systems, the total investment would be lower, although still considerable. Assume that a 50-Wp solar home system in future will cost $250 on average, then 400 million solar home systems (20 GWp) will require $100,000 million, or $4000 million annually for 25 years. These systems would have to be financed through long-term loans, not grants.

To put things in perspective, it is perhaps useful to mention the size of the predicted PV market and required capacities. Note that the present market in photovoltaics is about 60 MWp, of which about 5 MWp is for rural off-grid applications. Market analyst Paul D. Maycock, president of Photovoltaic Energy Systems Inc., Casanova, Va., expects the following markets for the off-grid rural segments in the years 1995, 2000, and 2010:

- For a business-as-usual scenario: 8, 20, ant 40 MWp.

- For an accelerated growth scenario: 15, 40, and 600 MWp.

Recall the estimate that the electrification of all 400 million households currently without electricity would require 20 GWp of PV capacity, or 800 MWp on average for a period of 25 years. This is even more than is predicted in Maycock's accelerated growth scenario. So probably this target will not be met unless bold new initiatives are taken.

Bold Ideas

One initiative of this nature is the Power for the World proposal put forward by Wolfgang Palz, division head of renewable energies in the European Commission's Directorate General XII, which handles science research and development. To reduce system costs and increase production volume, plants with an annual production capacity of 10 MWp must be built soon; by the year 2000, annual capacity must reach 100 MWp. This can only be tone if specific conditions are met, namely, policy changes, better financing options, and system improvements. But the environmental issue must be considered right now.

There are signs of policy changes and a beginning of acceptance by electricity companies, as in Mexico and the Philippines. But there is still a long way to go before solar PV systems are accepted by utilities in developing countries as a reliable means of pre-electrification or even electrification. Sources of capital can be instrumental in changing this attitude by requesting such policy changes (as well as financing renewable options) during the negotiations for conventional power loans.

Several financing initiatives have been offered by both national and international donors; but in terms of total funds required, the efforts have to be increased by orders of magnitude. The easy terms for large power loans should be made available for small off-grid options as well.

Manufacturers, importers, and distributors should ensure the quality of their PV products. National product standards should be established, leaving enough room for product improvement.

With the introduction on a large scale of PV battery-charging systems, the number of batteries in rural areas will soar. Environmental problems could ensue if no measures are taken beforehand. Manufacturers, together with local counterpart companies, should work out optimum and least-cost solutions. National battery recycling is already in effect in Indonesia, for example.

Acknowledgment

This article summarizes the plenary paper presented by the author at the 12th European Photovoltaic Conference, held in Amsterdam in April 1994. The full paper has been published in the conference proceedings.

To Probe Further

Costs of rural electrification are addressed in *Electricity for rural people* by G. Foley (Panos Publications Ltd., London, 1990) and in *Rural Electrification for Development: policy analysis and applications* by M. Munasinghe (Westview Press, Boulder, Colo., 1987).

R.J. Saunders is the author of "The World Bank's role in the electric power sector: policies for effective institutional, regulatory and financial reform," a 1993 World Bank Policy Paper, published in Washington, D.C. The costs of electrification are discussed by R. Turvey and D. Anderson *in Electricity Economics*, a World Bank Research Publication (Johns Hopkins University Press, Baltimore, Md., 1977).

A reference to an early photovoltaic system in Chile is included in *Photovoltaics for Development*, by R. Hill (ed.), United Nations ATAS Bulletin No. 8, 1993.

Integrated Rural Energy Planning was discussed by Y. El Mahgary and A.K. Biswas in a United Nations Energy Planning (UNEP) publication (Butterworth Scientific, England, 1985).

Solar home systems are discussed in *The Philippines' Rural Photovoltaic Electrification Scheme* by G. Santianez-Yeneza and H. Böhnke in a publication of the National Eletrification Administration, Manila, 1992. Photovoltaics applications were addressed by R. Schröer and P. de Bakker in their article, "It All Began on Burias Island," *GATE* magazine, July 1989. *Solar Rural Electrification in the Developing World; Four Country Case Studies: Dominican Republic, Kenya, Sri Lanka, Zimbabwe* was dealt with by M. Hankins, Solar Electric Light Fund, Washington D.C., 1993.

The financing of energy services for small-scale energy consumers (Finesse) was discussed during the World Bank workshop, Kuala Lumpur, October 1991. Paul Maycock examines *Photovoltaic technology, performance, cost and market forecast 1975-2010*, in a publication of PV Energy Systems Inc., Casanova, Va., June 1993.

Bold initiatives in rural electrification were proposed by Wolfgang Palz in his paper "Power for the world," which is to be found in the proceedings of the International Solar Energy Society (ISES) Solar World Congress, held in Budapest in 1993.

Energy sources are regularly written about in the papers in *IEEE Transactions on Electron Devices*, while energy conversion by renewable sources is regularly addressed in *IEEE Transactions on Energy Conversion*.

Water from the African Sun

Serge Makukatin

The most ambitious worldwide program in photovoltaics ever financed by the European Union (until a year ago, the European Community) is nearing realization. Its goal is to better the living conditions of those who live far from population centers. Both short-term and permanent improvements are envisaged.

The first task is to make available drinkable water, the next to irrigate fields under cultivation. A third aim is to supply small communities with electricity for lighting and essential refrigeration. As part of this 1200-kW (peak power) project, Siemens Solar GmbH faced special requirements involving a variety of systems and key components. The project had several important social aspects as well.

The project's beneficiaries are the members of a body set up in 1973 to fight drought in West Africa's Sahel zone, the Comité Inter-Etats de Lutte contre la Sécheresse dans le Sahel (Cilss). Present membership consists of nine countries that suffered greatly from drought in 1968 and 1974: Burkina Faso, Cape Verde, Chad, Gambia, Guinea-Bissau, Mali, Mauritania, Niger, and Senegal.

It was to help these nations that the Programme Régional Solaire (PRS) was established to make use of photovoltaic energy and to that end given 34 million ECU in funding by the then European Community as nonrepayable aid.

The program was divided into three parts, with Siemens Solar GmbH the first to be awarded a contract. The contract called for systems to be installed in five Cilss states—Gambia, Guinea-Bissau, Cape Verde, Mauritania, and Senegal. All in all, Siemens Solar will supply 550 kW, peak, of solar power. Most of this power will be used by 330 pumping systems, the largest number of high-capacity pumping systems of any part of the program.

Also to be provided are a total of 339 so-called community systems—240 for lighting 63 for refrigeration, and 36 for recharging lead-acid and nickel-cadmium batteries. The DM 30-million contract covers parts supply, installation maintenance, and after-sales support.

Under this contract, Siemens Solar had in addition to establish a service network, train local partners, and support their activities. The execution and coordination of this all-embracing contract required the establishment of a complex project organization. For instance, Siemens was obliged to find a local partner in each of the five countries.

These partners would be responsible for maintaining contact with the local building supervisors, coordinating all essential documents (dealing with orders for installations and technical information resulting from alterations) and dispatching them to Siemens, and stocking spare parts for repairs. The importance of reliable local partners cannot be overemphasized. A lack of spare parts or technical support has wrecked many a past project.

Numerous companies volunteered for the project. The challenge was to identify those that would be most suitable as partners. In the end, there were only a few serious candidates with adequate financial backgrounds.

The partnership benefits both parties. By being involved in the greatest PV project ever carried out, the local partner can earn a good sum of money for the services rendered. Siemens Solar, in turn, can extend its activities in the African market through the aid of the local partner.

For its partner in the Sahel region, Siemens Solar chose a French company that had already been a subcontractor on African projects, successfully performing installation and maintenance services. Wherever it has a local subsidiary in the five regions, Siemens' partner takes care of any tasks there directly. Otherwise, it picks a company in the area to do so.

Future Upkeep

As the main contractor, Siemens has to guarantee all systems and to deliver spare parts for five years free of charge (although consumable materials, such as light bulbs, have a one-year-warranty). After the termination of the five-year guarantee, funds will be needed for maintenance and replacement.

Once a village has inspected and provisionally accepted the PV system, those of its inhabitants who use it pay an annual sum determined by the individual system's maintenance costs. For example, a medium-sized P4 pumping system used in Mauritania will deliver 9000 m^3 of water in a year. Dividing the total US \$2000 yearly costs of maintenance (\$900) and replacement (\$1100) by the annual 9000 m^3 water output, results in 22 cents per cubic meter of water. This is the charge users must be able to afford to keep the system operational; it does not include money for new investments in future PV plants.

Siemens chose its own M50 module, a 50-W, peak, monocrystalline solar panel with an efficiency of 12.4 percent, as the major power component. A requirement of the EC project is that all components be of European origin.

The key components for pumping systems are the pumps themselves and their ac inverters. Standard centrifugal pumps and motors are used for high water output. These pumps are equipped with 3.5-kVA Simovert-P-Solar inverters. This inverter model—a slightly modified version of the more than 10,000 units thus far produced by Siemens—is designed for highly reliable operation even under severe conditions. It has an efficiency of up to 95 percent.

The Simovert-P's microprocessor allows it to be programmed for special site conditions. It drives common three-phase, 220-Vac pumps up to 2.2-kW rated power. There are no known competitive inverters with these features.

Centrifugal pumps with modified motors are employed for the smaller pumping systems. The Grundfos Solartronic SA1500 inverters drive the modified three phase, 65-Vac pumps. (The P1 types are for surface-pumping irrigation systems.)

Both Simovert-P and the Solatronic inverter have dry-running protection and can produce frequencies from 1 to 60 Hz. The actual output frequency at which the inverter operates depends on several factors: the input power from the solar modules, type of pump, piping, and the delivery head (defined as the height of the inlet to the cistern above the well's water level). The efficiency differs with frequency and also with pump type, piping, and the slope from the delivery head. Typical efficiencies of the combined inverter, pump, and motor are in the area of 40 percent at 50 Hz and 10-20 percent at 25 Hz.

Danger-Free

The installations need to be safe in two senses. They must be as immune as possible to external events, like lightning strikes, as well as harmless for people to approach and maintain.

There are two types of lightning protection: external and internal. The external variety consists of connecting all parts (not only the modules and inverters, but also the support structures and fences) to earth ground. This is accomplished by burying a ring of copper cable 1 meter deep in the ground around the system and inside its protective fence, and connecting the ring to an earthpole, or plate, in the ground. These measures ensure that, in case of an external overvoltage, no significant difference in electric potential exists between the different components.

The internal protection keeps any overvoltage from damaging the electronic devices—the inverter and solar-cell array. It consists of varistors in the junction box and in the inverter.

Since the operating voltage of the pumping system lies in a hazardous range, measures must be taken to protect the public as well as system maintenance personnel. For this reason, the systems were designed using German industrial safety standards (DIN/VDE-Standards). In addition, each pumping system is fenced off from the public.

The EC office awarding the contract imposed strict quality requirements on components and material for this project. It wanted to ensure that systems would be rugged enough to operate in harsh environments throughout a long service life.

To find accessories and components of suitable quality at acceptable prices, extensive market research was necessary. The materials and components selected had to pass severe tests performed at one or other of the four European research laboratories that are officially accepted by the Cilss organization: Technical Inspection Authority (TUV) Rheinland, Cologne, Germany; LVT/CEA, Cadarache, France; Global Renewable Energy Services (GRES), Swindon, England; or Ciemat, Madrid, Spain. The main purpose of the tests was to ensure that the technical data indicated by the suppliers reflected the specifications required.

For instance, in the case of the inverters, the test criteria used by TUV Rheinland included performance, efficiency, temperature and climate tests, electrical safety, and the examination of packaged devices after a drop from a height of 1 meter. Further, the fabrication processes of the inverters' suppliers were audited. During these tests, some possibilities for optimizing the devices came to light and were later integrated during production.

For instance, the degree of electrical protection was increased from IP54 to IP55, the mechanical mounting of several components was optimized for greater ruggedness, and the steering program within the microcontroller was improved. A 10-g vibration test was also added to production testing.

Although this testing raised the supplier's costs, in the end it was justified by the way the components operated; all devices work perfectly in the field and are highly reliable, which is not typically the case for photovoltaic inverters.

For all PV modules, a certificate (CEC specification 502) from the Ispra Institute of Ispra, Italy, is proof of qualification for the project. No problems arose in complying with the module data for any of the PV systems during the verification of the delivered power.

For the West-African region, the basis for the system design is 6 kWh/m^2 per day (which lasts from 6 AM until 6 PM there) and a daily output of water within a range of 30 percent (-10 to +20 percent). All design values (300 W, peak, to 3.8 kWp, rated generator power) were checked and confirmed by the customer.

For a specific site on an average day in a recommended month, a nomograph can be used to determine the characteristics of a photovoltaic pumping system (of the solar generator, the well, and the water output). Note that when water is drawn, its level in the well will drop; this so-called draw down and the rate at which the water returns to its previous level depend on the conditions of the site. No realistic statements on the delivery capacities of the systems can be made without these data. On this basis, characteristic variations for various frequencies were determined for all centrifugal pumps used.

First Results

The first of the project's PV pumping systems were installed in early 1991. As of April of this year, 55 out of the total of 330 deep-well pumping systems had been installed and had provided approximately 270,000 hours of trouble-free operation. The total efficiency (from sun to water) of the completed systems is about 3-4 percent. The efficiency of other systems is about 2-3 percent.

All systems work without any notable problems, so that the local populations can rely on receiving the precalculated quantities of water. The yield of the systems until now amounts to approximately 1,200,000 m^3 of water and is probably unique in its volume. In several villages the water output is so great (50-60 m^3 per day) that the cisterns can be filled up within two or three hours.

Cilss has installed several test PV plants that store all key data: delivery head, water output, insolation, voltage/current of solar generator, and water output. The goal is to measure performances and water output within a limited time period. So far, the stored data has shown that the systems' output exceeds the Cilss specifications by 10-20 percent (water output per day at a specific insolation).

As of April 1994, 30 of the 339 community systems had been installed, among them 11 cooling systems used for storing vaccine in Mauritanian first-aid hospitals and 6 lighting systems in Cape Verde schools. All the installed systems have satisfied their users and work without trouble.

Essential to this success were the contributions of the local companies. Following a period of well-structured instruction, these local companies assembled, installed, and maintained the pumping systems.

In this way, an excellent base of technical knowledge for system and component has been established within the Cilss organization. The local firms involved with the systems are now familiar with PV systems and their experience should form the basis for further successful applications in this and future projects.

Minor Problems

As with every project, there were some problems, but they were minor in nature. Some Gambian systems are in a region with frequent lightning strikes. To date, four lightning barriers at the input of the 3.5-kVA inverters have been destroyed by indirect lightning strikes. Nevertheless, the devices fulfilled their function because the inverters remained fully operational. The barriers were replaced with locally available spare parts.

The second event, and to date the last, was the failure of four float switches in boreholes, caused by corroding well casings. The problem was remedied by using an additional float switch filter.

Choice of Village

The selection of a village to be equipped with photovoltaic systems is governed by several criteria. There must be a real demand for water supply (population) and the basic infrastructure must be there (water hole, a small hospital). In addition, the villagers must be able to pay some money for replacement and maintenance. The water committees of the local villages take care of the administration of the money. Fees for the water can be individually paid if somebody takes water. Alternatively, it is also possible to pay an annual average per family.

Payment for the water is essential—it ensures the survival of the PV system. In Cape Verde, droughts have often lasted for as long as two years. When this happened, the villagers had to pay for water brought in tanks from the capital or places with higher rainfall. It was not difficult for these people to understand that water is not free of charge.

The Podor people of Senegal, on the other hand, have traditionally taken drinking water from the river free of charge. Even although this water was often polluted and caused many diseases, it is difficult to explain to the people that they must pay for clean drinking water. So the need to pay for water must often be clarified in lengthy discussions.

PV systems within the region have completely changed the lives of the African village people. Infectious diseases caused by polluted water have greatly diminished. Pure drinking water is available at water taps, and women and children no longer have to walk 3-5 km for water. Freed from this chore, children can go to school while women can tend a kitchen garden watered by the PV system. Because of the electrification of schools and public buildings, it is now possible to educate people after the workday ends at 6 PM.

In each case, the local population must recognize the need for a village organization that is responsible for seeing that the PV installation is kept in good condition. They must also realize that they, too, have an obligation to care for the systems; there cannot always be a solution from an external source for everything.

To solve the problem of collecting money, several sociologists, who are working on the problem of forging an "identification of people with the project," have in the meantime worked out insurance concepts. For example, in Gambia—a relatively well developed country with good business opportunities—a contract being negotiated between the Department of Water Resources and an insurance company covers the possible risks of maintenance and replacement. This had the advantages of lowering costs for maintenance and replacement and of placing financial administration outside the village.

Preliminary Findings

Three years into the project, some interim conclusions can be drawn. Because of its comprehensiveness—including the high requirements set on system quality and the reliance on local firms and local after-sales service, the training of local partners, and the stocking of spare parts within each country—the project is very likely to succeed and to set an example for others like it in the future.

Photovoltaic systems have proved to be a reliable way of offering essential services to rural communities off the electric grid. But for the successful implementation and operation of such systems, well-trained partners located in the developing communities are imperative.

That the components used in the project have shown themselves to be reliable and of high quality indicates that authorized inspection institutions play an important role in the success of large-scale projects. At the same time, projects like Cilss allow manufacturers and suppliers to optimize their systems and components and prove their reliability. This in turn is beneficial for the next customers, increasing confidence in the products.

Last, but by no means least, the Cilss project clearly demonstrates the benefits of appropriate technology to people in remote areas.

To Probe Further

More information about this project can be found in the paper, "PV Energy for a Sustained and Social Development in the Sahel Region," by F. Kabore, in *The Yearbook of Renewable Energies*, a publication of Eurosolar in collaboration with UNESCO sponsored by the Commission of the European Communities, 1994, pp. 146-149.

Acknowledgment

The author thanks Mr. Cunow and Mr. Theissen, engineers from the technical office of Siemens Solar, for their valuable support.

Article Questions

1. What type of energy technologies are most appropriate for improving the general well-being of Third World countries?

2. Compare the energy consumption (kW hour per capita) for the following countries:

    a. USA vs. Bangladesh

    b. UK vs. China

    c. France vs. Nepal

    d. Germany vs. Yemen

3. List the advantages and limitations of various energy technologies available to the developing countries.

Energy Technology	(+)	(-)
Solar		
Wind		
Hydroelectric		
Nuclear		
Biomass		

4. A number of developing countries are planning to construct nuclear power plants to meet growing energy needs. Due to scarce resources in the Third World, the nuclear energy seems to be the best viable option. The developed countries are trying to prevent the transfer of nuclear technology to the Third World. The developing countries consider this TECHNOLOGICAL IMPERIALISM.

    a. Do you agree that Third World nations should be denied access to nuclear technology?

    b. What alternate sources would you recommend for Third World countries to acquire instead of nuclear technology?

5. What is the future of solar power in developing countries? What are the obstacles?

Pakistan's Energy Position: Problems and Prospects

Karen Turner Dunn

Pakistan has one of the world's fastest growing economies, and energy resource development will be essential in its ability to sustain high growth rates through the 1990s. Three crucial characteristics must be considered in analyzing Pakistan's energy sector. First, a complex range of energy resources are available and each plays a different role in meeting national needs. Second, the gap between domestic energy supply and demand is widening because of inadequate production, poor transmission and distribution systems, and inefficient energy use. Finally, exploiting energy resources creates environmental hazards that threaten long-term development prospects and social welfare. Pakistani policy makers must address these issues by considering energy policy for the 1990s in terms of the political, institutional, and cultural constraints involved, while encouraging sustainable long-run growth.

This article reviews Pakistan's energy position, problems, and prospects. The first section examines the supplies of conventional resources, identifies inefficiencies in energy provision and consumption, and assesses sectoral trends. Next, the oil, natural gas, coal, and electricity sectors are discussed, followed by a look at alternative and traditional sources of energy—wood, biogas, small hydroelectric plants, solar, and wind energy. Finally, energy-caused burdens on Pakistan's environment are considered.

Trends in Energy Supply and Use

Industrialization, urbanization, population growth, and the shift in consumer demand toward energy-intensive products contribute to the sharply rising demand for conventional energy supplies in Pakistan. The country has the potential to approach self-sufficiency in energy resources but faces institutional and policy impediments that render current supplies inadequate. In the past two decades, the absolute gap between commercial energy requirements and production in Pakistan has more than doubled.[1] Figure 1 shows that the gap rose from three million tons of oil equivalent (TOE) in 1971 to five million in 1980 and is estimated to have reached over eight million in 1990.[2]

Inefficient use of domestic and imported energy supplies is largely responsible for this gap. A comparative analysis of the energy profiles of low-income countries shows that only 11 of 68 countries have higher ratios of energy consumption to GDP.[3] Pakistan's energy consumption per dollar of GDP is typical for an economy with 51% of its GDP from industry rather than only 24%. Also, contrary to governmental claims, Pakistan's per capita energy consumption of 210 kilograms of oil equivalent is not unusually low; this figure is consistent with the level one would expect from a country with a per capita GDP almost two-thirds higher than Pakistan's.[4] Further, commercial energy requirements are growing faster than GDP, indicating that the inefficiency is worsening. The average annual increase in the ratio of energy requirements to GDP from 1973 to 1987 was .726 TOE per million rupees.[5]

The conclusions drawn from these comparisons and trends are limited because aggregate energy consumption and income data cannot reflect the specific economic activities undertaken and their efficiency across countries. Nonetheless, the fact that Pakistan consistently exhibits high levels of energy use relative to other low income countries is a clear indication that this use is inefficient.

In absolute volume, energy consumption is increasing most rapidly in the industrial and transportation sectors, reflecting the rapid industrialization taking place in Pakistan. In percentage terms, however, this increase has been less dramatic, and the share of total energy consumption for industrial purposes and transportation has changed little since 1971. Residential energy consumption is increasing rapidly both in absolute terms and as a fraction of total energy consumption. This reflects the increasing consumer demand for energy-intensive products, the broadening of rural electrification, and policies that keep residential energy prices low. Agricultural energy use stayed fairly steady through the 1970s and then rose slowly in the 1980s. Hence, the share of energy consumption going to agriculture fell during the 1970s. This decline resulted from pricing policies that favored industry and the relative ease of switching to noncommercial energy sources in agriculture.

Conventional Energy Resources

Oil

Oil accounts for 40% of Pakistan's commercial energy use. During the 1970s, the country imported almost 90% of its oil requirements, and despite domestic oil production having increased four-fold in the 1980s, roughly three-quarters of Pakistan's oil requirement is still imported. This dependence on imports left Pakistan extremely vulnerable during the Gulf crisis; before August 1990, more than half of the country's imported oil came from Kuwait. In the early 190s, labor remittances from the Middle East were so significant that Pakistan was a net beneficiary of the oil price increases, but the 1990-91 crisis, in contrast, prompted a massive return of overseas workers to the domestic labor force. The cost in higher prices paid for oil imports, lost trade, lost worker remittances, and resettlement of the returning workers was expected to reach billions of dollars. The government has dealt with the situation by increasing domestic oil prices, encouraging energy conservation, and seeking soft loans from the international community.

The oil shocks of the 1970s first brought to the policy forefront the need to reduce reliance on foreign supplies. Since the mid-1970s, the government has encouraged the development of oil and gas reserves through its pricing policy, which raised local crude prices above international prices effective in early 1987, and by allowing joint exploratory efforts under production-sharing agreements between the government and private companies. Thirteen private-sector oil companies and the state-owned Oil and Gas Development Corporation (OGDC) are engaged in oil exploration and development in Pakistan,[6] and most of the crude produced in Pakistan now comes from fields operated by foreign firms. Considerable reserves have been found. The prospects for future discoveries remain reasonably good since more than 85% of the country has sedimentary rocks, and offshore geological conditions in the Indus Basin are similar to those of the Bombay High where India produces most of its oil and gas.

Bureaucratic, technical, and geological problems have impeded rapid progress. The bureaucracy has been slow in processing applications for concessions, emigration of technical personnel limits the human capital available to the OGDC,[7] investment in oil exploration carries a high risk and is very capital-intensive, and the paucity of foreign exchange reserves to finance the import of drilling equipment contributes to the difficulty of searching for oil in Pakistan's rugged terrain.

There are three oil refineries in Pakistan, two near Karachi and one in the north at Attock that is designed to process the heavy crude produced locally. The quantity of oil recently produced in the south exceeds the amount that can be handled at the Karachi refineries, which were designed for lighter imported crude, and an inadequate transportation infrastructure makes it impossible to ship the surplus local crude to Attock for refining. Hence, because of its limited refining capacity and inadequate infrastructure, Pakistan, an importer of large quantities of oil, has to rely on exporting to balance oil production with refinery capacity. The Seventh Five-Year Plan (1989-93) anticipates upgrading the refineries, and progress is occurring in constructing and improving the pipelines carrying oil to the refineries.

Of the oil consumed in Pakistan, 60% is used by the transportation sector where the substitution of other fuels is not economically feasible. The agricultural sector, in contrast, responded to the oil crisis of the late 1970s by substituting electricity for oil on a large scale. Oil's share in total residential energy use has fallen in the past two decades because of increased rural electrification and the substitution of wood, biogas, and other noncommerical and nontraditional energy sources for expensive kerosene oil. The industrial use of oil, which changed little in the 1970s, increased steadily from 4% of total energy consumption by industry in 1980 to 14% in 1986. This reflects policies that aimed to conserve diminishing supplies of natural gas.

Natural Gas

Pakistan produces all of its natural gas supplies domestically. The large Sudan natural gas field was discovered in Baluchistan shortly after independence, additional fields have continued to be found, and associated natural gas is often recovered from crude oil production. As a fraction of the total energy requirement, natural gas rose from 33% in 1971 to 41% in 1980, but during the early- and mid-1980s this proportion fell. Policies affecting natural gas development and consumption took several swings during the 1970s and 1980s. The wellhead price for producers was kept low in the 1970s, providing little incentive for new exploration. The price of natural gas to consumers was significantly below the rising price of fuel oil, causing a rapid rise in natural gas utilization. In the early 1980s, the government responded to natural gas shortages by restricting its use in power plants and industries such as cement where furnace oil could be used.

This policy has recently been reversed as the government recognized that using gas could limit oil imports and that it is cleaner and more economical than burning furnace oil. To encourage more natural gas production, the government has agreed to increase the price it pays to producing companies, and clear formulas for the pricing of gases associated with oil extraction have reduced the time lost in lengthy rate negotiations. Prices of associated gases are increased when international oil prices decrease and decreased when oil prices increase, thus guaranteeing profits to companies producing crude oil along with associated gases. Consumer prices for natural gas are being increased gradually and are likely to reach parity with petroleum product substitutes in the early 1990s.

Coal

Pakistan is endowed with an abundance of coal, but the sector is plagued by a number of production problems. As a result, coal has met less than 10% of the country's total energy requirements during the past two decades. It is used almost exclusively by the brick kiln industry which is seasonal in nature. Most coal is produced in Baluchistan—the sole coal-based power plant is located in Quetta—and Sindh where its contribution to employment is as important as its energy contribution.[8] The greatest problem with Pakistan's coal is its poor quality. It is mostly lignite or subbituminous coal with limited coking potential, a low calorific content, and a high sulfur content. The coal industry also exhibits a fragmented institutional structure. Most of the mines are small and privately owned, and the mine owners often do not have adequate capital, machinery, or technical personnel to increase production. In addition, coal is distributed mainly by rail, which limits the locations that can be served.

Efforts are being made to expand the production of coal because of its abundance and potential to reduce reliance on more scarce resources. The Pakistan Mineral Development Corporation (PMDC) is contemplating a plant to mold smokeless coal briquettes to replace kerosene as fuel for domestic heating, and plans are underway to set up three new coal-based power plants, two in Baluchistan and on in Punjab.

Conventional Electricity Sources: Hydro, Thermal, and Nuclear

Over one-half of the electric power generated in Pakistan comes from hydroelectric plants. The remainder is provided by thermal power plants, except for the 2% provided by the Karachi Nuclear Power Plant (KANUPP). There has been much bureaucratic controversy over the generating facilities to be constructed in the future. First, many existing plants are operating well below capacity, raising the question of whether attention should be focused on improving the efficiency of power production rather than on new construction. In the long run it is risky to depend on large future discoveries of oil and natural gas, and while there is much potential for increasing hydroelectric capacity, this avenue leads to environmental and water-distribution problems. The controversy over the advantages and disadvantages of nuclear power development parallels that in many other countries. Large gains could be realized by redirecting efforts toward improving power transmission and distribution facilities and reducing corruption. Transmission and distribution losses are at least 20%, and bribes are offered and accepted in exchange for the reduction of electricity charges.[9] A large amount of power is lost due to the low voltage capacity of distribution lines as well as to theft and inefficient metering.

Difficulties in policy planning are compounded by the rapid growth of electricity demand. Official reports indicate demand is growing at 11% annually, but it may be up to twice this rate.[10] Droughts, large seasonal fluctuations in the flows of rivers, and the priority given to irrigation make hydroelectric power generation unreliable, and hydroelectric installations must be backed up with thermal or nuclear capacity. The high siltation rates of the Indus and its major tributaries, largely caused by deforestation, present another problem. There are many sites in the mountainous north with hydroelectric potential that have not been exploited because of their remote location and the cost of transmission to the south.

Shortages of electricity that result from transmission losses, growth in demand, and weather conditions are threatening Pakistan's development. The Water and Power Development Authority (WAPDA) adopted a policy of load-shedding to handle the shortages in 1983 and this is likely to continue to the end of the century,[11] even though unprecedented load-shedding in 1989 caused large production losses. Some large firms have started using their own generators. Rural electrification has progressed. Over half of Pakistan's villages had been electrified by June 1987, 49% in Punjab, 82% in the North-West Frontier Province (NWFP) and the Federally Administered Tribal Areas, 86% in Sindh, and 23% in Baluchistan. These numbers can be deceiving, however, since on average, only one-quarter of the population in Pakistan's electrified villages has access to electricity.[12]

A nuclear power reactor, supplied by Canada, has been operational since 1972. Its record is poor, in part at least because Canada stopped all nuclear assistance to Islamabad in 1976 when many became alarmed that Pakistan's nuclear capabilities would make weapons production possible. KANUPP is now fueled with indigenous uranium and is maintained by Pakistani engineers and technicians with locally made components. It reached its peak output in 1975-76. The government several years ago approved another nuclear power plant, CHASNUPP, to be built at Chasma, south of Mainwali near the border between Punjab and the NWFP, but it has not yet been built.

The Case of Kalabagh Dam

Controversy over electricity generation is nowhere more intense than that surrounding the impending construction of the Kalabagh Dam. Initially conceived in 1953 as a water storage project for meeting irrigation needs, the Kalabagh Dam has the potential to become one of the largest generating stations in Asia with an ultimate capacity of 3,600 megawatts. Proponents argue that construction of the dam is essential because of the power and water resources it would provide and because its cost is low relative to that of constructing a thermal station of equivalent capacity. Technical opposition to the project centers on its anticipated short life span due to siltation, its location in an active seismic zone, and the fact that for three months each year the dam would neither generate power nor store water.

The strongest protests against the dam have been on political grounds. Many people in the smaller provinces feel that provincial rights are being overlooked, that they will be adversely affected by the dam, and that they will not get their shares of the power, irrigation water, and profits it generates. In particular, the NWFP will face increased flooding and waterlogging of fertile land, dislocation of people, and the destruction of civic works. In

Sindh opponents fear that the province's share of irrigation water will be curtailed, that the cost of transporting power from Kalabagh to Sindh's main demand centers will be prohibitive, and that a disproportionate share of the power Kalabagh generates will be consumed in Punjab. Promises of compensation and resettlement arrangements do little to assuage the smaller provinces' concerns; many believe such efforts were ineffective and insincere when earlier dams were built.

Leaders in Sindh and the NWFP argue that public debate should have been opened and a consensus reached among the provinces before massive federal funds were committed to Kalabagh Dam. Sites farther upstream, such as Basha and Skardu, might have allowed more power generation and greater water storage with less siltation. These were given lower priority than Kalabagh because of their location in areas of seismicity and poor infrastructure, but some of the political difficulties delaying the dam's construction might have been avoided if these possible sites had been studied more seriously. The controversy continues to escalate: it enters election campaigns, evokes demonstrations, and rages in the media. One NWFP leader has even threatened to blow it up if it is constructed. Consensus remains a dim prospect.

Alternative and Traditional Energy Resources

Alternative resources have the potential to improve energy availability in isolated areas and to offset the pressures on nonrenewable resources. Noncommercial resources account for more than half of Pakistan's total energy consumption and in rural areas this share is much higher.[13] Policies influencing energy provision in the villages have important social consequences since control over resources will change hands. Women will be strongly affected since they are the primary users and collectors of household energy supplies. The traditional noncommercial resources used in Pakistan are predominantly biofuels—that is, fuelwood and animal and vegetable waste. Alternatives ways of producing energy include biogas plants, small hydroelectric facilities, and solar- and wind-powered plants.

Fuelwood

In spite of Pakistan's scant forest resources, wood provides an important source of energy, particularly in rural areas where four-fifths of all households use fuelwood for cooking. Wood is vital for domestic heating in certain areas. Population pressures, expansion of cultivation, and overgrazing have caused much deforestation, affecting those who rely on wood for energy. River siltation results from deforestation and reduces the useful life span of hydroelectric and irrigation projects. Wood is primarily a noncommercial fuel source but it is sold on the market with increasing frequency.[14] Fuelwood prices have risen sharply in recent years as demand has risen and the resource base has diminished; hence, commercial purchases of fuelwood are absorbing a growing share of household expenditures of the rural poor.

Biogas

Animal, human, and vegetable waste can be converted into biogas to provide both a decentralized electricity source and a fuel for cooking, heating, and lighting. Animal waste is already in wide use in the rural areas of Pakistan. As oil prices rose in the 1970s, there was an abrupt shift toward use of dung instead of kerosene for cooking fuel. The increasing scarcity of wood is also leading farmers to use more dung for fuel, which reduces fertilizer supplies and lowers crop yields.[15] The government has been helping villagers utilize dung more efficiently since 1974 by constructing family and community biogas plants, and over 4,000 biogas units have been installed.[16] The largest, which is operating at Halloki near Lahore, was set up as a joint venture between a private firm and the Appropriate Technology Department Corporation, an auxiliary of the Ministry of Science and Technology. This unit was expected to generate 10 kilowatts of power to run tubewells and provide 900 kilograms of fertilizer daily.

Biogas has considerable potential for use in cooking, heating, lighting, and operating irrigation pumps, allowing savings in other energy sources. It is cleaner and more healthful for cooking than dung cakes, and the energy yield from biogas is greater than that obtained from burning the original dung.[17] Further, the fertilizer value is not lost when dung is converted to biogas as biogas plants can produce both fuel and fertilizer supplies. One study suggests that the initial investment for a family biogas plant can be recovered in three to four years.[18] A functional plant is expensive to construct, however, and requires that the family have at least three to four cows, which restricts the operation to the fairly well-to-do. An analysis of biogas potential in India concludes that using biogas for power generation rather than as a direct fuel is generally less cost advantageous than centralized power production and distribution.[19] This conclusion holds except when biogas is employed as a transitional source of electricity or in very remote villages.

The human factor must be considered in any attempt to institute a biogas program. Like all community development programs, a biogas scheme would deeply affect the lives of villagers. Existing rules governing the sharing of dung would be supplanted by market distribution, which would affect the distribution of incomes and resources. Community biogas facilities are often constructed on the property of powerful villagers who then charge others for the benefits. This can increase dependence on landlords for credit and often results in peasants' refusal to bring dung to the facilities.

Small Hydroelectric Projects

Small hydroelectric plants for local power production are an attractive alternative method of producing energy because they utilize a renewable resource and the technology involved is well proven and simple enough to allow use of domestic inputs and local participation in the construction process.[20] Further, such units are viable where streams provide hydroelectric potential in remote hilly areas not easily reached by the national electricity grid. Small hydroelectric plants are classified by size as micro-hydel units (less than 50 kw) and mini-hydel units (50 to 500 kw). These plants may be constructed according to the "conventional" approach, with contracted labor and utilizing standards and materials like those the national electric utility uses, or the "participatory" approach, using simple designs, community labor, and low-cost locally available materials.

An analysis of a small hydroelectric program being developed in the NWFP shows strong economic justification only for micro-hydel schemes using the participatory approach. This study probably exhibits a downward bias in its estimates of the rates of return for conventional schemes, however, because these may be more reliable even if more costly. An ideal economic analysis of small hydroelectric projects would take into account induced demand resulting from the higher quality of electricity supplied and the degree of reliability

Karen Turner Dunn

provided under different design standards. The greatest problem faced in developing small hydroelectric systems is institutional. Identifying the national or provincial government organization best suited to oversee projects involving such significant local input is a challenge.[21] The national electric utility has the technical skills needed but not necessarily the interest or incentive to become involved. Private and voluntary organizations concerned with local economic development may be interested but lack the technical expertise.

Solar and Wind Energy

The potential advantages of solar energy deserve close attention as solar systems may be viable for use at household and community levels in areas not reached by transmission lines. The solar cell method is not practical for Pakistan due to its cost and other factors, but solar collectors could be used economically for crop drying, room heating and cooling, and water heating, distillation, and pumping. A recent report said that 18 solar village electrification systems have been installed.[22] Harnessing wind energy is a realistic possibility for raising underground well water and for small-scale irrigation projects in some regions, especially near the coast; overall wind velocity is not adequate to produce substantial quantities of electric power. The greatest problem with wind energy is storage. Using it for work that has an inherent storage capability such as water pumping, water heating, and refrigeration is one solution,[23] and WAPDA has experimented with windmill irrigation pumps.

Energy-Related Environmental Issues

Environmental considerations are of crucial importance in evaluating the methods available for providing energy in Pakistan. Oil spills are a likely result of offshore oil development, acid drainage from coal mines pollutes water supplies, and the combustion of Pakistan's low-quality coal presents a serious air pollution hazard. The growing use of motor vehicles is accelerating air pollution problems in urban areas.[24] Air quality is also threatened by the combustion of biofuels in residential stoves, a method of cooking and heating used by many in both rural and urban areas. Compared to gas, oil, and even coal in some circumstances, biofuels appear to have high emissions of some important pollutants, including particulates, carbon monoxide, and polynuclear organic materials. The eye diseases and respiratory illnesses caused by indoor air contamination from the use of these stoves in poorly ventilated housing are among Pakistan's most widespread and most neglected health problems, affecting mostly women and children.

Another serious environmental problem is the destruction of forests, which results from, among other causes, the collection of wood for fuel. River and reservoir siltation resulting from deforestation links fuelwood energy problems with difficulties in hydroelectric power production. Pakistan's forests are already in precarious ecological balance because of their location in areas of extreme aridity, very high or very low temperatures, and precipitous slopes. Once deforestation occurs, reversal is difficult and sometimes impossible. Poor management combined with vague records of ownership rights and historic land claims by traditional residents impede efforts to enforce forest conservation.[25]

Environmental threats are the least documented of the energy-related issues, and very little political pressure for environmentally sound policy planning exists. In a country where many people are struggling just to meet basic needs, environmental damage often seems remote. The perception is mirrored in the view that environmental protection can be achieved only at the expense of economic development. The tradeoff between meeting the needs of today and the needs of tomorrow is nowhere more clearly demonstrated than in the complex of damages ensuing from deforestation. Pakistan's political chaos is particularly conducive to environmental neglect. The management time horizon necessary for environmentally targeted plans exceeds the time period that a politician or planner can expect to influence. Administrative authority is often too weak to enforce measures needed to ensure a safe, healthful environment. Educating people about the likely effects of their actions on their natural surroundings would be a start, which means that policies must be formulated at a decentralized political level incorporating the ideas of those most directly involved. Different approaches will be appropriate in different areas, depending on traditional institutions, structures of property ownership, and cultural attitudes.

In tackling the deforestation problem, policies aimed at the proper selection of trees for cutting and programs for replanting with adaptable, fast-growing species may be called for in some areas, while changes in the structure of land tenure or fuel or newer technology would be appropriate in others. The poor and the landless constitute a large portion of the users of fuelwood, so improved management of forests partly involves strategies for the alleviation of poverty. Acceptance of new fuels and technologies will be a gradual process, and policy makers must take into consideration their cultural implications, including their effects on the roles of women who are the primary rural energy users and collectors of traditional energy supplies. Integrated energy planning is crucial so that the new technologies designed to improve health conditions are compatible with those designed to improve efficiency.

Conclusions

The task of designing an energy policy in Pakistan that takes into account all the relevant perspectives is challenging indeed. Meeting the needs of the poor, reducing reliance on imported energy resources, and preventing the over-exploitation of domestic resources are goals that lead to advocacy of conflicting policy measures when evaluated independently. Policy makers must therefore weigh the benefits of different approaches with a view toward the overall energy situation. This will require integration among the now fragmented agencies responsible for different aspects of the energy problem. Energy development has been slowed by bureaucratic power struggles between such organizations as WAPDA, OGDC, the Pakistan Atomic Energy Commission, the Ministry of Petroleum and Natural Resources, and the Ministry of Science and Technology. Policy coordination is also lacking between the central and provincial government authorities.

Growing conventional energy requirements reflect Pakistan's expanding industrial base, increasing mechanization in agriculture, and rising residential demand for energy-intensive appliances. Prospects for developing domestic sources of oil, natural gas, and coal appear good, and continued efforts to determine the recoverable amount of these resources will permit calculations of their optimal rate of extraction to meet the growing demands. Funds need to be directed toward improving capacity utilization in power production. Comparative analysis of Pakistan with other low-income countries indicates there is also much room for greater efficiency in energy use. This calls for improved distribution facilities and incentives to conserve energy. Further attention to the development of decentralized energy sources such as solar energy and biogas may reduce reliance on nonrenewable sources and improve energy availability for people in remote locations, but the social and political implications of introducing alternative methods of energy provision must be carefully evaluated. Population pressures in poor rural areas are reducing the availability of wood, the heavy use of which has already contributed to deforestation and consequent soil erosion and silting of rivers. Reduced reliance on fuelwood can be accomplished by using more efficient technology (e.g., improved stoves) or substituting modern energy resources for traditional ones. Changing to new methods, however, requires altering deep-rooted cultural practices, and policies to encourage such changes will be most effective when local groups participate in their design and implementation.

Notes

[1] The data used to extract the trends in Pakistan's conventional energy consumption, requirement, and production discussed in Sections 1 and 2 were taken from International Energy Agency, *World Agency Statistics and Balances 1971-1987* (Paris: OECD/IEA, 1989, pp. 403-14.

[2] Energy requirement and production figures for 1990 were estimated based on coefficients obtained from a regression using data for 11 years between 1971 and 1987 inclusive.

[3] The data (for 1988) used for comparative analysis in this section were taken from the World Bank, World Development Report 1990 (New York: Oxford University Press, 1990).

[4] The result per dollar of GDP is obtained by regressing the ratio of energy consumption to GDP on the percentage of GDP arising from industry for 65 low-income countries and comparing actual with fitted values; the per capita result is obtained by regressing energy consumption per capita on per capita GDP for 68 low-income countries and comparing actual with fitted values.

[5] This figure is the slope of the regression line obtained by regressing Pakistan's ratio of energy requirement to GDP on time, using data for 11 years between 1973 and 1987 inclusive.

[6] Economic Adviser's Wing, Ministry of Finance, Economic Survey 1988-89 (Islamabad: Government of Pakistan, 1989), p. 45.

[7] Abu Mohammad Izhartul Haque, "Energy Planning in Pakistan: Problems and Prospects," in United Nations, *Energy Planning in Developing Countries* (New York: Oxford University Press, 1984), p. 262.

[8] Charles K. Ebinger, *Pakistan: Energy Planning in a Strategic Vortex* (Bloomington: Indiana University Press, 1981), p. 18.

[9] *Economic Survey 1989-90*, p. 85, and Emma Duncan, *Breaking the Curfew: A Political Journey through Pakistan* (London: Penguin Group, 1989), p. 42.

[10] Majid Sheikh, "Demand and Power Supply," *Pakistan and Gulf Economist*, June 3-9, 1989, p. 12.

[11] Ibid.

[12] *Economic Survey 1987-88*, p. 131, Asit K. Biswas, "Environmental Concerns in Pakistan, with Special Reference to Water and Forests," *Environmental Conservation* 14:4 (Winter 1987), p. 324.

[13] Ebinger, *Energy Planning in Strategic Vortex*, p. 125.

[14] Biswas, "Environmental Concerns," pp. 324-25.

[15] Ebinger, pp. 30-31, 125.

[16] *Economic Survey 1987-88*, p. 138.

[17] Wallace E. Tyner, *Energy Resources and Economic Development in India* (Leiden, Netherlands: Martinus Nijhoff, 1978), pp. 120-21.

[18] M.M. Qurashi, "Renewable Sources of Energy in Pakistan," *The Pakistan Development Review* 23:2 and 3 (Summer-Autumn 1984), p. 465.

[19] Tyner, *Energy Resources,* pp. 111-112, 120.

[20] Mark Gellerson, "The Economics of Small Hydro Power," *Pakistan Economic and Social Review* 23:1 (Summer 1985), p. 26.

[21] Ibid., pp. 34, 28, 36.

[22] Rafique Akhtar, *Pakistan Year Book,* 17th ed., 1989-90 (Karachi: East and West Publishing Company, 1989), p. 667.

[23] Qurashi, "Renewable Sources," p. 469.

[24] The number of motor vehicles on the road in Pakistan increased three and one-half times between 1977 and 1987 (*Economic Survey 1989-90*, Table 6.3).

[25] Jeff Romm, "Forest Land Issues in a Developing World: Management for Intensified Use," in *Ecology, Environment and Afforestation*, National Seminar Environment and Urban Affairs Division, Government of Pakistan (Islamabad: Pakistan Press, 1975), p. 25.

Article Questions

1. The proposed Kalabagh Dam project has a potential of generating 3600 MW at a relative low cost compared to thermal stations. The construction of the Dam will shorten the gap between the energy supply and demand of the country. Should the government go ahead and finish the project and disregard the concerns expressed by the smaller provinces?

2. What energy technologies in Pakistan can be effective in making the country self-sufficient in the energy sector?

Development, Democracy, and the Village Telephone

Sam Pitroda

I was born in 1942 and raised in a poor village in one of the poorest areas of rural India, a place with kerosene lamps and no running water. In 1980, at 38, I was a U.S. citizen and a self-made telecommunications millionaire. By 1990, I was 47 years old and nearing the end of nearly a decade back in India as leader of a controversial but largely successful effort to build an Indian information industry and begin the immense task of extending digital telecommunications to every corner of my native country, even to villages like the one where I was born.

That effort persists today at an increased pace, but it remains controversial. Some of the controversy has centered on me and my methods. Most of it focuses on the efficacy and logic of bringing information technology to people who are in global terms the poorest of the poor.

Common sense and accepted thinking about economic development have long held it ridiculous to supply Third-World villages with state-of-the-art technology. What subsistence farmers need is not high-tech science and complex systems, the argument goes, but immunizations, basic literacy, disease and drought-resistant cereals and oilseeds, simple pumps, deep-drop toilets, two-phase electrification—all the "appropriate" technologies that the unsophisticated rural poor can use and understand.

I agree with this argument as far as it goes. Third-World farming villages need water, hygiene, health, and power, and the need is usually great. But the argument falls short in its definition of "appropriate." It ignores technology's profound social implications. And it comes dangerously close to consigning the Third-World poor to a life of third-rate capacities and opportunity. The policies of development agencies like the World Bank too often limit "appropriate technology" to the two-dimensional, twopenny solutions that bring the poor to the doorway of the modern world but not actually across the threshold.

For me, three facts about Third-World development stand out with great force. First, high technology is *already* an essential element in effective water sourcing, sanitation, construction, agriculture, and other development activities. Geohydrologic surveys are carried out from satellites. Bioengineering has revolutionized crop production. Appropriate technology has moved well beyond the water screw and the inclined plane.

Second, modern telecommunications and electronic information systems are thoroughly appropriate technologies even in those regions of the world that still lack adequate water, food, and power. The reason is simply that modern telecommunications is an indispensable aid in meeting basic needs. If a U.S. community needed, say, widespread immunizations or replacement of a power grid, would the telephone seem a vital or an irrelevant tool in getting the jobs done? Would the telephone seem more or less critical if the job were tied to a natural calamity such as flood or drought and required the mobilization of diverse resources over a broad area?

Third, as a great social leveler, information technology ranks second only to death. It can raze cultural barriers, overwhelm economic inequalities, even compensate for intellectual disparities. In short, high technology can put unequal human beings on an equal footing, and that makes it the most potent democratizing tool ever devised.

In 1942, the village of Titilagarh in the Indian state of Orissa, southwest of Calcutta, had a population of 6,000 or 7,000 and no electricity or telephones. My early education took place in one-room schools, and most of my classmates had no shoes or books. My family was of the *suthar* caste—lowly carpenters—yet my father was an ambitious man. He never learned English until I brought him to the United States to enjoy his retirement, but he did business with the English and used what opportunities he had to build a prosperous trade in lumber and hardware and to send most of his eight sons and daughters to high school and on to university. For 12 years, I lived with one or more of my brothers and sisters in towns and cities far from home and studied hard to get the kind of grades that would outweigh my origins. In 1964, I succeeded. I was only 21 years old, and I had never used a telephone. But my masters degree in physics, specializing in electronics, from Maharaja Sayajirao University in the city of Baroda in Gujarat state, gave me membership in a new technological caste that superseded the one I was born to.

My older brother and I decided that I should apply to a university in the United States to do postgraduate work, and my father readily agreed to give me $400 toward this education, expecting me in return to bring my brothers and sisters to the United States one by one as I made my way in the world. I applied to the University of Oregon and the Illinois Institute of Technology but did not apply for scholarships, on the theory that an expression of need might reduce my chances of getting in. I was accepted at both schools and chose Illinois. The state of Orissa gave me a travel grant of $600, just enough for a taste of every form of transport: a boat to Genoa, a train to London, an airplane to New York, and a Greyhound bus to Chicago.

I arrived in December, 1964, with my father's $400 in my pocket. Tuition for the first semester was $700. I paid half on account, found a cheap apartment to share with another Indian, and landed a job in a physical chemistry lab to earn my keep and the rest of my tuition. A year later, I had a master's degree in electrical engineering. I had not only learned to use a telephone, I had, in essence, learned to make one. More important still, I had learned enough to design an electronic telephone switch.

Telephone switching is what operators used to do by hand in the early days of the century. Using a board with cords and plugs, the operator created a manual connection between the telephone in the caller's hand and the phone being called across town. Voice transmission then took place by means of analog electrical signals derived from a vibrating diaphragm in one handset and translated back into sound waves in the other. The system was marvelously simple, but, by technological standards, dreadfully labor intensive. If all the calls in the United States were handled that way today, every U.S. citizen would have to be a telephone operator.

Fortunately, electromechanical switching appeared in the 1920s, allowing the system to locate and connect two phones entirely by means of electrical signals opening and closing metallic contacts. These switches were automatic, but they had moving parts, and any device that moves wears out. So, while they required no operators, they did need people to carry out routine maintenance and regular replacement.

Finally, in the 1960s, I myself was involved in the invention and evolution of digital electronic switching equipment, which has two huge advantages over its analog predecessor. First, without moving parts and able to perform its own automatic maintenance, it never wears out. Second, it uses microchips as its basic building blocks and therefore takes up very little space. A large metropolitan switching station for 50,000 phones once occupied a six-to-ten-floor building and needed hundreds of people to keep it operational. The same capacity can now be housed in one-tenth of the space and requires a staff of perhaps ten people to operate its computer and software controls. Indeed, the only serious remaining drawback is that digital switches still produce heat and must be air-conditioned to prevent overheating.

Over the next few years, I worked for GTE in Chicago, designing and refining digital switching equipment and analog-to-digital conversion technology. I was responsible for nearly 30 patents and enjoyed a prominent position at GTE's annual patents banquet in the late 1960s and early 1970s. I married an Indian girl I had met at the university in Baroda, started a family, brought my parents and most of my brothers and sisters to the States, and began to become a middle-class American.

But my father kept telling me I was too young to get into the habit of working for other people, and I was beginning to tire of pats on the back for the patents I'd won, so I quit. In 1974, with two local telecom entrepreneurs, I founded Wescom Switching Inc.— their money, my technical expertise—and we began manufacturing digital switching equipment that I designed. In 1980—six years and more than a dozen patents later—we sold out to Rockwell International. As part of the deal, I agreed to work for Rockwell for three years and undertook not to compete in telecommunications for five years. My 10% of the company came to roughly $3.5 million in cash.

I left Titilagarh in 1951 to go to boarding school in Gujarat; I left India in 1964 to go to graduate school in the United States; now, in 1980, I was a millionaire, and to my own surprise I felt nearly as much guilt as satisfaction. All my life, I had dreamed of wealth and success, but now I suddenly confronted the fact that I had walked out on India. The sheer immensity of India's problems, the huge gap between my luxurious U.S. suburb and the struggling poverty of villages like the one where I was raised, the selfishness of my own success so far, all of it weighed on my mind and set me off in pursuit of another American dream: the exploration of a new frontier and challenge. In my case, that challenge was to use telecommunications as an agent of change—a bridge between the First World and the Third.

As I began my new job as vice-president at Rockwell, I began observing telecommunications at work in underdeveloped countries. What I saw disturbed me. On the whole, telecommunications was not so much closing as *widening* the gap between the rich countries of the north and the poor countries of the south. The First World, inventing and deploying new technology as if it were fast food, seemed headed in the direction of unlimited and universal information access. Even in the Second World, information technology had penetrated far enough to destroy the information monopoly that supported totalitarianism and to launch Eastern Europe toward the West. However, in the Third World, telecommunications and information technology remained an urban luxury, and an unreliable one at that. India had fewer than 2,500,000 telephones in 1980, almost all of them in a handful of urban centers. In fact, 7% of the country's urban population had 55% of the nation's telephones. The country had only 12,000 public telephones for 700,000,000 people, and 97% of India's 600,000 villages had no telephones at all.

What was worse, India, like most of the Third World, was using its priceless foreign exchange to buy the West's abandoned technology and install obsolete equipment that doomed the poor to move like telecom snails where Europeans, Americans, and Japanese were beginning to move like information greyhounds. The technological disparity was getting bigger not smaller. India and countries like her were falling farther and farther behind not just in the ability to chat with relatives or call the doctor but, much more critically, in the capacity to coordinate development activities, pursue scientific study, conduct business, operate markets, and participate more fully in the international community.

Worse still, I was perfectly certain that no large country entirely lacking an indigenous electronics industry could hope to compete economically in the coming century. To survive, India had to bring telecommunications to its towns and villages; to thrive, it had to do it with Indian talent and Indian technology. In other words, there were two goals to work toward: telecommunications and other information technologies could not only help Indians create wealth in every walk of life, a telecom and information industry could also create wealth of its own. Unless we had both, we had no future as a nation.

Worst of all, I began to see that information technology played an indispensable role in promoting openness, accessibility, accountability, connectivity, democracy, decentralization—all the "soft" qualities so essential to effective social, economic, and political development. India needed the capacity to network people, ideas, and initiatives. Telecommunications was as critical and fundamental to nation building as water, agriculture, health, and housing, and without it, India's democracy could founder.

I began looking for an entry into Indian telecommunications, a rigid bureaucracy with about a quarter of a million employees: one for every ten telephones.

In 1981, a friend in Bombay sent me a newspaper clipping reporting that Prime Minister Indira Gandhi had set up a high-level committee to review telecom development. I wrote to its chairman and asked for an interview. From my name and location, he concluded that I was an Italian-American with telecom products to peddle. I wrote back at greater length to say I had nothing at all to sell except the conviction that India possessed all the talent necessary to pursue telecommunications modernization on her own. He invited me to India. He could not absolutely promise me an appointment—and I would have to pay my own way—but he did ask me to come. Ultimately, I spent two hours with the entire high-level committee.

My message was that India should abandon electromechanical switching and move immediately toward digital systems for switching and transmission. My reasoning was twofold. First, electromechanical switching was ill-suited to the Indian climate and to Indian conditions. With few available telephones, most lines were intensively used, and electromechanical equipment was much more likely than digital to malfunction from overuse. (We later discovered that some public phones in India generate as many as 36 calls per hour at peak volume, compared with maybe 10 to 12 in the United States.) Electromechanical switches are also more vulnerable to dust and moisture. Analog transmission, finally, suffers over distance, while digital transmission is what gives those astonishingly intimate connections halfway around the world. In a country with low telephone density like India, distance—and therefore static—were nearly unavoidable.

Second, the development of digital technology would help build native industries in electronics, software, and related fields. Moreover, India needed one piece of digital equipment that no other country manufactured but that many developing nations could use: a small rural exchange. In the United States and Europe, the smallest exchanges built will accommodate 4,000 to 10,000 lines, and, in small towns and rural areas, these exchanges are installed and then deliberately underutilized. This kind of waste may be tolerable in a country where the number of small exchanges is tiny. In India, exchanges with a vast overcapacity would have to be installed in hundreds of thousands of villages, and waste on such a scale was unthinkable. Development of an efficient exchange for 100 to 200 telephones would not only solve India's problem, it would give the country a valuable high-tech export.

The committee was impressed by my enthusiasm if nothing else—and suggested I meet the prime minister, Two weeks later, Mrs. Gandhi's office agreed to give me ten minutes of her time. Because I needed at least an hour to get my message across, however, I turned the offer down. New Delhi was full of people who had been waiting *years* to get ten minutes with the prime minister, but I really did need an hour. By pushing what few connections I could muster, I eventually got my background papers into the hands of two advisers to Mrs. Gandhi's son Rajiv. One of them spent several hours studying the file, and in November, after five months of trying, I got an hour with Mrs. Gandhi, her senior cabinet colleagues, the chief ministers of several Indian states, and Rajiv, whom I met for the first time that day but who was already an advocate for my point of view.

I began my slide presentation almost as soon as Mrs. Gandhi walked into the room. There was a lot of ground to cover, and I covered it as swiftly as I could. I summarized world telecom statistics and correlated telephone density to productivity, efficiency, prosperity, and gross national product in about 50 countries. I pointed out that only a handful of countries had achieved universal service and raised the possibility that it was not so much wealth that created telephone density as telephone density that created wealth. I reminded them that Indian telecom was characterized by high unsatisfied demand, low accessibility as well as density, poor connectivity, lack of dependability, substandard maintenance, superannuated technology, overcentralization, bureaucracy, bad management, and limited capital. I underlined India's reliance on imported equipment of traditional, not to say obsolete, design, and tied that equipment to poor service and system inflexibility. I laid out a program that emphasized rural accessibility, customer service, digital switching, and large-scale technological innovation and integration, all of it accompanied by privatization, deregulation, and organizational restructuring. I outlined plans for design, production, installation, networks, fax, E-mail, telex, and more. At the end, I spoke of resources and management and then offered three alternatives.

The first alternative—obviously unacceptable—was to do nothing at all and let the system limp along until it failed completely. The second was to pursue the present development plan, using imported technology to address some problems and ignore others. But the present policies meant that India would fall steadily farther and farther behind the developed world, with dire consequences for India's economy, government, and people.

My third alternative was to adopt radical new technologies, products, and programs, hire new people—in particular, a core group of young research-and-development engineers to develop new hardware and software—and set India on the path to universal telecommunications accessibility by the turn of the century. I suggested the creation of new organizations with the power to issue bonds and sell stock to raise massive sums of capital. I talked about large-scale manufacturing plants to meet domestic and export demand. I proposed a telecom commission to oversee regulatory requirements. I spoke of the need for a generational change in telecommunications thinking.

Prime Minister Gandhi listened attentively to the entire presentation, and when it was over, I answered a number of questions. In the days that followed, the word went out that the prime minister was interested in a plan to modernize Indian telecom, and I began three years of commuting between Chicago and New Delhi to put together a strategic framework, plan the program, give shape to an R&D entity for developing human resources and new technology, and lobby it all through India's parliament and intricate governmental bureaucracies.

Living in the United States for the most productive years of my life had altered my values and perceptions beyond recognition. My approach to business, and for that matter to life, had become performance oriented. But every few weeks I left Chicago for New Delhi and a set of standards and values that were feudal, hierarchical, and complex beyond belief. From my now thoroughly American point of view, India was in desperate need of modernization. And my frustrating efforts to install some of the modernizing mechanisms only underscored how badly the country needed technology to organize, simplify, economize, and create the infrastructure to meet basic human needs. I saw so much potential for technology's problem-solving capacity that even as I struggled through quagmires of social and political confusion, I was near to drowning in ideas and excitement.

Through all of it, Rajiv Gandhi was my ally. I saw in him a young, energetic, modern man, direct and honest, eager to explore telecom's role in Indian development. He and I had clicked at our first meeting and quickly became friends. Over the next few years, we fought together for dozens of administrative experiments and reforms using information technology—computerization of railways, for example, and of land records, which was vital to the progress of land reform. At the moment, however, we worked together for the creation of the Centre for Development of Telematics, C-DOT as it came to be known.

The battle was uphill. Every important decision had a political as well as an economic impact. For example, a few months after my meeting with Mrs. Gandhi, India signed a deal with a French multinational to manufacture a digital switching system, so those who stood to profit from this arrangement opposed our concept of an indigenous digital industry and labeled it redundant. One European CEO wrote a strongly worded letter to Mrs. Gandhi pointing out that his company had already spent $1 billion developing digital technology and questioning the wisdom of so massive an investment by the Indian government. Given India's limited resources and the vast needs of its people, that argument had wide political support.

In 1984, the breakup of the U.S. Bell System set in motion a process of deregulation and privatization around the world and gave our proposals the extra boost they needed. In August, C-DOT was registered as a nonprofit society funded by the government but enjoying complete autonomy. Parliament agreed to give us $36 million over 36 months to develop a digital switching system suited to the Indian network. An executive director was appointed, we found five rooms in a rundown government hotel, and we went to work using beds as desks.

A few months later, in October, 1984, Indira Gandhi was assassinated and her son Rajiv became prime minister. He and I decided that I should press the initiative for all it was worth. Since I could not simply pull up stakes and move to Delhi—back in Chicago, my father was dying of cancer—I began spending about half my time in each city. I did not finally move to India with my wife and children until August, 1986, after my father's death. In the meantime, I continued to commute, now more often than ever.

From 1984 on, I was a principal adviser to C-DOT with a salary of one rupee per year, an arrangement I modeled on Roosevelt's dollar-a-year men during the New Deal. I wanted the chance to work for a cause, an Indian cause in particular, and I knew that in order to succeed, I had to place myself above the suspicion of greed or self-interest. In any case, what could I have earned? The top government salary at that time was 5,000 rupees per month—then about $400—and I was spending more than ten times that amount of my own money just on plane fare and hotels. In any case, it was an arrangement that no one in New Delhi understood. One day the deputy minister for electronics took me aside and said, "Mr. Pitroda, what is it you really *want* out of this!" My answer, "Nothing," puzzled him. Whether or not he believed me, my motives remained a subject of discussion in New Delhi for the next six years, with eventual dire results for me.

For the moment, however, activity was bliss. Our engineers were conspicuously young, and they never seemed to sleep or rest. Most had been ready to leave India when this opportunity came along. Now they threw themselves into India's future and worked with an energy that the underdeveloped world is not commonly supposed to generate.

From the outset, C-DOT was much more than an engineering project. It did of course test the technical ability of our young engineers to design a whole family of digital switching systems and associated software suited to India's peculiar conditions. But it was also an exercise in national self-assurance. Years earlier, India's space and nuclear programs had given the country pride in its scientific capability. Now C-DOT had the chance to resurrect that pride.

From the outset, consequently, I was interested in process as well as product. Technology may be complex, but human motivations and interactions are even more so. I knew India had great young engineers, and I believed there was nothing they couldn't accomplish if we challenged them and gave them a proper environment to work in. Part of our mission was to inspire a whole generation of young talent and thumb our noses at the nay-sayers, the political reactionaries, and the vested interests whose prosperity rested entirely on imports. I set impossible targets. I cheered people on. Knowing as I did that young Indians did well in the United States, I tried to create an American work environment. I set about instilling a bias toward action, teamwork, risk, flexibility, simplicity, and openness. I was almost brutal in my determination to root out hierarchy and bureaucracy: I once shouted and made a thoroughly mortifying scene in order to get typists to stop leaping to their feet every time a manager entered their work space to use one of the two telephones we started out with. I did my best to shield our young engineers from bureaucrats, politicians, and business interests. At the same time, I opened our doors to the media, which responded with excitement, optimism, and the kind of hero worship that we hoped would attract more young people to technology careers.

By 1986, C-DOT had sprawling, chaotic offices, 425 employees (average age 25), and the drive, activity and optimism of a U.S. presidential campaign. My methods had been highly unconventional for India and highly unpopular with a lot of the old guard, but within C-DOT we had accomplished wonders.

By 1987, within our three-year limit, we had delivered a 128-line rural exchange, a 128-line private automatic branch exchange for businesses, a small central exchange with a capacity of 512 lines, and we were ready with field trials of a 10,000-line exchange. Better yet, the components for all these exchanges were interchangeable for maximum flexibility in design, installation, and repairs, and all of it was being manufactured *in India* to the international standard: a guaranteed maximum of one hour's downtime in 20 years of service. We had fallen short on one goal—our large urban exchange was well behind schedule—but, overall, C-DOT had proved itself a colossal, resounding success. In addition to the four exchanges, we had licensed some 40 public and private companies to manufacture and market C-DOT products and more than 100 businesses had sprung up to manufacture ancillary parts and components.

Moreover, these rural exchanges were small masterpieces of "appropriate" design.

As I mentioned earlier, digital switching produces heat, so switching equipment has to be air-conditioned in order to function dependably. But in the countryside, the Indian electrical grid is notoriously undependable, and we couldn't give villages exchanges that were certain to overheat the first time the electrical system went down. The solution was simple but ingenious. First, to produce less heat, we used low-power microprocessors and other devices that made the exchanges work just slightly slower. Second, we spread out the circuitry to give it a little more opportunity to "breathe." The cabinet had to be sealed against dust, of course, but by making the whole assembly a little larger than necessary, we created an opportunity for heat to rise internally to the cabinet cover and dissipate. The final product was a metal container about three feet by two feet by three feet, costing about $8,000, that required no air-conditioning and could be installed in a protected space somewhere in the village and switch phone calls more or less indefinitely in the heat and dust of an Indian summers as well as through the torrential Indian monsoon.

Our 512-line exchange was designed for the somewhat larger market town nearby, where it could handle intervillage and long-distance calls for a dozen villages or more. What now remained was to disseminate this new technology through the Indian telecommunications system and actually reach out to the towns and villages that needed it.

In 1987, I chaired a national conference that proposed the establishment of a new, streamlined, semi-autonomous Telecom Commission to replace the old, heavily bureaucratic Department of Telecommunications. Before the government could act on that proposal, however, Rajiv Gandhi appointed me adviser to the prime minister on National Technology Missions, with the rank of minister of state. I had to give up my U.S. passport to take the job, but I couldn't turn down such a marvelous opportunity. The Technology Missions existed to marshal, motivate, and manage the efforts of more than ten-million people and lots of technology involved in meeting six basic human needs: drinking water, immunization, literacy, oilseeds, dairy production, and telecommunications.

Our specific goals were straight-forward. Make clean, potable water available to about 100,000 problem villages in the amount of 40 liters a day per person and 30 liters a day per head of livestock. Immunize 20-million pregnant women and 20-million children every year. Teach 80-million people in the 15 to 35 age group—about 75% of adult illiterates—to read and write at a rate of 10 million each year. Increase oilseed production by as much as 18-million tons and reduce, eliminate, or reverse India's annual 10-billion-rupee import bill for edible oils. Increase dairy production from 44- to 61-million metric tons per year over eight years, raise dairy employment and incomes, and expand the number of dairy cooperatives by 42%. Last but hardly least, improve service, dependability, and accessibility of telecommunications all across the country, including rural areas.

The six mission directors worked for different ministries, so my job was to cheerlead, set agendas, and integrate the activities of ministries, state governments, national laboratories, and voluntary agencies. For two years, I traveled the country visiting tribal areas, villages, towns, cities, and state capitals. Every day I made two or three speeches, took part in half a dozen meetings, talked to scores of people, made dozens of phone calls (if a telephone could be found). I was doing my best to generate ideas, communicate goals and enthusiasm, fight red tape, clear obstacles, tie up loose ends, assess progress, mend bureaucratic fences, and bridge bureaucratic ravines. It became by far the most hectic period of my life, but I got swept up in the romance of making a difference and began working and traveling nearly around the clock. I saw enormous commitment from tens of thousands of people and solid resistance to change from entrenched interests. I began to sense an unholy alliance among many politicians, bureaucrats, and businessmen to stop people from taking power into their own hands through literacy and community-based programs—and through communication.

I was learning the ropes of development in action, and everything I saw strengthened my conviction that telecommunications lies at the very heart of progress. This is true in the political and social sense—people must be able to reach out to government, media, institutions, and allies if they're to make their voices heard—and it is true in the more practical sense that development depends on communication for logistical efficiency. Let me give two examples of what I mean.

One of our greatest assets in the oilseed and dairy missions was Dr. Verghese Kurien, chairman of the National Dairy Development Board and winner of the World Food Prize in 1989. In the 1950s, Dr. Kurien started the farm cooperative movement in India and in 30 years built it into a multimillion-dollar enterprise with a membership of one-million farmers in 50,000 villages. Forgetting for the moment the added years and extra toil it took to build such an organization by word of mouth and personal recruitment, aided only by a postal system famous for incompetence, just imagine the task of galvanizing this organization into concerted action without the ability to computerize membership roles or to contact members by phone or telegraph. In spite of that limitation, Dr. Kurien has succeeded in stabilizing oilseed prices by buffer-stocking large quantities of oil and in building a cooperative milk-distribution system that reaches 170-million people. Telecommunications makes the efforts of men and women like Dr. Kurien incalculably less onerous and more effective, which is one of the reasons a dozen agribusiness lobbies in New Delhi oppose the spread of rural telephones.

Another example comes from the drinking-water mission. One group in the Rural Development Ministry was pushing for the purchase of 40 imported drilling rigs at a cost of several million dollars. Unfortunately, there were two vital pieces of information that no one seemed to possess: first, the number of drilling rigs already in the country, and second, the length of time it took to drill a well and how long it took to move a drill from one village to another.

We found a UNICEF official who was able to tell us that India already owned 1,200 drilling rigs, and several weeks of research revealed that, on average, it took about ten hours to drill a well and roughly ten days to move a rig. These were not ten days of travel time but ten days of bureaucratic wrangling and communication disarray in picking a site, negotiating political priorities, and getting the equipment on the road for a trip of a day or two. If a proper telecommunications network allowed the ministry to improve its planning and coordination even enough to cut that time to *five* days, India would gain the equivalent of 1,200 new water-drilling rigs without importing a single one.

Yet many of those who asked such questions and argued in favor of such solutions were accused of promoting technology *at the expense* of development and, to add insult to injury, of not understanding the plight of the drought-affected poor.

The fact was that no one in India had previously investigated and articulated the role that information systems play in development. Once we started, the practice and the insight grew and grew. After two years at the Technology Missions, I was given a chance to shape that practice even more directly.

In 1989, after two years of debate and study, the government decided to reorganize Indian telecommunications and create the Telecom Commission recommended in our 1987 report. Rajiv Gandhi appointed me the commission's chairman.

I met for three days with the heads of all telecom companies in the country: service providers, manufacturers, laboratories, C-DOT, and others. Then I met with the leaders of 37 telecom unions and the telephone white-collar bureaucracy. At the moment I took over, Telecom had 500,000 employees managing five-million lines, and it took me nine months to get their leaders to buy into my plan to quadruple the lines by the year 2000 without adding to the work force.

Once the unions were on board, we faced three fundamental challenges: connectivity, accessibility, and rural expansion.

First, we replaced all our existing electromechanical long-distance exchanges with digital equipment manufactured in India on license from a French company. We set up two factories to manufacture fiber optics and built high-speed fiber-optic highways to connect the four largest metropolitan areas: Bombay, Delhi, Calcutta, and Madras. We connected 400 district headquarters to automatic dialing, increased our population of digital switching exchanges by 50%, expanded the capacity of switching-system manufacturers, and increased automation at the operator level. We launched a multimillion-dollar program to computerize telecommunications operations nationwide. We introduced international direct dialing to more than 120 countries.

In a country the size of India with only five-million phones, it is difficult to have a significant impact on telephone *density*. Quadrupling the number of lines still means only one telephone for every 50 people, compared with more than one phone for every two people in the United States. *Accessibility* is another matter. By providing more phones in public places, we could put millions of people within reach of telecommunications.

In most areas, coin-operated phones seemed a poor idea for any number of reasons, including the fact that they cost a great deal to manufacture. Instead, we equip ordinary instruments with small meters, then put these phones into the hands of entrepreneurs who set them up on tables in bazaars, on street corners, or in cafes or shops whose owners feel they attract customers. These telephone "owners," frequently the handicapped, take in cash from their customers but are billed only six times a year, with 20% to 25% discounted as their commission. The phones are in such constant use that, in most cases, the revenue is enough to support a family. We launched a drive to install 200,000 such phones in public places nationwide, creating more than 100,000 jobs along the way. Today, the small yellow signs indicating a public telephone can be seen all across India.

The third piece of the program was rural communication, close to my heart because of my own background, and I now set in motion an ambitious program that envisioned nothing less than universal telecommunications accessibility by the year 2000. For us, accessibility was to mean that every Indian citizen should live within three or four kilometers of a dependable instrument, a goal that may strike Westerners as trivial, though I believe it will alter the face of India.

Several years earlier, C-DOT had run a test in Karnataka state with hugely encouraging results In one town of 5,000 people with almost no previous telephone service, business activity rose many times following installation of an automatic digital exchange for 100 lines. Suddenly, it was possible for a truck owner to chase his drivers, line up goods and labor by telephone, and monitor the movement of his vehicles Local farmers could call nearby cities and get real prices for their produce. Artisans could speak to customers, machine operators could arrange for service and repairs, shopkeepers could order goods—all by phone and in real time. In the six months after the introduction of service, total bank deposits in the town rose by an impressive 80%.

There were also social benefits. The townspeople could call doctors and ambulances, order pumps and textbooks, call newspapers, speak to politicians, share experiences with colleagues, and organize community ceremonies and functions. One villager told me that when his father died seven years earlier, he'd had to send 20 messengers on trains and buses to inform relatives in nearby villages. More recently when his mother followed, the villager went to the local tea shop and phoned all 20 villages—instant, certain, and far less expensive.

One-hundred phones in a town of 5,000 is a laughable density to an American and a miracle by Indian standards. Among other surprises, we found considerable long-distance traffic not just to Delhi and Bombay but also to London and New York. The villagers, it seems, have relatives and friends in all four cities.

In 1989, we set a goal of installing one rural exchange a day. By 1993, Telecom was installing 25 rural exchanges every day, and the rate continues to accelerate. By 1995, 100,000 villages will have telephone service. By the turn of the century or very shortly after, almost all of India's 600,000 villages will be covered. Once in place, the village telephone becomes as critical as water, food, shelter, and health services. Once exposed, people in rural areas want a village telephone more than they want any other community service.

Of nearly equal importance for me, the community phone becomes an instrument of social change, fundamental process of democratization. With telecommunications networks now spreading across the Second and Third Worlds, I believe that no amount of effort can put information back in the hands of the few, to be isolated, concentrated, and controlled.

My own effectiveness with the Indian Telecom Commission ended in 1990. Rajiv Gandhi was defeated in parliamentary elections in November, 1989, and I came under political attack a short time later. Eventually I was accused of corruption. Businesses owned by my family in the United States were said to have profited by contracts I awarded while at C-DOT. A thorough investigation by the Comptroller and Auditor General of India turned up no evidence to support this allegation. Moreover, to my gratification, hundreds of scientists, colleagues, academics, and thousands of citizens came to my defense. But the strain was very great. My family moved back to the United States, and in October, 1990, I had a heart attack. A few months after quadruple bypass surgery in Delhi, I went back to work as chairman of the Telecom Commission, with high hopes that Rajiv Gandhi would be returned to office in the 1991 elections. When Rajiv was assassinated in May of 1991, I resigned from my job as chairman and rejoined my wife and children in Illinois. The only post I now held was adviser to the new prime minister on Technology Missions, the same position I had held under Rajiv Gandhi but resigned when he left office.

Though I don't think of my telecom work in India as finished, I have begun to alter my focus somewhat over the last two years. Specifically, I've been struck by the preconditions that the First World has set for Third-World development. Europe and North America built their economies with the help of coercion, work-force exploitation, child labor, and environmental plunder, but the First World has announced to the Third that these and other violations of human and ecological rights are quite unacceptable.

The developed countries are forcing human rights and environmental sensitivity on the world's poor, setting all kinds of new conditions and restrictions on economic growth. This is not fair, of course, but it is an excellent policy.

Still, the First World must understand that it is not likely to achieve this policy goal except with the help of telecommunications and other information technologies, for two simple reasons.

First, telecom makes abuses infinitely easier to monitor. It gives watchdog groups as well as the victims and witnesses of human and environmental outrage access to one another. Local stories become international news, and local events become global events.

Just as information technologies helped make totalitarianism impossible in Eastern Europe, they can help destroy exploitation in the developing world.

Second, telecom helps to create wealth, and prosperity is everywhere a force for civilized behavior. Take child labor. It is poverty that puts children to work, and it is unskilled labor that children are able to perform. When telecommunications comes to the Third World, it brings with it new economic activity, new higher-paying jobs for parents, and new technologies that reduce the utility of unskilled child labor. Countless towns and villages in India can bear witness to telecommunications' electrifying effect on entrepreneurialism, employment, and the overall standard of living. On top of all that, of course, information technologies create their own skilled jobs.

The dreadful human and physical conditions that the industrial revolution created in the West are now avoidable. But it is not some fundamental improvement in human nature that makes such progress possible. Growth without freedom and responsibility can still take place. It is technology, and information technology in particular, that makes human development feasible.

The fact is, the telecom revolution has hardly begun. In addition to new products, systems, and integrated services, we will soon have new information-based relationships with our society and environment. But if sustainable progress of this kind is not to be limited to the developed world, then there is one initial hurdle still to clear.

The Third World still lacks adequate investment in telecommunications. Telecom in the developing world needs about $30 billion a year, of which only $3 billion is presently available. The World Bank devotes only 2% of all its funding to telecommunications. Corporations are attracted by the prospect of immense long-term profit but frightened by political risk and the certainty of social and economic experimentation.

Along with a number of fellow telecom engineers and executives, I am now working to organize a special funding agency, similar to the World Bank, to support Third-World telecommunications. Without proper telecom institutions and infrastructure, sustainable development with freedom will be difficult to achieve. Without telecom development, we will never deliver 75% of the world's people to the civilization of the information age.

Article Questions

1. The exponential growth in the field of telecommunications has transformed the world in to a global village. But there still exists a wide gap between the first world and the third world. In developed countries the telecommunication has played a key role in the economic growth. In most developed countries a good majority of people have telephones and the literacy rate is 80%+. In contrast, a vast majority of the population in third world is illiterate and does not have access to a telephone. In most developing countries there are only 1 to 5 phones per 1000 people, and the illiteracy rate is more than 70%. How can telecommunications be used in the developing countries to increase the literacy rate, which in turn can improve the economic well being of people?

2. Comment on the author's statement: "The developed countries are forcing human rights and environmental sensitivity on the world's poor, setting all kinds of new conditions and restrictions on economic growth. This is not fair, of course, but it is an excellent policy".

The Moral Equivalent of War— in the Middle East

By James Gaffney

When William James coined one of the most luminous of modern phrases, "the moral equivalent of war," a coinage reissued in the Presidential rhetoric of John Kennedy and Jimmy Carter, he was acknowledging something that modern moralizers about war tend to overlook or underrate. Pacifists perceive war as a form of human behavior so saturated with maleficence that it cannot be exonerated by any good it might conceivably secure. "Just war" theorists likewise perceive war as fraught with maleficence, but as nevertheless sometimes defensible as the only practical recourse for averting far greater evil. William James, while siding with the pacifists, also insisted on a more adequate perception of war as being, partly but really, what more romantic observers have always seen it to be—for at least some of its participants—a field of honor and school of virtues, the virtues mainly of courage and comradeship. Any reader of the interviews Studs Terkel assembled in *The Good War* (World War II) will discard any doubt that, even in our century, war has often been experienced, not simply imagined, in terms very reminiscent of chivalric romance.

James's practical concern was that in rejecting war we should try to retain or restore, in more wholesome settings, the kind of moral opportunity and moral stimulation that had always been the only good thing about war. He thought that other areas of modern life offered similar opportunities and stimuli for a kind of virtue we can ill afford to lose. And he called for the exercise of social imagination to envision, as great religious founders have often done, benign tasks that would foster and employ the same ascetical capacities and austere loyalties that had always been the justifiable pride of good soldiers.

This Jamesian theme came back to me in a new way as I attended in recent days to the public claims and counterclaims of George Bush and Saddam Hussein. Both rely for the moral components of their rhetoric entirely on denunciation. Saddam Hussein can ridicule George Bush's pretended outrage at the forced occupation of foreign territory by pointing to his Government's easy acceptance of similar behavior by Israel. George Bush can ridicule Saddam Hussein's pretended commitment to Arab solidarity by pointing to his blitzkrieg in Kuwait and his bloody purges of domestic adversaries. Each can show convincingly that any claims by the other to moral idealism in Middle Eastern foreign policy is patently hypocritical. Each can also show convincingly that in the present confrontation the effective motivation of the other is fundamentally economic. Unquestionably, the facts of recent history exhibit Saddam Hussein as an extraordinarily detestable person, while George Bush emerges from the same record as a decent enough sort. Nevertheless, the present conflict is not a struggle between their respective characters, but simply between the interests they represent as, on the one hand, a greedy oil-consumer and, on the other, a very greedy oil-producer. That, and that alone, is what they are prepared to get people killed for.

What occasioned my relating this situation to that old Jamesian conception of the "moral equivalent of war" was hearing, in close succession, George Bush telling his people that we were not prepared to tolerate any change in our "way of life," and Saddam Hussein telling his people they should prepare to reduce consumption, endure discomfort, risk danger. In his own perverse way, Saddam Hussein was appealing to a "moral equivalent of war" in evident expectation that it would challenge and inspire his followers. George Bush's insistence on the inviolability of our "way of life" had, in the circumstances, the very opposite implication.

But is it really quite unthinkable that in this ignoble quarrel over changing the prospects for sellers and buyers of oil, a critical eye might be cast on how very much of our "way of life" is a colossal and unparalleled waste of oil, of other forms of energy derived from oil, and of a natural environment that is wasted precisely by that waste? Is it simply inevitable that a tightening of belts should be the kind of response to a national threat that only fanatical Arabs dare appeal to? Is it altogether impossible that in this dreaded prospect of more costly oil importation we should feel the challenge not of war, but of a moral equivalent of war: of a prudent restraint, a wholesome austerity, a recognition of reasonable limits to greed and growth, and a courageous, imaginative pursuit of decent feasible alternatives to the most wanton aspects of our "way of life"?

Such possibilities, including prospects of emancipation from national indenture to the merchants of a non-renewable energy-source, were seriously entertained in the pre-Reagan era. To cultivate such possibilities with vigor and resolve would exemplify very much the sort of thing William James meant by the "moral equivalent of war." As things are developing in the Middle East it might well turn out to be our only real moral alternative to war. Saddam Hussein confronts us as a would-be extortionist, ruthlessly preparing to present us, in an oil-market he largely controls, with an offer we cannot refuse. George Bush's absolutization of our notoriously energy-wasteful "way of life" no doubt assures Saddam Hussein that if he did get into such a position, his offer would indeed be one we couldn't refuse. What the Bush rhetoric seems to be announcing, apart from its well-deserved rejection of Saddam Hussein's claims to high moral ground, is that, faced with a threat of much more costly oil, we are ready to kill, we are ready to die, but we are eternally unready to curb our environmental prodigality or attempt a practical reorganization of our economic priorities.

It must not be forgotten that in the present conflict our "way of life" no longer means what it did in either the Cold War or the World War that preceded it, namely the security of a free democracy menaced by totalitarian adversaries. That is not what we are defending against Saddam Hussein. What George Bush means by our "way of life" is the "lifestyle" we have constructed on a basis of affordable imported oil. It is easier to apply notions of sacredness and inviolability to the former conception of our "way of life" than to the latter one. "Better dead than red" was an incantation that sustained national bellicosity right up to *glasnost* and *perestroika*. If we were to risk lives in conflict with Saddam Hussein, it is hard to guess what prospective victims might consolingly regard themselves as better dead than. "Better dead than adaptable" just does not have the right ring. Even "better dead than frugal" seems unlikely to quicken the pulse.

I have significantly more respect and admiration for George Bush than for many of his predecessors. Yet if an oil-rich President should appear to assume that the human costs of a major war can be compensated in petro-dollars, I should think it time to seek a second opinion—except that by then it would almost certainly be too late.

Article Questions

1. Is it moral and ethical to endanger hundreds and thousands of human lives in a war just to get oil at a cheaper price?

2. What does the author mean by the phrase "moral alternative to war?"

Discussion Questions

1. What can be done to curb population in less developed countries?

2. Define the changing role of women. What part does education and employment play for women in determining their future in Third World countries? Discuss.

3. Why is world population one of the most important issues for the 21st century? What other issues are closely connected to population growth issues?

4. What is the role of technology in relationship to the quality of life in Third World countries?

5. Identify some of the medical issues and ethics of birth control. What are some of the issues in transferring this technology to Third World countries?

CHAPTER NINE
TECHNOLOGY OF THE FUTURE

Is Anybody Out There?

Dennis Overbye

Giant space stations in the sky, underground cities on the moon, galactic empires that have forgotten the earth, interstellar war with telepathic ants, voyages to go boldly where no man has gone before. Such were the predictions about the glories of the space age. No wonder the failure of events to live up to the predetermined history bequeathed by science fiction has disappointed the baby boomers.

But that future may still be realizable, believe many scientists in and out of NASA who meet now and then to try to imagine the technology that could bring the space age to life. In their eyes, those first moon landings represented a false dawn of space exploration, just as the early Viking voyages to America were ahead of their time. Only when technology makes space flight cheap enough, as one astronomer put it, "to hock your socks and go," will the real space age begin. What will that age produce?

For starters, rockets will go the way of the dinosaurs. Future spacefarers will look back on the notion of sending people (or anything precious) aloft on huge, lumbering towers of flame and smoke as primitive, brutal and notoriously unreliable. Before the next millennium is very far along, humans will get their lift from space planes that take off and land like conventional jets but are powered by "scramjets" that, once aloft, will enable them to swoop into orbit or go halfway around the world in two hours. Cargo will be shot into orbit by electromagnetic rail guns that ramp up the sides of mountains, or will be flung upward by looping orbital tethers, sort of like David's slingshot.

Probes and people would sally forth into the deeper universe, propelled by thin sails filled by the feeble but inexorable pressure of sunlight or traveling on ion drives that get their boost by shooting high-energy electrified particles out of the rear of the vehicle. Other possible vehicles for space travel may be propelled by a series of tiny thermonuclear explosions using pellets of fuel mined on the moon, or by mass drivers employing electromagnetic fields to expel bucketloads of dirt from the back.

Once the transportation is ready, Mars will be a popular destination. According to scenarios worked out by a group of scientists who call themselves the Mars Underground, the first voyagers would be preceded by ferries carrying equipment for setting up a permanent base. Early visitors would face a hostile environment: a thin atmosphere of mostly carbon dioxide, temperatures that fluctuate from -10°F to -190°F and hurricane winds. People would live chiefly underground, grow vegetables in greenhouses, wear space suits and explore the countryside in dirigibles.

After a few decades of familiarization and exploration had established that there was no indigenous Martian life, humans might be ready to undertake the ultimate real estate-development project: the greening of Mars. The first step, according to one recent study, would be to warm the planet by releasing large amounts of chlorofluorocarbons into the atmosphere. These gases would act like a greenhouse, trapping the sun's heat. As the planet warmed, the polar caps would begin to melt, releasing water vapor and carbon dioxide into the Martian air, thickening it and increasing the greenhouse effect. Eventually the permafrost, where most of Mars' water is locked up, would melt, and rivers and lakes—if not oceans—would flow across the Red Planet again.

The next task would be to oxygenate Mars' atmosphere and introduce life. The "gardeners" on Mars could import anaerobic organisms—for example, the blue-green algae that flourished on earth billions of years ago. Other genetically engineered organisms would follow until one day, probably millenniums from now, the new Martians could breathe freely under clear skies.

Most of the work of investigating and colonizing the solar system (and perhaps beyond) would be done by robot probes smaller and smarter than those of today. Advances in computer technology and genetic engineering, predicts physicist Freeman Dyson of the Institute for Advanced Study in Princeton, New Jersey, will enable scientists to squeeze the capabilities of a Voyager spacecraft, say, into a 2-lb. package that is half machine, half organism. This he dubs the astrochicken. Launched as an "egg," the astrochicken would sprout solar-panel wings that would double as radio antennae during flight. Arriving at its destination, the craft would nibble on the ice in planetary rings and shoot around like a bombardier beetle exploring moons.

Robot probes no bigger than bacteria will eventually be possible. According to K. Eric Drexler, author of Engines of Creation, they will use nanotechnology to assemble devices atom by atom or molecule by molecule. His colleagues have already made motors smaller in diameter than a human hair. Drexler believes a bundle of nanorobots, weighing practically nothing, would be the perfect interstellar emissaries. Having arrived at a planet or asteroid around some distant star, perhaps in a solar sailship pushed to high speeds by a powerful laser beam from earth, they would go to work, antlike, building radio transmitters and other gear to report home for new instructions. They could also reproduce themselves and their ships in order to send off a new set of explorer robots.

Could humans follow their robots to the stars? Because people and their life-support systems are so massive, it would take gargantuan amounts of energy and time to get anywhere. By one estimate, a round trip to a nearby star at one-tenth the speed of light would take 500 times the energy the U.S. produces in a year. Many scientists argue that no society would ever find the trip worth it, unless perhaps the sun were threatened with imminent destruction—an event not due for 5 billion years.

Nonetheless, within 500 years humans may be ready to pack their belongings into starships—as the early Polynesians did into canoes—and set off in search of new worlds. With a possible 1 trillion people spread out over the solar system by then, a trip into the galaxy beyond will not seem so daunting, contends Eric Jones, a physicist at the Los Alamos (New Mexico) National Laboratory, and his collaborator Ben Finney, an anthropologist and expert on migration at the University of Hawaii. In their scenario, robots will have transformed the planet Mercury into a giant solar-power station, beaming energy to the rest of the solar system in the form of microwaves, and the moon will be a mining and construction center.

A starship could be accelerated to interstellar-travel speeds by having one of those powerful microwave lasers on Mercury push against a vast, thin sail constructed perhaps of diamond fibers. At its destination, the starship would then hunt out an asteroid, upon which microrobots would descend and begin mining and constructing a colony. Perhaps in a few hundred or a few thousand years. the inhabitants of this new world would be ready to send a migratory ship even farther. In this way, Jones and Finney argue, humans could colonize the galaxy in a few million years.

But it might not be necessary to send people's bodies. The answer, says Konstantin Feoktistov, a former Soviet cosmonaut, could be the human fax. Feoktistov has pointed out that it might be possible someday soon to "download" the entire contents of a human brain into a computer, the way a file on a PC can be transferred onto a floppy disk, and broadcast it to a robot in a remote star system. After a few days or years of exposure to this strange world, the surrogate brain would "fax" its new information back to earth and its original owner. Feoktistov suggests that human faxing would be even easier if we could contact some extraterrestrial and have them build receiving stations for us.

What about those extraterrestrials? In that regard, the future is already here: a new search for extraterrestrial intelligence (SETI to astronomical aficionados) is about to start. On Columbus Day, radio antennas in California and Puerto Rico are scheduled to begin a survey of the heavens, monitoring 8 million radio channels simultaneously for signs of life. By the end of the decade, if they get lucky, NASA'S radio astronomers may discover the signal that ends mankind's loneliness. SETI theorists hypothesize that even advanced civilizations might find interstellar travel an expensive and time-consuming way, at best, to meet the neighbors, and would instead set up radio beacons to call out to one another—a cosmic ham radio club.

The detection of an extraterrestrial signal would be one of the greatest events of this or any other millennium. Direct contact with aliens, who would probably be vastly more powerful than we ourselves, could have a demoralizing and destructive effect on human culture, much as white men destroyed Native American life. It might also pose a challenge to the world's religions.

Fortunately, perhaps, the odds against physical contact are, well, astronomical. Even if another civilization were in our own corner of the galaxy, it could be several hundred or a thousand light-years away. With signals propagating at the speed of light, the distances involved suggest that all communications would essentially be monologues. Frank Drake, a California radio astronomer and SETI pioneer, once said that the most likely signalers would be races of immortals because they could afford to wait almost forever for the return message.

Dennis Overbye

Others speculate that humanity will tap into a galactic radio network, a cosmic encyclopedia in which the cultures and histories of civilizations—some of them by now dead—would be preserved and broadcast eternally. The development of radio astronomy technology would constitute the entrance fee for this cosmic lonely-hearts club. Since we have reached that level of technology only in the past 50 years, humans would almost by definition be the most junior members of an association of cultures thousands or even millions of years older.

Moreover, the human race would probably not even understand any signals from outer space. SETI people liken the task of decoding and understanding such signals to biblical scholarship or the deciphering of ancient hieroglyphics. The obstacles have led Philip Morrison, a Massachusetts Institute of Technology physicist who helped invent SETI, to call the task "the archeology of the future." How would humanity respond to signals from other beings? The writer and physician Lewis Thomas once proposed that we should send the music of Bach, acknowledging that it would be bragging but holding that we had a right to put our best foot forward.

And what if, after a millennium of listening and looking, there is only silence—what if we still seem alone? If interstellar migration is as easy and inevitable as Finney and Jones have outlined, and if the galaxy, 10 billion years old, is populated by other advanced races, critics of SETI argue, E.T.s should have come calling by now. There is no scientific evidence that they have, and the lack of it has led some scientists to argue that there is no life out there at all. One answer to the dilemma, popular in SETI circles but not very flattering, is called the zoo hypothesis: extraterrestrial ethics would bar other creatures from interfering with quaint, developing species. Somewhere out beyond the orbit of Pluto there may be a sign bearing the astronomical equivalent of DON'T FEED THE BEARS.

Article Questions

1. What does the author predict about the vehicles for space travel?

2. What does Dennis Overbye feel about the role of Mars in the future? What will happen to Mars?

3. What is an astrochicken?

4. What would be the function of nanorobots?

5. What would be the role of the human fax?

6. What would be one function of radio astronomy technology?

How the World Will Look in 50 Years

Bruce W. Nelan

Just as wars—two World Wars and, equally important, the cold war—dominated the geopolitical map of the 20th century, economics will rule over the 21st. All the big questions confronting the world in the century ahead are basically economic. Is the U.S. in an irreversible decline as the world's premier power? Will Japan continue its competitive conquest of international markets? Can Europe manage to hold together the world's largest trade bloc in the face of strong centrifugal forces? And does the future hold any hope at all for the poverty-stricken Third World?

This concentration on economics will be made possible by the prospect of general peace in the 21st century, heralded by the lifting of the nuclear arms threat in the 1990s. In the century ahead, the world will contain more democracies than ever before, and they will dominate in Europe, the Americas and the countries of the Pacific Rim. Since it is a truism that democratic states do not make war on one another, warfare should become essentially irrelevant for these nations, most of which will reduce their armed forces to the minimum necessary for individual or collective defense. "We're not going to see nation-states bullying one another as they have in the past," predicts senior analyst Carl Builder of the Rand Corp.

New realities will also curb the old acquisitive impetus toward imperialism. Raw materials of all sorts, for example, will lose much of their importance because the manufacture of 21st century products will use fewer and fewer of them. Even the need for oil, now the most vital of interests in the West, will fall from the strategic agenda as it is replaced by solar power and controlled nuclear fusion. The end of the petroleum age will make the Arab states of the Middle East poorer and less stable but of declining interest to the West. The Islamic world, powerfully resistant to modernization, will tend to isolate itself.

Unfortunately, the lifting of the nuclear threat in the 1990s will continue to create opportunities for mischief among some nationalist ideologues and local despots. In the decades ahead, the major powers will ignore most petty tyrants and the brutal but small-bore wars that they foment—unless they seriously endanger their neighbors or threaten their own people with genocide. When that occurs, the United Nations will, in most cases, authorize joint armed intervention. When it does not, the U.S. and other states that share its views will act on their own.

But cooperation with the U.N. will be the norm, in both warlike and peaceful pursuits. The world will have to utilize the powers of the U.N. to solve other overreaching problems, such as environmental pollution, global warming and damage to the ozone layer, that cannot be approached piecemeal. John Steinbruner, director of foreign policy studies at the Brookings Institution in Washington, foresees "a much more advanced form of international politics, involving more sophisticated coordination and more consequential decisions made at the international level."

The U.S. will remain the one reigning military superpower in this less heavily armed world. Its forces will shrink considerably to enable it to concentrate more of its energies on economic and social advances, but it will continue to provide global outreach with state-of-the-art weapons and an invulnerable nuclear arsenal. The U.S. will have to preserve this role because the technical know-how to build nuclear weapons cannot be abolished no matter how carefully arms-control treaties are drafted. Truly determined governments, among them many smaller nations that covet prestige and power, cannot be prevented from buying or building nuclear arms. The U.S. will have to be prepared to deter nuclear-armed dictators, and to intervene against them if necessary, in order to protect its friends and head off nuclear blackmail.

The competition that is normal and inevitable among nations will increasingly be played out in the 21st century not in aggression or war but in the economic sphere. The weapons used will be those of commerce: growth rates, investments, trade blocs, imports and exports. "The move to multinational trade blocs around the world has suppressed nationalism," says Gregory Schmidt of the Institute for the Future in Menlo Park, California. "Economics will eventually win out in the 21st century."

In his new best seller *Head to Head*, M.I.T. economist Lester Thurow writes, "World trade in the next half-century is apt to grow even faster than it did in the last half-century: any decline in trade between the blocks will be more than offset by more trade within the blocks."

The big winner will be Europe. At the opening of the 21st century, the European Community will comprise an integrated market of 20 countries, newly including such advanced economies as Switzerland, Sweden, Norway, Finland and Austria. By the middle of the century, it will have added the Czech republic, Hungary and Poland, and its members' population will total more than 400 million. By then, Ukraine, Russia and most of the rest of Eastern Europe will have achieved associate membership in the Community.

That last stage of Europe's growth will demand a lot of work. Eastern Europe's conversion from communist central planning to democratic market economies is one of the most difficult undertakings imaginable. As the Carnegie Endowment's National Commission referred to it in a report last July, "You can make fish soup out of an aquarium, but you can't make an aquarium out of fish soup."

What exists in Eastern Europe—mostly antiquated factories, worthless currency and a socialist hangover—will have to be replaced. What does not exist—a commercial banking system, marketing networks, cost accounting—will have to be created from scratch. The biggest hope for the future of the old socialist world is its very well-educated work force and a high level of science and technology.

Another major plus for the emergent democracies will be the eagerness of governments in the West to do everything necessary to build prosperity in the East in order to keep waves of economic migrants from rolling over Germany, Italy, France and their neighbors. As Western investments and technical assistance take hold, the East will forge ahead. East Europeans will drop their most extreme nationalist and ethnic preoccupations in order to qualify for the economic payoffs they expect from association with the E.C. Of course, some countries, including Romania, Bulgaria and Albania, will simply not be able to transform themselves.

On the other side of the world, the astonishing Asians will continue their success story, but with more diversity and less coordination than Europeans. Japan will not have things so much its own way in the next century. Its ultramodern and finely calibrated economy will not falter, but several factors will impose limits on its once seemingly boundless growth.

To begin with, Japan's special sort of samurai work ethic will be under assault. Coming generations of your "salary-men" will be less willing to work such grueling hours. They will want more leisure time, larger apartments, shorter commutes. Japanese men and women alike, no longer content to be poor people in a rich country, as they describe themselves, will demand a larger share of the national wealth they create. The resulting higher consumption at home will inevitably mean more imports and a reduction in Japan's trade surpluses.

Problems for Japan are already building up in the Pacific Rim and are bound to intensify. Tokyo's long-range plan for growth is to bring in the raw materials it needs from Russia and steadily increase its sales of manufactured products to what it envisions as a vast market in China. But things will not work out quite that way. Communism will collapse in China, clearing the way for the powerhouse of Taiwan to join Hong Kong as a special economic zone of the Chinese motherland.

Even with their help, however, China cannot grow into an industrial giant in the 21st century. Its population is too large and its gross domestic product too small (it is expected to reach only $900 per capita by the year 2000). China's economy seems to be growing at 7% in 1992, but, as the former Soviet Union and East Germany once did, Beijing cranks out phony statistics. Moreover, China's growth projections are based essentially on light industry.

China will have a potential alternative supplier in Korea, where communism will be abolished in the North. The merged Koreas will prove to be a strong competitor to Japan. Right now, all Asia's "little tigers"—South Korea, Taiwan, Hong Kong, Singapore—run considerable deficits in their trade with Japan. In the 21st century, they will be as much Japan's rivals as its trading partners. Like the rest of the world, they will be less willing to buy from a Japan that does not buy much from them.

The hard laws of economic life also decree that in the 21st century, the rich will generally get richer and the poor poorer. In order to rise to a level of prosperity, a developing country must achieve decades of high growth rates while simultaneously holding its population stable. Few will be able to manage that trick successfully. India in 2025, for example, will have 1.4 billion people. By 2050 the world's population is likely to have surged from the present 5.5 billion to 11 billion, and its production of goods and services will have quadrupled. But almost all the population increase is projected for the less-developed countries, while most of the increased output will occur in the industrial democracies.

Moreover, developed countries are already buying less from the Third World and more from one another. Even now, trading by the three main economic regions—Europe, North America and the Pacific Rim— accounts for 75% of the world's total. Over the past decade, 20 of the world's 24 largest industrial powers have signed bilateral agreements that regulate their trade and set up new barriers to imports.

If the dynamics of the 21st century produce a gloomy outlook for the poorest countries, the most bothersome question facing much of the world is about the fate of the U.S. There is no doubt, of course, that America will be a major player on the world scene.

Bruce W. Nelan

319

Its military power, its 20% share of the world's gross national product and its mastery of such cutting-edge fields as biotechnology, microprocessors and information technologies guarantee that. It will bestride the North American Free Trade Agreement like a colossus.

But serious worries shadow the U.S. future. The country has run a $1 trillion trade deficit over the past 10 years, and its national debt is more than $4 trillion. One day the U.S. will have to pay those bills. And the only way it can do so is to stop devouring the products of other nations, put more of its wealth into investment at home and greatly expand its exports.

Aside from the skewed balance sheets, there are serious doubts about the country's intrinsic health. Its educational system is in crisis, its industries faltering, its investment in itself too meager. "In a world whose workers require ever more basic education, technological savvy and specialized skill," Marvin Cetron and Owen Davies write in their book *Crystal Globe*, "America's schools are the least successful in the Western world." Says Brookings' Steinbruner: "There's no way of overcoming disparity in economic fortune without overcoming the disparity in education." U.S. spending on civilian research and development is 10th in the world, a level that M.I.T.'s Thurow estimates will "eventually lead to a secondary position for American science and engineering and lower rates of growth in productivity."

Will the U.S. be able to diagnose its ills and swallow cures that are certain to be bitter? Probably. The country is good at rising to occasions, once it recognizes them. The end of the cold war has released immense resources and millions of talented people who can now turn to the repair of America's damage. Because the U.S. is, among other things, an even-handed superpower and a vast market, most of the world has a stake in its continued success. But if the U.S. is to be counted among the winners in the next century, it will have to make gravely important decisions—and act on them—before the end of this one.

Article Questions

1. What is the the underlying force for the 21st Century according to the author?

2. How would this force be made possible?

3. What will be the importance of raw materials and oil? What will be the role of the U.N.?

4. What will the U.S. look like? What will Europe be like?

5. What will be the future of the Asian countries—especially Japan and China?

6. What will be the world economic profile?

7. What are some of the central concerns for the future of the U.S.?

Dream Machines

Philip Elmer-Dewitt

Try this sexual fantasy on for size: author Howard Rheingold, who writes about the you-are-there technology known as virtual reality, predicts that consenting adults in the not too distant future will be able to enjoy sex over the telephone. First they will slip into undergarments lined with sensors and miniature actuators. Then they will dial their partner and, while whispering endearments, fondle each other over long-distance lines. For those who prefer something tamer, Nobel physicist Arno Penzias believes that in the 21st century it will be possible to play Ping-Pong (or any other sport) with phantasms that look and talk like the celebrity of your choice. And that's just the beginning. Someday, says visionary engineer K. Eric Drexler, molecular-size machines will be able to assemble objects one atom at a time. Using this method, they could manufacture everything from prefabricated skyscrapers to computers small enough to fit inside a living cell.

When asked to close their eyes and imagine the shape of technology in the 21st century, scientists and industrial planners describe a world filled with intelligent machines, multisensual media and artificial creatures so highly evolved they will seem as alive as dogs and cats. If even their most conservative projections come true, the next century may bring advances no less momentous than the Bomb, the Pill and the digital computer. Should the more radical predictions prove correct, our descendants may encounter technological upheavals that could make 20th century breakthroughs seem tame.

For the first few decades of the next millennium, new advances are likely to fit within familiar forms. People will still drive cars to work, albeit lightweight cars running on strange new fuels. Office workers will toil before computers, although those machines will probably respond to commands that are spoken or scribbled as well as typed. Families will gather around TV sets with big, high-definition screens and a large menu of interactive options. After a few decades, those familiar forms will blend together and begin to lose their distinct identities. TVs, VCRS, CD players, computers, telephones, video games, newspapers and mail-order catalogs will merge to create new products and services that can only be dimly imagined today.

Somewhere around the middle of the century, many scientists predict, technology may enter a transitional phase, a shift in the ground rules that will put what is now considered pure science fiction well within society's reach. "We're at the knee of a curve, after which all those intimations of the future may actually come true," says John Holzrichter, director of institutional research and development at Lawrence Livermore National Laboratory. Among the scenarios he and his colleagues anticipate:

Communications

People in the 21st century will wear their telephones like jewelry, with microphones hidden in necklaces or lapel pins and miniature speakers tucked behind each ear, predicts Nobelist Penzias, vice president of research at AT&T Bell Laboratories. Every phone customer will have long since been issued a personal number that follows him everywhere—home, the office, the beach. Thanks to a telecommunications system that will link phone networks, cable-TV systems, satellite broadcasts and multimedia libraries, getting connected to anything or anyone in the most remote parts of the world will be a simple matter. This easy access will spur the rapid growth of "virtual communities." If picture phones finally become widely accepted, people will begin to make network friends whom they may never meet in person. These communities will flourish as the cost of transmitting voices and images keeps falling.

Computers

The stand-alone machines that dominate office desktops today will eventually insinuate themselves into the walls and furniture, perhaps even into clothes. Exotic display devices will serve as windows onto great, interconnected networks. These windows could be as big as chalkboards or as small as Post-it notes, according to scientists pursuing "ubiquitous computing" technologies at Xerox's Palo Alto Research Center. Computer screens could even be etched onto the lenses of eyeglasses.

The networks of the future will become increasingly populated with new kinds of software entities known as personal assistants, or "agents." These agents will monitor the outside world, gleaning pertinent information, filtering out unwanted clutter, tracking appointments and offering advice. A travel "agent," for example, would be indispensable to a foreign traveler by doing simultaneous translations or pointing out sites of interest. A virtual lawyer could give expert legal opinions, a Wall Street agent timely investment tips.

Home Entertainment

The shift to digital entertainment media, which began with compact discs in the 1980s, will open up new dimensions in leisure. Nicholas Negroponte, director of M.I.T's Media Laboratory, predicts the availability, before the end of the next century, of "full-color, large-scale, holographic TV with force feedback and olfactory output," which is to say home movies that can be seen, felt and smelled. The trend will be toward entertainment that is customized for the individual, including do-it-yourself multimedia fantasies as well as newspapers and magazines edited to suit each subscriber's interests.

As overpopulation makes the real world less congenial, artificial realities will become more attractive. Fifty years from now, the ability to put oneself in the shoes of another character in another place—Rambo rafting down the Orinoco, say—could be a metered commodity, like pay TV. Stewart Brand, creator of *The Whole Earth Catalog*, thinks these experiences might provide the kind of mind-expanding thrills people once got from psychedelic drugs, but without the mental and physical side effects.

Robotics

Long predicted but slow to arrive, robots may finally have their day. Within decades, says M.I.T. robot designer Rodney Brooks, the world could be filled with small, single-purpose semi-intelligent creatures. He describes, for example, tiny insect-like vacuum cleaners that will hang out in dusty corners scooping dirt into their bellies. When they hear the big vacuum robot coming, they will scurry to the center of the room, empty their innards and run back under the sofa.

Robots will eventually learn a human trait: reproduction. And the smart ones will be able to improve on the original pattern with each new copy. Self-replicating devices that are mobile, can find their own sources of energy and evolve from one generation to another could satisfy many of the criteria that have come to be associated with living things, says Steve Levy, author of a new book called *Artificial Life*. In the next century, says Levy, "we'll relate to our machines as we now relate to domestic animals."

The most important self-replicating machines, says Eric Drexler, will be microscopic atom-stacking factories, or "assemblers." Drexler, the author of *Engines of Creation*, believes that within the new few decades, armies of assemblers will be programmed to turn out a wide range of consumer goods, from featherweight spacecraft to paper-thin television screens. "Many of the things we can expect to see in the next 100 years will resemble the wild ideas of the 1950s and 1960s," he says.

Transportation

The future's lightweight, superefficient cars will still be equipped with conventional steering and accelerators for knocking around the neighborhood and countryside. But highways will be embedded with electronics to monitor and control speed and traffic patterns, so that driving on the most heavily traveled freeways will become increasingly effortless. Commuters in the latter half of the century will simply get on the freeway, punch in their destination and let the electronic control systems take over. Collision-avoidance software could speed cars along at 200 km/h (120 m.p.h.) with no more than a few feet between each vehicle.

For medium-distance travel, new forms of mass transit are likely to dominate. Magnetically levitated locomotives will zip along at up to 500 km/h (300 m.p.h.). Lightweight materials will enable aircraft to carry as much as three times the passenger load of today's jumbo jets. For those who can afford the tickets, a few airlines might even offer services on a supersonic, suborbital *Orient Express* that would hop from Los Angeles to Tokyo in only two hours.

Philip Elmer-Dewitt

Energy

Fuel sources will probably change as dramatically in the coming century as they have in the current one. Scientists may find that the environmental effects of carbon dioxide and other greenhouse gas emissions are far worse than expected, which would prompt a virtual ban on the burning of hydrocarbons, says Livermore's Holzrichter. But what's next? Some experts believe so-called inherently safe reactors will have progressed so much by that time that the environmental movement will embrace nuclear fission. Others see a mix of solar, geothermal, tidal and wind power. By the end of the century, the big industrial nations may begin to rely on fusion, a safer form of nuclear energy that creates far less radioactive waste.

These varied sources would produce electricity for local consumption and clean-burning hydrogen for distribution via pipelines. According to one estimate, a single solar-cell farm covering roughly one-quarter the area of New Mexico could supply enough electrically produced hydrogen to replace all the fossil fuels consumed in the U.S. If the necessary real estate can't be found on the planet's surface, the solar collectors could be parked in orbit, beaming energy to earth via high-power microwaves.

Warfare

The weapons of the future will look like they came straight out of *Star Wars* or *RoboCop*: everything from hand-held laser swords to autonomous robots programmed to kill. The long-term trend, as demonstrated in the Persian Gulf last year, is toward short battles conducted at long distance by increasingly intelligent machines. Defense experts predict that the next arms race will be to develop the smartest, stealthiest and most accurate weapons and to demonstrate their superiority convincingly enough in advance to avoid risking lives and expensive hardware on the battlefield.

The biggest problem will be proliferation, not only of nuclear fuel and arms but also of poison gases, biological toxins and other awful things no one has yet dreamed up. If tin-pot dictators and drug cartels get hold of the technology, they will become increasingly troublesome. Even a cheap, radio-controlled model airplane can do a lot of damage if, say, it is carrying a genetically engineered anthrax spore.

As a rule of thumb, says Bell Labs' Penzias, technology will provide for people of the future what only the wealthiest can buy today. Where the rich now hire chauffeurs to drive them to work, for example, the working stiff of the future will be transported to work in his robocar. None of these advances are without their costs and risks. Drexler's assemblers, for example, could create bounties of goods and services—or they could unleash artificial pests of unimaginable destructiveness. One nightmare creature from Drexler's book: an omnivorous bacteria-size robot that spreads like blowing pollen, replicates swiftly and reduces the biosphere to dust in a matter of days.

None of this, of course, is etched in stone—or in silicon. In the end, what propels science and technology forward is not just what can be done but also what society chooses to do. As the brief history of the nuclear age has taught, powerful technologies are hard to rein in once they've been loosed on the world. Is humankind mature enough to handle the possibilities of intelligent robots, self-replicating machines and virtual sex? Fantastic new opportunities are sure to come. The hard part will be deciding which ones to pursue and which to bypass.

Article Questions

1. Describe the "shape" or overview of technology in the 21st century. What will happen in the next few decades? What will technology be like by 2050?

2. Predict your view of what communications, computer, home entertainment, robotics, transportation, energy, and warfare with that of the author.

3. Of these seven areas, which do you think will undergo the most change from today? Explain your answer.

4. What is the biggest challenge for the future according to your view after reading the article?

5. Is the author's view of the future pessimistic or optimistic? Contrast that with your view. Explain your answer.

Discussion Questions

1. Evaluate the following statement: "technology will provide for people of the future what only the wealthiest can afford today."

2. How will the future development of technology affect communications? Home entertainment? What social consequences, if any, do you see as a result of such developments?

3. What are some of the ways technology will change space exploration?